EARTH UNLIMITED

FUGRO 50 YEARS – WHAT'S NEXT?

FUGRO N.V.   1962 - 2012

JAN DAAN HILLEN

CONTENTS

I

EARTH UNLIMITED

IN ADVANCE

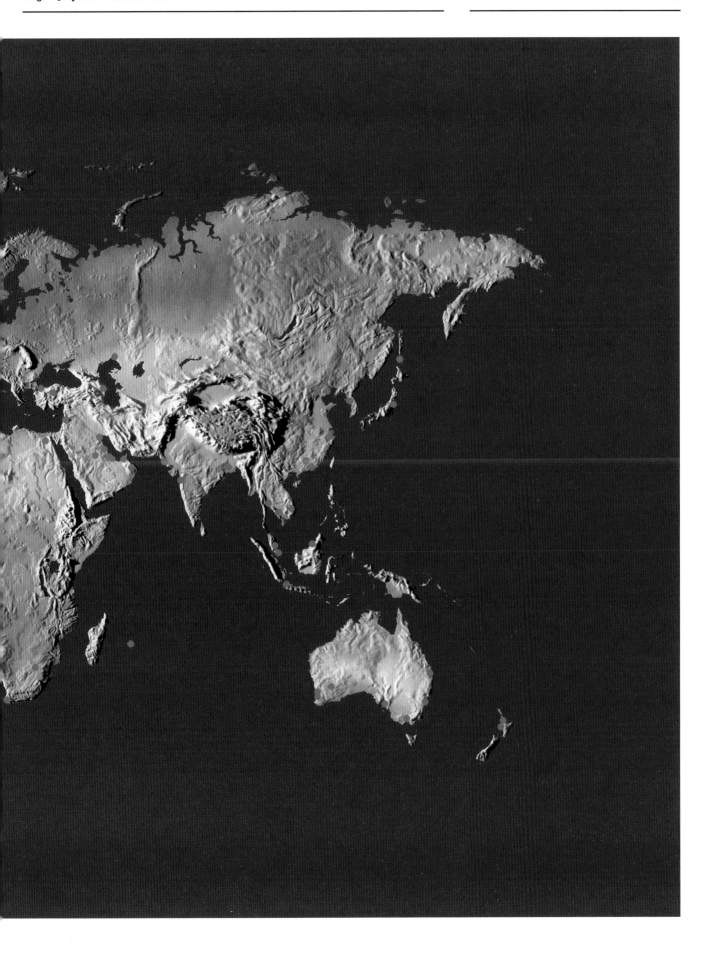

FUGRO 50 YEARS – WHAT'S NEXT?

In 2012, Fugro is celebrating its 50th anniversary: clearly a reason for festivities. This is the tenth edition of the traditional five-yearly celebration, organised for the first time by Fugro's founder Kees Joustra in 1967, and this 50th anniversary justifies a commemorative volume.

Ten years ago we published *Down-to-Earth and Up-to-Date,* a book describing Fugro's history. The company's history was captured in forty chapters against a backdrop of significant events in the world, one for each year.

Five years later, we published *Moving On,* outlining major company events. The book you are now holding, *Earth Unlimited,* summarises the historical review begun in the first book and goes on to present a concise account of the company's exploits and developments during the past ten years.

Our Earth still has almost boundless opportunities on offer, for Fugro too. That is why we have chosen the present and the foreseeable future as themes for *Earth Unlimited.* Managers and employees voice their thoughts on the actions and decisions of the past decade that have given Fugro its current leading position in energy, transport, infrastructure and mining. These narratives have been divided among the book's three sections: Earth, People and Energy.
We also give the floor to external experts on such relevant themes as worldwide water issues, ethical aspects of technological design, and shifts in the field of fossil and renewable energy.

But there's more. Managers of the global Fugro Group sent us their views on the developments expected in their regions and/or disciplines and on the position of their operating companies or branches by the time of Fugro's 65th anniversary in 2027.

We thank all of them for their contributions and opinions, which together give a good picture of recent advances in all the fields in which Fugro operates, the current geopolitical situation and future perspectives and challenges. Not that Fugro will rely solely on these individual opinions when making strategic decisions!

During the past half-century Fugro, despite the occasional dip, has been moving from strength to strength. Now, in 2012, the company is stronger than ever. Almost 14,000 employees in over 280 branches in more than 60 countries are performing outstanding technological feats and offering first-class services. This not only gives individual job satisfaction and an excellent reputation, but also very healthy financial results. This benefits the company and its continuity and, consequently, the people who work there as well as future employees.

All good reasons to celebrate together and then to continue on our illustrious course. This explains the book's subtitle: *Fugro 50 Years – What's Next?* Full steam ahead to 2027 and beyond!

Klaas Wester
President

EARTH UNLIMITED

E arth Unlimited. An audacious title to be sure, at a time when everyone is talking about climate change, corporate social responsibility and the transition from fossil to renewable sources of energy! The oil and gas industry with its impressive technological advances admittedly continues to discover and exploit previously inaccessible oil resources and other fossil sources of energy; but doesn't it realise that the Earth's resources are finite? How can such a title be reconciled with the growing awareness that we are approaching the limits of what is attainable and affordable? This awareness is also growing within Fugro, closely connected as it is with the global oil and gas industry. Are the people at Fugro self-seekingly burying their heads in the sand?
Far from it.

An unimaginable reality

Quite the reverse, in fact. Fugro is well aware that easily exploitable fuel resources are dwindling, whereas the demand for energy is on the increase due to a swelling world population and the rising average standard of living. (Older people who themselves are used to walking or cycling see their children and grandchildren using motorised means of transport, whether to flaunt their wealth or to keep up with their fast pace of life.)
But after fifty years of soil investigations, Fugro knows – maybe better than anyone – that the Earth has much more to offer and that there are sources of energy other than coal, oil and gas. *Homo technologicus* never stops questing for alternatives. He will continue to amaze the world and himself by devising smart solutions: what was quite unimaginable fifteen years ago is commonplace today. Add Mankind's staggering inventiveness to the endless potential of the planet (and the Sun), and an inexhaustible source of opportunities unfolds, one that fully justifying the title of this book. Human creativity knows no limits when it comes to survival on this planet, many of whose secrets are still to be revealed.

Fugro began preparing for a world ruled by renewables a long time ago. Its engineers are closely monitoring developments and even come up with new ideas themselves. As a result, this fascinating company has a head start in getting to places that Jules Verne scarcely dared dream of. The most improbable things turn out to be feasible and achievable, and this justifies Fugro's positive outlook, not least where the consequences of pressing climate issues and looming energy shortages are concerned. The title reflects Fugro's self-confidence and built-in drive to seek out and develop practical solutions to the problems caused by the behaviour of the Earth and its inhabitants.

Earth, people, energy

Earth Unlimited takes an in-depth look at the steps Fugro has taken to retain its leading role in the geotechnical, survey and geoscience disciplines (and in any others it may choose to add), so that the company can continue contributing worldwide to mankind's increasing prosperity and well-being. The book gives a picture of the challenges most likely to accompany this leading role.

The text is compiled from a number of elements. To start the ball rolling, there is *'The top stone'*, the final chapter of *Down-to-Earth and Up-to-Date*, the 40th anniversary commemorative volume published in 2002. Now, ten years later, this vision of yesterday's future deserves a front-row seat in the theatre of prospects for the next few decades.

'The quest for Odysseus' destination' takes us back even further; here you can learn what the connection is between Homer and Fugro's ingenuity. The remaining text is based on interviews with Fugro employees and external experts. The individual pieces are grouped under three headings: *Earth, People and Energy,* the stuff of human survival. These three factors, singly or in combination, at times present challenges that humanity should boldly face if it is to move forward. The dissatisfied among us, or at least those in a position to do so, move to places where the grass is greener still. Those who are forced to live on hope, seek conditions where life may be slightly less menacing. We all want a room (or something like it) with a view. They accept that even there life is seldom easy and survival may be a still greater challenge. Many settle on the fertile slopes of volcanoes or in swampy deltas, where the only certainty appears to be an ample food supply. They ignore the risks of devastating earthquakes, volcanic eruptions or floods. Nor are they alone in this – in 2012, more than half of the seven-billion-strong world population lives in river deltas where the soil is fertile and the climate agreeable. Those who opt for living on a volcano ignore seismologists' forecasts in the hope that there will be no eruptions until after their death by natural causes – after me, the deluge (or the lava flow). Tomorrow can take care of itself. Food first, the rest will follow.

2027 and beyond

Technical illustrator and futurologist Rudolf Das made a drawing for each of the three main sections of the book: a Remotely Operated Vehicle that can work at extreme water depths (Earth), a dyke of adjustable height (People) and his design for a floating wind farm (Energy).

The three above-mentioned sections are accompanied by a summary of Fugro's fifty-year history in a column of its own.

It is astonishing just how much can happen in fifteen years – just think of all the things we didn't know and couldn't do in 1997. The *2027* feature presents the expectations and forecasts of Fugro managers from all over the world for 2027, the year in which Fugro will turn 65.

Earth Unlimited ends with a section entitled *What's next?*, with its sights primarily set on Africa. That continent will see a rapid development in the near future and may, thanks to its huge natural resources, catch up economically. Fugro is ready to assist.

It has been fascinating, instructive and a great honour to have played a part in this impressive publication. Even those only indirectly involved in Fugro's corporate culture and technological capabilities feel a sense of pride. It feels good to know that Fugro employees are themselves filled with this pride, and occasionally astounded by each other's achievements, wherever they may be on this limitless Earth.

Jan Daan Hillen
May 2012

2027

At the beginning of Fugro's next step into the future it is interesting to know the ideas and visions of those who are leading the Fugro organisation, worldwide. The managers were asked to gaze into the crystal ball and freely answer one or more of the questions listed below. They contributed to this book by answering one or more of these questions.

1   What are the consequences of climate change until 2027, notably sea level rise, for the work in your operational company?
2   How far along will we be with the transition from fossil to renewable energy, and, in 2027, which renewable energy sources will be getting most attention?
3   How will geopolitical developments have influenced your region and/or operational company instability
4   How will Fugro have developed from an organisational point of view?
5   With which technology will Fugro be predominantly active?
6   In which new geographic areas will Fugro be active in 2027?
7   How large and what will be the composition of your work force in 2027?
8   In 2027, how will staff recruitment and their mobility within the Fugro organisation take place?
9   Which communication methods will people be using in 2027 on a daily basis?

▸
Surveyor with satelite positioning equipment, Rocky Mountains, Canada

◂
Fugro's seismic vessel Geo Caribbean

THE TOP STONE

—
—
—

The concept of the future is one of man's most important inventions. It is an everyday and at the same time world-encompassing, often grand concept which is applicable everywhere that is close to the feeling of *hope*, which is also a means to offer progress to our lives. Not every future is hopeful. Many Europeans, children of politically conscious parents, remember the period after January 1933 when for years and years every day covered itself with an increasingly fierce threat and more intense hopelessness. A new future could only be started in mid-August 1945.

These seem rather strange sentences to conclude a book about Fugro, whose history coincides with one of the greatest, most prosperous periods in our Western world – so far. Future was stacked onto future and hope after new hope was fulfilled. The already historical wall between the two Germanies crumbled in 1989, suddenly and sooner than anyone had dared to presume. Hope was in more of a hurry than the future. That year, 1933 had finally tumbled down and was over. There were no dictatorships left in Western Europe.

This book contains a company history and that is something different than a novel or a short story. These all have inevitable endings. A literary work is completed with its final word, like an Egyptian pyramid is finished with the last stone. It is closed for always and forever. This is the only way a pyramid can be made. The drawing dictates this. Like that, or not at all.

Indeed, a commemorative book about the inception and progress of a company end with a final word, but that word is in the air because those concerned with the company are thinking more about tomorrow than about yesterday.

PASSING THE BATON
Fugro celebrated its fortieth anniversary in 2002 by publishing a book titled *Down-to-Earth and Up-to-Date*. It presented a year-by-year account of the company's origins and growth. Max Dendermonde (1919–2004), a well-known Dutch author in his day, wrote a concluding piece to the chronology. His essay considered the part played by the future in human thought and action over the centuries. The passage of time has since gobbled up another ten years of the future, as it was then. As always happens, developments in countless areas have taken a surprisingly different course from what was anticipated. Progress may have been slower, or may have taken a different direction, but it never stops. *Panta rhei:* everything flows, meandering left and right as time advances but unstoppable.
New generations are taking over the baton from their predecessors. They think and act differently because that goes along with their sharper view of the times ahead. As a way of inaugurating the relay race, this book starts by recapitulating the conclusion of the previous edition.

The end is their beginning. Therefore the commemoration has already projected its thoughts on other matters and is opening its mind to a greater future, a reverberating final chorus, that takes the reader to tomorrow's world. People understand that there is still a lot to be gained, after the great deal that has already been achieved (despite this and despite that). The future is impatient to get going.

Which elusive, exclusively human attainments were there first? Language? The future? Language was already used early on by man in order to record future plans. Small-scale plans for the short-term came first. The fact that it was special was not yet considered – in that misty prehistoric era. Animals have also used sounds. The feeding bowl – half a coconut? – full of future scraped across the rock-bed and made an introduction of the concept of award. A monkey was eating.
Homo sapiens continued on this road and unwittingly used grammar. Twaddle became repeatable and furthered the creation of the common message. A future was recorded in words.
Trees and other flora citizens had not come that far yet but they felt a future in their sap. Even before autumn has arrived, the branches that are losing their leaves bend together towards a new winter.

The future has always been more complicated than those making plans imagined. Through the centuries, the history of a building of churches shows how people had to compromise on the original plans. Church towers were cancelled, new places of worship demanded introverted austerity.

Social changes also demanded new thinking where the construction of factories was concerned. A confident feeling for the new brought grandeur. Buildings like factories, for instance, could become monuments. In East Groningen, where engineers tapped into a huge amount of natural gas in the middle of the twentieth century, the deteriorated shell of a building can be found that is called *De Toekomst* (The Future). It was built a hundred years before that gas field was found when there was an extensive, new trade in Western Europe in strawboard, the plastic of that time. The old steam castle is just rotting and rusting there, like a pathetic, superfluous dream castle.
In Gizah, not far from Cairo, a great piece of carefully completed future has been standing for centuries before the western era. The builders had two options during construction: stopping the impossible job, or completing the job according to the only plan. No deviations were possible. It was a mathematical plan that could only be completed without any alterations, and only with that irreplaceable final stone.

1962

Taking the plunge
–
–

After graduating in Civil Engineering at what was then Delft Polytechnic in 1950, engineer Kees Joustra joined the employ of, successively, the Zuyder Zee Works Service, the Habo construction company in The Hague and the Delft Laboratory for Soil Mechanics (LGM, Laboratorium voor Grondmechanica). On May 2, 1962, he launched his own firm, whose name translates as Engineering Company for Foundation Technology and Soil Mechanics, in short 'Fugro'. 95% of the financing came from Ab Schreuders, director of Verenigde Bouwbedrijven Nederhorst, a major contractor domiciled in Gouda, after Joustra had written down his business plan for him on a single A4 page.
He silenced sceptics who were claiming that the cone penetration testing technique (CPT) had reached its limits; the CPT cone still needed plenty of improvement. Joustra saw the possibilities. Fugro did what no one else was doing: it combined the practice of soil analysis with the theory of advice on foundation design. The company began life in The Hague, but moved to Leidschendam in the

>

The builders forced themselves to be true to the future. And that is really the biggest miracle of Gizah: that it could only be built in that one way, stone by stone, metre by metre, without room for deviation. The people held the reigns of the future. That rarely happens.

These are a lot of introductory words to say that the future throws a spanner in the works. The old future should end in Leidschendam in the spring of 2002. Then Fugro is forty years old. Those celebrations will now take place with much more restraint than the planners had thought. Because it's true that what happened in New York on September 11, 2001 is, hopefully, a completely isolated event, yet it has also taken place in a new, universal context which affects the whole community.
With the celebration of Fugro's fortieth anniversary a future is planned. This is done carefully, with building bricks, stacked on top of each other, one by one.
No matter how it is done: carry on.

1962

>

autumn of 1962. Fugro sought to operate at the top of the market as a soil investigation consultant and as a contractor, as both price-setter and trendsetter, and become better known.
The first, and for years the biggest order came from an American engineering company, Frederick Harris, for CPTs for the construction of 50 kilometres of motorway in the south of Belgium. The order gave the company a flying start, but the paid-up capital was not enough for the necessary investments; Fugro had to borrow an additional € 90,000. That same year brought a second foreign order, for CPTs in Curaçao.
—
And John Glenn orbited the earth three times.

THE QUEST
FOR ODYSSEUS' DESTINATION

Close on three thousand years before Fugro proposes a toast to its 50th anniversary, the Greek poet and singer Homer had his own reasons to celebrate, namely the completion of his *Iliad* and *Odyssey*.

At least, if he really was the author of the two epic poems. Some scholars seriously question whether a blind bard could have written both the *Iliad* – about the siege and battle for Ilion, as Troy as also known – and the *Odyssey* – about the Greek king Odysseus' ten-year-long journey home to his native island of Ithaca after the Trojan War. Sceptics base their doubts on linguistic research, claiming that phrases in the stories reflect different periods in the development of the Greek language, and therefore cannot have been written by one person. *Homerists* counter this by suggesting that Homer may have written the *Iliad* when he was a young man and that the *Odyssey* was a work of his old age.

Other scholars point to Homer's blindness and claim that he didn't write the stories but recited them, as a born storyteller blessed with a good memory. (Was he really blind, or did he only close his eyes while reciting, to improve his concentration?) They claim that the poems were not written down until after Homer's death. And these writers may have occasionally dipped their pens into well-filled pots of their own fantasies to make the stories more attractive. Or they may have watered down the original epic poems with other tales with no links to Troy or Odysseus at all. What is currently believed to be the standard version dates from the third century BC, when adepts of the Alexandrian School removed later additions in their attempts at uncovering the original text. Unfortunately, there is no reliable information about Homer as an individual – if he ever really existed at all. Some people claim that Homer is just a collective name for a number of authors.

2027

SIZE AND COMPOSITION OF WORKFORCE

GRANT AITCHISON
FUGRO SUBSEA SERVICES, UK

Based on current workforce of just under 400, then we can see this potentially rising to 800 in 15 years time. The skills set will be predominantly computer technology and applications engineering based, with an increased focus on management systems and operating efficiency. There should be a reduction in the number of personnel needed to work offshore on vessels, as systems and technological efficiencies (e.g. communications systems sending data from offshore to onshore) come into effect.

1963

A flying start
—

Fugro's enthusiastic CPT team was much more efficient than its bureaucratic rival LGM (attached to Delft Polytechnic) and largely forced it out of the market. The growth was encouraging, but brought its fair share of worries. There was a shortage of office space, Fugro had no workshop of its own and there was a constant need for new funding for investments to prolong the success. Fugro charged an extra ten guilders (€ 4.50) for each CPT so as to be able to continue investing.

Fugro rapidly gained ground in the housing foundation market through the speed and efficiency with which it dealt with its projects. The oil and gas industry focused on developing production fields off the Dutch coast.
—

And Martin Luther King led a march on Washington where he delivered his legendary speech: *I have a dream.*

Another suitor for Penelope

The *Odyssey* describes the voyage of the Greek king Odysseus to his home port on the island of Ithaca, after he had helped defeat the Trojans. (He was the one who devised the strategy with the giant wooden horse.) His wanderings around the Mediterranean took ten years, because Odysseus and his crew encountered many misfortunes on the way: storms, temptations and other threats that delayed his return. All this misery was caused by Poseidon, the god of the sea, who cursed Odysseus for blinding his son, the Cyclops Polyphemos. Fortunately, the goddess Athena favoured Odysseus; she made sure he could eventually return to his wife Penelope, who had been faithfully waiting for her husband for all those years. In the meantime, Penelope had to fight off hundreds of obnoxious suitors, who, in the absence of her husband were dancing around her loveliness like moths round a light. Penelope no longer trusted anyone and it took a while for her to recognise her husband in that weather-beaten wandering beggar, as Athena had disguised him. After having made perfectly clear who had the oldest rights in Odysseus' house, and – with the help of his son Telemachus – having taken care of the suitors, Odysseus could once again embrace his Penelope, twenty years after he had left for Troy.

Where was Ithaca located?

Homer and the works attributed to him are now, almost three thousand years later, still the subject of much scholarly study and discussion. Many geographical names that feature in the *Odyssey* are still found on the map of Greece, and that makes it possible to trace most of Odysseus' wanderings. But scholars are divided as to the final leg of the journey because the exact location of Ithaca is disputed. Archaeologists and other scholars are keen to start digging at Ithaca, expecting to find clues there that could also solve the mysteries surrounding Homer.

But what about the small island of Ithaki, east of the island of Cephalonia, in the Ionian Sea? This Ithaki (New-Greek for Ithaca) was named in the first century BC by Greek geographer Strabo. He identified the island as being Homer's Ithaca. But present-day archaeologists agree that this cannot possibly be Odysseus' homeland. Excavations have unearthed archaeological objects that bear no relation to the Bronze Age of Odysseus' time. No, the scholars say, the shape and dimensions of Ithaki differ too much from Homer's description ('a low-lying, wooded and rugged island with one high mountain top') to maintain that this is the original Ithaca. But then where was it that Penelope waited so longingly?

How an island became a peninsula

This intriguing question had also puzzled British businessman and amateur archaeologist Robert Bittlestone since 2003. He came up with the hypothesis that the present-day Paliki peninsula, on the western side of Cephalonia, was once an island. It became attached to Cephalonia – maybe because of tectonic movements or because sea level in the area was once higher. Bittlestone succeeded in interesting John Underhill (Professor in Geology at Edinburgh University) and his learned colleague James Diggle (classical scholar at Cambridge University) in his proposal that Odysseus' Ithaca could be found in the Paliki peninsula. Tectonic movements may have lifted up the ground; and the present-day Thinia Valley between Ithaca and Cephalonia would have been a marine channel 3,000 years ago. The three Englishmen founded an organisation, Odysseus Unbound, in order to seriously investigate the problem. They asked Fugro for technological support and, bearing in mind its Corporate Social Responsibility objectives, Fugro offered to become technological sponsor for this cultural project. They launched a research programme for gathering and interpreting data that might be used by scientists to prove that, some 3,200 years ago, Paliki was not a peninsula but an island.

Pull out all stops

Once the Greek authorities and local landowners had granted permission, Professor Underhill could start his geological, geophysical and geomorphological research. Fugro marshalled the expertise of all its divisions to investigate the soils of Thinia Valley down to a depth of approximately 150 metres. Helicopters equipped with lasers and geophysical sensors flew across the area for high-resolution airborne terrain mapping *(FLI-MAP)*. Shallow-marine seismic and sonar surveys were used to produce detailed profiles of the shallow sea floor. On land, gravity, electrical and refraction seismic surveys were conducted to assist the traditional geological field mapping. Fugro also drilled shallow boreholes, took cores and soil samples, and analysed the latter two to determine the sediment packages and stratigraphy. Armed with all these data Fugro produced geological maps that can shed light on possible past tectonic movements. This would have to prove whether the Thinia Valley had ever been a marine channel and Paliki an island. If that was the case, the palaeogeography of Paliki would match Homer's description of Odysseus' homeland Ithaca. The former channel would then be called Strabo's Channel, after the man who pointed out the wrong place two thousand years ago.
[www.odysseus-unbound.org]

2027 CONSEQUENCES OF CLIMATE CHANGE

IDAR HORSTAD C.S.
FUGRO MULTI CLIENT
SERVICES, NORWAY

Although the causes of climatic change and the influence by man still remains to be fully understood, societies across the earth have experienced extreme weather and large damages caused by mother nature. It seems like we are in a transitional period where the weather and possibly climate is changing in many regions at the same time, and as with any unwanted change this has a large impact on our way of living. Our daily life and many of our constructions are based on observations and experiences from a relatively short period of time ... the rest is based on models prone to revisions. While it still remains uncertain how the climate will evolve over the next decades, our ability to predict has to improve and as in any transitional period there will be a strong demand for services and knowledge that plan and build structures that will survive a change I climate. Climate change and sea level rise or fall is a rule in geology not an anomaly ... we just have to accept that, like any geologist does.

▲

*View from Argistoli Bay
on Southern Thinia*

▼

*Drilling on Cephalonia,
Greece*

2027

CONSEQUENCES
OF CLIMATE CHANGE

BIGHNA N NAYAK
FUGRO SURVEY,
INDIA

Climate change will have an impact
on Fugro Survey in India as we are
dependent on monsoons. We already
see the impact of extended monsoons
and higher periods of weather down
time during the season. We forecast
reduced working season in future.
With sea level rise and frequent flooding in coastal cities, we expect more
survey work for Fugro in India.

50 YEARS
OF RECOGNISING AND SEIZING OPPORTUNITIES

'One thing led to another and I eventually returned some two months later. The international experience gave me a taste for more but Fugro had nothing to offer me at the time. I joined a dredging company, which posted me abroad. After seven years we had to choose: either send our children to an international school or return to the Netherlands. We opted for the latter and I rejoined Fugro in 1981 – we had always kept in touch. I had many different jobs in the company; which job I did depended on happenstance. Whenever something happened somewhere, we came up with ad hoc solutions. You know such situations can arise and you seize your opportunity.'

CEO by surprise
'I was running the Onshore Geotechnics Division, which operates globally, when I was appointed second in command in 1996, as a back-up for Gert-Jan Kramer. I became involved in corporate matters such as investor relations and the annual report. There's little difference between our ages and we were to retire at about the same time, but Gert-Jan left in October 2005, sooner than expected. So the fact that I succeeded him took me by surprise. But it was a pleasant surprise, and because all the business line managers report to the CEO and the CFO, I became widely involved in the entire company. The short reporting lines keep you in close contact with operations and the day-to-day running of activities.
'In those days, the oil and gas industry started operating in ever deeper waters, requiring larger ships with more equipment. Until then we leased or converted vessels. But then we started a building programme for a new seismic fleet. That was a new activity for Fugro. We built state-of-the-art vessels according to our own ideas, not only because these best met our own operational requirements, but also because we wanted to keep our operational expertise in-house, enabling us to retain our leading position. We are pursuing a 50/50 balance between owned and leased vessels in the fleet, which enables us to adjust to market fluctuations as best as possible.'

Shortly after graduating as a civil engineer and fulfilling his military service obligations, **Klaas Wester** joined Fugro in 1971. Being one of the few young people with a driver's licence, he was almost immediately sent to England with a box full of cones for cone penetration testing, as Fugro was carrying out soil investigations there. At the time, he didn't have a clue about customs formalities and was surprised by the fact that the British drove on the left.

*Fugro's seismic vessel
Geo Celtic offshore Dutch
Harbor, Alaska*

▲
*Sportsday Fugro's
Managers Meeting,
The Netherlands*

2027

TRANSITION FROM FOSSIL
TO RENEWABLE ENERGY

JORGE HILDENBRAND
FUGRO LASA GEOMAG,
BRAZIL

I believe that the transition from
fossil to renewable energy sources
would take place around 2050. My
expectation about changes in the
energy matrix is for a progressive
elevation of the use of renewable
sources. My view is that the
renewable sources would achieve
50% of the energy matrix of the top
10 countries in 2027. Solar and wind
energy sources would attract more
attention that time. The bio-energy
will be facing strong competition with
food producers and would not be an
option as a renewable source.

Cause and effect

'Another focus point was to prepare for closer collaboration between operating companies, for which we now have the right conditions. After expanding our services over the past fifteen years, we now want to cluster them, prompted by market developments. Clients want to have their increasingly complex projects handled by a single partner. They focus on contract management and hiring expertise; the growth of our organisation is partly due to this trend. In the large oil companies, project managers have taken over the technicians' deciding roles. This change hasn't come unexpectedly for Fugro. It's not a ground-breaking new development. Fugro devotes a lot of energy to restructuring itself – and rightly so – but I believe that it's much more important that our people focus on questions such as *Where are the projects?* and *In what direction is the market moving?* Any organisational restructuring will follow automatically. That's an effect, not a cause; we won't change the market by changing our organisational structure.

'Anticipating market developments and responding pragmatically have always been key factors in Fugro's success. We didn't go offshore of our own accord, but in the oil companies' wake. We are following our clients as closely as possible and seize opportunities as soon as they arise. That's what is really important. An organisational structure can be adapted whenever the business volume requires it, but that's only a shift of emphasis.'

Market developments in oil and gas

'Some fifteen years ago, large international oil companies called the shots. The balance of power is now shifting to national oil companies; they own approximately 80% of the oil and gas reserves. In the past, the national oil companies got themselves a dollar or two through royalties, nowadays they are exploiting their resources themselves. That's good for these nations' development, but means a huge shift in the balance of power. Multinational oil companies are still indispensable in developing new technology, because of their vast knowledge. They have become super-technology innovators. 'There are also geographic shifts: into remote areas with fossil fuel resources but virtually no infrastructure. The national governments of these frontier areas are dependent on foreign expertise for the time being, but as soon as they have their own in-house expertise, they'll take control of production, as happened in Norway, Brazil, Saudi-Arabia and India. This shift has far-reaching implications for Fugro too. In the past, we could focus on a limited number of big players, who hired us for their projects. As a consequence, we covered a large part of the market. We are staying in touch with these familiar clients, because we want to keep following their technological innovations. But now that the national oil companies are awarding the contracts, we are adapting our company's geographic structure in order to have a physical presence in the operating areas. Fugro

1964

Electric cone penetration testing is the future

—

A dispute raged in the CPT branch regarding the viability of an electric cone. Fugro felt that an electrical system gave better results and was indispensable for the further development and automation of the CPT process. TNO, the Netherlands Organisation for Applied Scientific Research, made two new electric cones at Fugro's request. The tests were a success, but the extremely sensitive components were expensive and vulnerable. The cones kept breaking and TNO needed three weeks to repair them. Fugro was neither willing nor able to wait that long. So it forced TNO into teaching the technique to Fugro's own instrument makers. From then on, Fugro assembled and repaired the cones itself. By devoting a great deal of time, energy and conviction, Joustra turned an idea into an efficient new product.

—

And the miniskirt arrived on the scene.

has long been accustomed to setting up local organisations: we established local presences in, say, Hongkong, Dubai and Nigeria which enable us to respond to developments in a logical, natural way. Contacts with national governments are greatly facilitated by the fact that our local staff is familiar with the language, culture and manners. That is also acting pragmatically. 'Dutch entrepreneurship has always proven very successful for Fugro: giving the different cultures their dues, but with a joint focus on a single, clear objective. Every manager is free to interpret this one way or another. Freedom with a joint purpose is one of the management challenges at corporate level, also because autonomy sometimes clashes with the need to collaborate.'

Leading in exchange for the best solutions

'By 2027, Fugro's know-how and expertise will ensure that we will still be involved in both fossil and renewable energy, and will have grown much stronger in transport, infrastructural projects and mining. We will be front runners in those activities too, with a focus on new developments, which means acting in a more risk-bearing capacity at times. Fugro's successes traditionally resulted from seeing a client's next step as a challenge, and responding rapidly by offering the right solution as soon as a client faces a problem. We built our strong position – and are able to retain it – by going with the flow and continuously succeeding in staying one step ahead of our competitors. The sooner a client involves us in his plans and allows us to think along about upcoming problems, the better our solutions will be when they are actually needed. This requires that our clients treat Fugro as their preferred supplier instead of opting for competitive pricing – that's the price for the best solution. What the client spends on Fugro is only a small part of their total investment, but it may be fundamental to their success and to optimising that investment. Clients have greater expectations on the basis of our reputation and performance and so we have to meet stricter requirements than other companies – and that's the price Fugro gladly pays for being involved in projects at an early stage and thus retaining our competitive edge.

'For these solutions, we need young, smart technology graduates, but proving our quality also requires experienced people. This last-named aspect poses a dilemma: we deploy our most knowledgeable and experienced staff preferably in jobs with the most external contacts, but their knowledge and expertise also make them attractive for our clients. By matching them, we run the risk of experienced staff leaving us for our clients. That could, however, also turn to an advantage when the good relationship with a former employee, who knows Fugro's capabilities, continues. There's a tendency to assume that our *Fugro Academy* is training people for the entire industry, but the *Academy* is key in maintaining an

2027

NEW GEOGRAPHIC AREAS

MELINDA ROBINSON
FUGRO CONSULTANTS,
USA

While the oil and gas sector will continue to figure prominently in Fugro's onshore practice, emphasis could shift noticeably to the cold regions. We see expansion of our presence into Alaska and eastern Russia (Siberia).
Mining, energy (especially nuclear) and mega infrastructure projects will create the bulk of Fugro Onshore Geotechnics growth in the coming decade. Consequently, we envision a much larger footprint in countries where we currently have some presence, namely: Australia, Brazil, India, South Africa and Canada. Onshore Geotechnics expansion will also be seen in countries with limited to no presence, including: Chile, Peru, Malaysia, Southern Africa, the Philippines and Indonesia (mining related); Poland and other east European countries (energy related); along with Iraq and perhaps Venezuela (oil and gas related).

edge on our competitors. As soon as we relinquish that position, Fugro will just be another also-ran.'

Getting the best out of people

'All the aspects mentioned above are interconnected and determine the balance between internal freedom and the ability to anticipate external developments. My philosophy has always been: look outwards and accept that internally not everything is perhaps exactly as it should be – this will yield better results in the long term than rigidly regulating everything, which reduces people who stand out from the crowd to the lowest common denominator. Levelling is not Fugro's way of operating. Management should get the best out of their staff, use everybody's individual capacities to the full, and support everyone. That's the way to achieve the best results.

'I retire at the end of May 2012 and clear out my office in June. What will I miss most? The day-to-day dealings with the people, the direct involvement in operations and the resulting successes. The most fascinating aspect of Fugro, in my opinion, is the fact that 14,000 people with dozens of nationalities and cultural backgrounds are working at hundreds of locations towards a single, common goal. When you talk to them, you hear they are proud of working at Fugro. I share that pride and it has motivated me in the job I have so much enjoyed doing.

'Fugro is in excellent shape, and well positioned to thrive wherever the current economic and geopolitical events may take us. By staying close to our clients, and sticking to the strong points of our own traditional pragmatic culture, Fugro can look forward to a brilliant future.'

1965

You don't know everything

—

Fugro commissioned TNO to develop the electric friction cone penetrometer to measure the friction along the shaft of the CPT cone. It had received orders for it even before the testing stage was completed. Joustra was so convinced of its success that he dared to offer the friction measurement on a no-cure, no-pay basis; he wanted to add practical experience to theory and laboratory tests. 'You don't know everything', he stated. 'You have to make mistakes first to find out what they are. An instrument like that develops itself.'

Fugro's CPT Crew One drove a heavy-duty CPT truck across the Alps to a job in Trieste. The team knew nothing about the situation on site; they'd find out when they got there. In Leidschendam Joustra negotiated the purchase of an industrial site with enough room to park Fugro's appliances and build a better laboratory.

—

And The Beatles were awarded the OBE.

II

EARTH UNLIMITED

EARTH

SHIFTING

Fugro's fiftieth anniversary comes at a time of global changes (or premonitions thereof) in the economy, demographics, geopolitics, climate and technology. These changes astound those who thought things wouldn't come to this. They will take place over a period of many years, but are, considering their scales and consequences, radical nonetheless. Movements in the Earth's crust can show a similar picture. **Bill Lettis** of William Lettis & Associates Inc. is an expert on earthquakes.

The Earth's crust consists of a layer of solid rock. Below that solid crust, hot magma is slowly flowing. The huge forces of the convection currents in the magma drag the crust along, breaking it up into so-called plates. Being irresistibly dragged along by the magma currents, these plates slowly drift across the globe, moving jerkily past and over each other along so-called fault planes. Stresses build up along the fault planes between the plates, while no movement is detected for many years. Then suddenly, the plates move with a jerk: an earthquake occurs. Other types of earthquakes are caused by volcanic eruptions. Volcanic eruptions and earthquakes in the ocean floor can displace the seabed sufficiently to cause a tsunami: a huge wave. If such a wave approaches the shore, it can reach gigantic proportions and develop a devastating force.

Japan

We know the locations of the main fault zones in the Earth's crust: the largest are around the Pacific Ocean, in the Mediterranean region, in the Himalayas, south of Indonesia, and east of China and Japan. These are the world's most earthquake-prone regions. The point on the surface directly above the focus of an earthquake is referred to as the epicentre. Seismometers measure the force of vibrations caused by an earthquake. This force is expressed as a magnitude on the *Richter scale,* a scale developed by US seismologist Charles Richter in 1935. The *Richter scale* quantifies the energy released by the seismic waves. The magnitude measured by a seismometer at a particular observation station is corrected for the distance between that station and the epicentre: recorded vibration signals become weaker with an increase in distance.

Earthquakes can change the face of the Earth within seconds. The tsunami that followed the strong seaquake east of Japan in March 2011 paralysed the country and destroyed the Fukushima nuclear power plant. Safety systems had automatically shut down the power supply, but the emergency generators didn't function properly, because they were flooded. Consequently, the pumps that circulate cooling water through the reactors ceased working and meltdown was unavoidable, adding to the catastrophe. The reactions to this tsunami caused another shock wave around the world. Ministers, conservationists and others lost sleep over it, even on the other side of the globe. Debates about the risks of nuclear energy had abated in many countries. Dozens of plans for new nuclear power plants were on the drawing boards: the global increase in demand for energy motivated the search for alternatives to fossil fuels. Nuclear energy was in the picture again, but *Japan*, as the events in Fukushima came to be called, rekindled discussions and doubts. German chancellor Merkel only briefly discussed the issue; immediately after the extent of the disaster had become known she completely cancelled all building plans for this type of power plant in her country and decided that the existing plants would be dismantled. Germany decided to bid farewell to nuclear energy and switch completely to wind energy for generating sustainable energy. People in other countries were also shocked by these events, but many in reaction pointed out the increased safety of procedures, processes and power plants.

Earthquake-proof nuclear power plants

Fugro acquired geological consultancy William Lettis & Associates Inc. in 2007. Its head office is in Walnut Creek, California. There are few people in the world who know more about earthquakes, earth tremors, tsunamis and landslides or about the associated risk analyses than the staff of William Lettis & Associates. They are experts on earthquakes and the consequences for technical structures, know the effects of climate change, and know how to strike a balance between the natural and the built environment. As Bill Lettis says: 'Many dams were built all over the world in the mid twentieth century for hydraulic power generation. Are these dams still earthquake-proof? How would earthquakes affect their foundations; how do we build safer, earthquake-proof nuclear power plants? Painstaking research is being done into earthquake hazards in the vicinity of nuclear power plants. The stringent US design codes are being adopted all over the world and the companies involved must meet the highest standards. 'William Lettis & Associates Inc. joining the Fugro group meant a big change for our relatively small business. We originally focused on the US market, but the take-over suddenly opened up the entire world. To understand the risks posed by natural disasters, one should compute the chances of these events happening and their potential consequences. We know the probabilities and risks of virtually any place on earth. We apply this knowledge in jobs such as site investigations prior to building large infrastructure projects and nuclear power plants. Many countries (especially countries that are developing very fast) are developing plans for nuclear

1966

A thousand and one orders

—
—

Fugro's electric friction cone penetrometer, a world first, became operational. The post-war reconstruction effort was a source of much work for Fugro in housing and non-residential building construction and in industrial projects in the port of Rotterdam.

—

And the marriage of Princess Beatrix to Claus von Amsberg led to riots and smoke bombs in Amsterdam.

2027

NEW GEOGRAPHIC AREAS

GRANT AITCHISON
FUGRO SUBSEA SERVICES, UK

Compared to the current situation, we will develop further in the Arctic and Antarctic regions. Also we will see increased involvement in the deeper water areas of the Atlantic and Pacific as the capability of technology to operate in ultra deepwater develops.

power plants, but wonder where to start. The first step is to determine safety criteria, which depend on local conditions in the area of the intended building site.'

Criteria

'Some want more stringent criteria than others, depending on the local situation – building a nuclear power plant is a one-off job. Most government authorities apply the general, international criteria of the International Association of Electrical Inspectors (IAEI). Some states apply the very specific criteria of the US Nuclear Regulatory Commission (NRC). Because of the very low probability of an earthquake ever occurring in the United Arab Emirates (UAE), the regulations for building the Abu Dhabi power plant were relatively liberal, but the UAE authorities nevertheless established a special Federal Authority for Nuclear Regulation. Fugro experts assisted again, as they did before in Israel, Switzerland and South Korea. The UAE subsequently created the Emirates Nuclear Energy Corporation (ENEC), which asked Fugro to develop a package of conditions and criteria. ENEC commissioned the Korean Electric Power Company (Kepco) to build the plant, in accordance with the guidelines developed by Fugro; and Kepco also called in Fugro.'

Bridging cultural differences

An adviser may become involved in this kind of project through different channels: a government, the owner, the designer and/or the building contractor. The government commissions investigations of the intended building site. Companies such as Arriva (France), Westinghouse (US), Kepco (South Korea) and Mitsubishi (Japan) also involve Fugro at the design stage. The government usually commissions a provider, who subsequently is responsible for the entire project. A building company, such as Suez or Tractabel, is eventually engaged for the actual construction of a power plant.

'Each country follows its own procedures. Each situation is different, no two contracts are the same. Sounding out the market is a sensitive process. For a Western company, it is obviously easier to work in areas where people are familiar with the Western mentality and use Western-style contracts. Globally operating consultants have to be able to turn their hand to anything. Bridging cultural differences, for instance concerning contract legislation and negotiating habits, is challenging for both parties. The client is always right, so the adviser and contractor adapt. For that matter, not only the client's wishes matter. The International Atomic Energy Foundation (IAEF) and local authorities also require in-depth investigations into soil properties and risk analyses before they issue permits. And rightly so: *Japan* and previous calamities are proof of the disastrous effects of earthquakes. When building the Abu Dhabi nuclear power plant, the client

---

2027

FUGRO TECHNOLOGY

MARK HEINE
FUGRO SURVEY,
THE NETHERLANDS

Geographic data will remain a growth area for Fugro. New data-acquisition techniques for all the services Fugro currently provides will result in a further growth of opportunities, in which automation and remote operation will be key elements. The accessibility and easy acquisition of reliable geographic data will become essential for the industries that are currently Fugro's clients. Fugro's strength will be mainly in linking the acquired data and related services. In addition to expertise in data acquisition, Fugro will focus increasingly on data management and smart presentation of these data. Expectations are that the oil and gas industry will gradually move away from the production of fossil fuel and become general energy suppliers.

realised that an integrated top-down approach is preferable to several contractors sharing the job, with none of them possessing an integrated overview and understanding all the data.'

Bridging a fault line

Western Turkey's North Anatolia is one of the most active fault regions in the world. The likelihood of earthquakes there necessitates special precautions when building infrastructure and building projects, such as constructing a more than 400-km-long motorway between Bursa and Izmir. The proposed route includes a suspension bridge across the Gulf of Izmit. The Turkish government gave the contract for designing, building and operating the bridge to NÖMAYG, a joint venture of Turkish building contractors. Seismologists expect another earthquake in this area within thirty years, easily within the bridge's planned lifespan. Therefore, the client required an earthquake-proof bridge. Much research was needed to design the structure of the two pylons on either side of the gulf. Where exactly is the location of the fault? What is the type of rock at and below the surface? How will the soils react to an earthquake? What is the best spot for a pylon? What kind of geotechnical foundation is required? What data are needed to turn the project into a success?

'NÖMAYG followed standard procedures and hired a geotechnical consultancy. And that was it; one subcontractor would study the fault, another the motorway trajectory, the third the abutments, etc. But none of them would have an overview of the entire set of data or understand them all. Nobody would be capable of successfully integrating the research results. It was even doubtful whether anybody would be able to compile all the research results eventually into a single, consistent recommendation that would lead to the best end result. Splitting up the job would probably mean longer data gathering, less efficiency and higher costs.'

Integrated approach

Fugro was asked to drill some offshore boreholes at the bridge location in the gulf. Not very exciting, as boreholes – even at weird locations – had been part of Fugro's standard line of business for many years, so Fugro didn't blink an eye. But Fugro stood out from all the other subcontractors involved because the Fugro group also possesses in-house expertise to perform all the other studies in onshore and offshore geophysics, seismic surveys, geological mapping, geotechnical laboratory tests and earthquake studies. This enabled Fugro to interpret, combine and integrate all the investigations into a single, coherent recommendation that gives the client insight into all aspects of his project. Fugro's many years of investing in specialist knowledge and expertise and experience, by acquiring specialised companies, started to pay off. It was time to reap dividends.

Fugro explained to NÖMAYG what aspects needed to be considered for

▲
Slope failure, Hongkong

2027

STAFF RECRUITMENT AND THEIR MOBILITY

KELLIANNE MEAGHER
FUGRO AIRBORNE SURVEYS, AUSTRALIA

I imagine there will be a more structured career development path in place within Fugro which would result in a good deal of staff recruitment being trans global between operating companies. There will be greater networking with referrals and/or head hunting becoming a good sourcing channel. The Fugro brand will be a dominant recruitment tool. I envisage a shift in the demographic mix of the labour force in all regions (giving a wider pool of talent globally).

this specific project. Maximum safety required a full study into the local fault line in order to pinpoint its location and subsequently be able to compute what the earthquake and landslide risks imply for the design of the foundation of each separate pylon and of the entire bridge. This was so as to be able to predict the way vibrations would be transmitted into the roadway of the bridge – each part of the total construction would react differently to an earthquake. Gathering all these data is a good idea, but it's only a start. You also need to know how to interpret and integrate research results. NÖMAYG realised that in this case a bridge design would involve much more than they had thought and that such complicated projects require an integrated approach. This top-down approach not only offers qualitative benefits, for instance in the field of risk management, but also quantitative ones: time savings through a greater efficiency, for instance. NÖMAYG accepted the unasked-for advice; Fugro combined all the aspects of the job into a single project, took on project management and concluded a single, comprehensive contract.

Partners

Because of the benefits in terms of efficiency and risk containment, the Turkish government was also interested in this type of project model for the planned construction of a pipeline from the Black Sea to the Mediterranean: one contact point where all the aspects come together, one agreement for research into and advice on building the filling station, the pipeline itself, six or so pumping stations and the unloading station in the Mediterranean. This approach is obviously more attractive than separate contracts with different subcontractors who take care of individual parts.

Fugro is currently positioning and promoting itself in this way for major projects. The group seeks to identify which countries have plans for new nuclear power plants in order to become involved in the process as early as possible, preferably as soon as government negotiations on a nuclear power plant begin. The further the process is advanced, the more difficult it is to reverse decisions and decide on better options.

By now, Fugro's relationships with major engineering firms and building companies are so good that these will call Fugro as soon as they are approached themselves, in order to subsequently discuss future possibilities as partners and work together on marketing aspects.

2027

ORGANISATIONAL DEVELOPMENT

JIM MANN
FUGRO SUBSEA SERVICES, UK

The decentralised organisational style that characterises Fugro today will be refined and adapted to suit the ambitions of the next generation workforce. There will still be an influx of entrepreneurial management through acquisition, but many future leaders in Fugro will be *home grown* and bereft of the 'baggage' that comes from having lead a business to the level that makes it attractive to merge into the bigger entity that is Fugro and then coming up against the 'barriers' that are in place as a consequence of the decentralised corporate approach. This home grown managerial talent will be more adept in the Fugro style and able to work more potently within the refined organisational situation. Such adaptation/refinement is likely to embrace some elements of matrix style management in order to truly globalise the products and services of Fugro future.

▲
*Fugro Seacore jack-up
platform in the Bosporus
Strait, Istanbul, Turkey*

◀

*Diablo Canyon
Nucleair Power Plant,
California, USA*

DYKES –
A MASSIVE MARKET

Flood-control activities are a growing business for Fugro Geoservices in the Netherlands. During the past decade, the number of Fugro advisers in this field almost quadrupled to around twenty, in the Netherlands alone.

Fugro already had a good reputation in the network concerned with legislation, standardisation and drawing up guidelines. So the client base for this new business was already there and easy to contact. Fugro originally used to chase projects rather than clients, but will now act more as a network organisation.

Dutch Regional Water Control Boards are obliged by law to test the safety of the dykes in their district every five years. And anyone who wants to build, say, a wind turbine on or near a dyke needs permits. Fugro can assist by investigating the structure and condition of a dyke or levee. The results of these studies show whether water is seeping through the body of the dyke and whether it carries soil particles. Tiny leaks must be detected before they become any larger and threaten the dyke's soundness.

From large-scale to fine-scale

This technology's development has a clear link with other Fugro applications such as *FLI-MAP* topography, which surveys geometries, heights and other conditions and records these in 3D models, combining the various data. In conjunction with Deltares, Fugro has developed special modules for application in the US, where interest has grown considerably since *Hurricane Katrina*. By linking our numerical models, we are able to compute thousands of profiles within a few hours and locate weak spots very rapidly. The US operating company Fugro West has conducted successful tests in this field. The automated computation of failure mechanisms is an attractive spin-off.

2027

CONSEQUENCES OF CLIMATE CHANGE

MAARTEN VAN DER HARST
FUGRO MIDDLE EAST,
UAE

There is a lot of land along the coastline in the Arabian Gulf, which are very low and just above sea level. Apart from the so called Sabkha areas, which are just above mean sea level, there are many developed areas in Dubai and Abu Dhabi for instance, which are also just above sea level. A substantial rise in sea level, say 0.5 to 1.0 meters, would result in those developed areas needing to be protected by levees. This by itself would create a lot of opportunities for Fugro in terms of soil investigations, land survey and aerial surveys.

▲

*Deltaworks barrier
in The Netherlands*

▼

*Fli-Map helicopter
above levee,
California, USA*

So-called flood control is becoming increasingly important all over the world, not least because of the climate issue. Fugro possesses all the expertise required, from large-scale to fine-scale: from general images through satellite observations and detailed airborne images from planes and helicopters, to observations on and in the ground. Topographic maps are made with contours (lines of equal altitude) that indicate the deeper parts, where flood waters will enter and how that water will subsequently spread. These maps are used as input for inundation models: useful information, say for planning evacuation procedures.

VEERMAN ON WATER

Sea level will rise and fall, and will keep doing so. According to geologists, the present-day rise is nothing new – geologists think in terms of tens of thousands of years. For the inhabitants of low-lying delta regions, however, short-term protection against high water levels is a matter of great urgency, one could even say: a matter of life and death! Anno 2012, they don't need to worry about the situation in 10,000 years' time, but they do worry about the world in which their grandchildren will live.

Food supply

Veerman: 'My grandson is ten years old now. By the time he retires, sea level may have risen by 60 centimetres – so he will live to see it. Today's newborns' life expectancy is almost a hundred years. The predicted sea-level rise will occur within a lifetime. Governments of low-lying countries all around the world will have to take measures. If you wish to continue farming, fertile deltas will have to be protected from flooding and salinisation, and fresh water will have to be brought in. Plants can be made more salt-resistant by genetic modification, but this won't be sufficient. Organic agriculture will not nearly be capable of supplying the world with food; organic produce is a luxury, intended for prosperous Western consumers. We won't be able to escape genetically modifies crops. Eighty per cent of all the soya in the world is genetically modified, and 60% of all the corn. In a famine situation, the sources and compositions of food are irrelevant. Many years ago, people in the Netherlands said: Let's forget about our petty-scale farming – let's simply get our food from Brazil! That works well if everybody agrees, until there is a hitch somewhere. The EU needs a billion meals per day. No regime has ever stayed in power with a hungry population. Hungry people are capable of anything.

'The looters in London in 2011 were people who felt they had lost control of their own lives because of the advent of other cultures and habits. They're experiencing the negative effects of scaling up and globalisation first hand.

Cees Veerman, professor in Sustainable Rural Development at Wageningen and Tilburg Universities, had held many senior management positions and has been a member of several supervisory boards throughout his career. After he stepped down as Minister of Agriculture, Nature and Food Quality in 2007, he was appointed Chairman of the *Sustainable Coastal Development Committee,* also referred to as the *New Delta Committee* or *Veerman Committee.* This committee presented its recommendations on protecting the Netherlands from the consequences of sea-level rise in September 2008. Veerman has also been a member of the executive committee of a *Water Purification Board* and an acting dike reeve – Veerman and water belong together.

Globalisation has tightened the web; when the Chinese have a problem with an additive in their baby food, Dutch dairy farmers notice it in their milk prices. Now agriculture is becoming a more local affair again. Production closer to home is better – one still has some influence there.'

What is a plan?

'Many people feel they have lost control of their own lives and are, moreover, uncertain whether their children will be better off than they are themselves. That urge has existed always and everywhere: children should be better off than their parents. Parents in Asia are also scrimping all their lives to save up for a good education for their children. Children grow up with the problems of their own generation and find their own solutions. Thanks to computer technology, we can post our messages for free and in no time at all across the world – fascinating! My father wouldn't have believed that I can call Australia on my mobile phone, sitting peacefully in my own easy chair, and yet the call is coming through crystal clear. These technological advances bring together different cultures at the same moment. This requires adaptations and coping emotionally, and that sometimes causes confusion. I've noticed it in discussions with Asians about their delta plans. Their definition of a plan differs from the Dutch one. For us, a plan is an idea, a possibility, a vision, a series of connected thoughts on a particular concept, meant to be discussed, cleaned up, rounded out, and subsequently implemented step-wise. We stay open to advances in understanding. In Asia, a plan is a previously determined line of marching, a railway timetable, a script. They are used to working with detailed five-year objectives, deadlines and interim results.'

The Netherlands and water

'The (economically) most important part of the Netherlands lies several metres below sea level. The fundamental causes of a rise in sea level and larger river discharges are known. Doom mongers complain that everything will go awry, but they should see things in perspective. The Dutch have many centuries' experience in defending their country against high water levels. This has aroused international interest, from all parts of the world. *The Delta Committee,* which prepared the integrated plan for the Netherlands, regularly receives invitations to come and speak at international conferences about the way these things are tackled in the Netherlands. It is common knowledge that we have been managing water for years. They respect our technology, but above all our warning systems, and technologies for spotting and averting threats. There is widespread interest in the way we have organised our water boards. That governance structure has been in place here for over five hundred years, with a direct link between the common good, the burden that can be shouldered by the community

1967

Onto the North Sea

—
—

The management set up a Geodesy and Project Measurement department. It wanted to process the land measurements for plotting out CPT locations in a more scientific and responsible way.

Fugro took on research jobs for large infrastructure orders. It made maps for zoning plans and industrial developments and did measurement work for the maintenance and inspection of plant in the oil and gas industries. Fugro got its first job in Saudi Arabia, when Nederhorst built an airport in Riyadh.

Oil rigs made an appearance in the North Sea, where enormous oil and gas fields had been discovered. The American companies brought along their own expertise in the shape of McClelland. Based in Houston, this company had been engaged in offshore ground investigation since 1948. Heerema, a Dutch constructional company, was specialised in building oil rigs. After months of experiments carried out from the *Explorer*, Heerema's ship, to discover the ways and means of drilling in the North Sea for ground investigation in order to construct platforms, Heerema realised that there should be a laboratory on board. LGM declined the offer to equip it but Fugro's Herman Zuidberg happily arrived on board with a laboratory but with no experience. He had to get started straight

and the associated democratic decision-making process. How finely woven should a governance structure be to be effective and efficient? Most people have no idea of the intricacies of the subject.'

Delta Alliance

'After a flood, the government may claim that the dykes were strong enough and that there is less damage than expected, but that's not the way it works. As long as nothing serious happens, dyke maintenance is postponed. Deltares, an independent knowledge institute and adviser on delta technology, has developed modelling software for forecasting dangerous situations on the basis of rainfall and river-discharge patterns. It helps, but more is needed: one has to take physical action, move ground, build sluices. 'Global delta problems have resulted in the so-called *Delta Alliance,* a platform for sharing knowledge. The Netherlands is the place to come to. We have two lines of approach now: blue and green water. The places to go to for blue water are Delft University of Technology, Deltares and Rijkswaterstaat – they are in charge of dams, dikes and sluices. For green water, one can consult Alterra in Wageningen – they are building with nature. A new combination between green and blue was devised in the Netherlands. The construction of the Eastern Scheldt dam is fascinating and world famous, and yet not entirely successful; an 80% tidal flux is apparently insufficient to maintain an ecological balance. We have to integrate the expertise from the domains of blue and green water.'

Exporting know-how

'More than half the world's population lives in river deltas and more than half of all the world's food is grown there. But population growth rates in the Nile and Mekong deltas and the Bangladesh river area are the fastest in the world and poverty is worst there. This creates major problems. Vietnam has asked our *Delta Committee* for help with their *Mekong Delta Plan.* Approximately 25 million people live in the Mekong Delta. A Dutch team is helping to formulate that plan, by analogy with the Dutch one. The basic ideas must be ready by September 2012. After that they want to tackle the Red River, near Hanoi, where problems are similarly severe. Abstraction of groundwater is causing Ho Chi Minh City (formerly Saigon) to sink approximately ten centimetres a year, irrespective of the rise in sea level. So that adds to the effect locally. The Vietnamese government takes matters seriously and has only one wish: an effective plan.
'Since the Vietnam War, Vietnam's population has doubled to over 80 million people. Agriculture is still vital there. More than half of all Vietnam's rice is grown in the Mekong Delta and the country is South-East Asia's main rice exporter. However, the infrastructure leaves much to be desired. There are only bumpy roads, over long distances. The entire infrastructure needs

1967

> away with a small order from Shell. The client was impressed by Zuidberg's explanation of his tests but it failed to supply Fugro with much work initially. The tried and trusted McClelland landed almost all orders for ground investigation through drilling.
—
And Andy Warhol's painted soup cans made him a star of the art world, adored and vilified in equal measure.

2027

TRANSITION FROM FOSSIL
TO RENEWABLE ENERGY

GRANT AITCHISON
FUGRO SUBSEA SERVICES,
UK

Based on the current estimate which is that right now, 95% of global commercial energy is based on fossil fuels and nuclear power, we believe that by 2027 this will have reduced to around 60%. Wind power will continue its present situation and still be getting the most attention, though solar energy will be pushing hard in second place.

to be renovated, because of the rapidly growing population, industrialisation and the increasing number of small businesses with their specific transport problems. That's a rather tall order. An integrated approach for such a plan is new for these people.'

Risk and protection

'All over the world, people are seeking out the fertile soils of deltas and volcano slopes. They take risks and are inclined to underestimate the dangers. One of the most important tasks of a government is to protect its citizens against calamities, irrespective of these being aggressive nations or natural disasters. Every country has to arm itself against that. All over the world, protection against water involves a lot of effort. One metre of sea-level rise means this or that, and therefore requires such-and-such a measure to avert a catastrophe. There is a continuing debate on the minimum or maximum expected rise in sea level, but estimates are getting higher. The likelihood of sea level rising by a metre within a certain period is unknown, but a government must be prepared to face up to the worst-case scenario and know its potential consequences.

'The appealing side of the rising sea level is that the process is so gradual. One can prepare for it at leisure, consider what to do and discuss it, take only those decisions that can't be postponed, and subsequently build on these. Our *Delta Committee* has recommended responding to the growing knowledge and understanding of climate developments. Then, measures can be adjusted accordingly. One has to be prepared to face up to the worst but there's no need for the solution to be ready the day after tomorrow.

'When discussing the possibility of using the IJsselmeer for water storage, one of the ladies present wondered whether that meant she should bring in her garden furniture tomorrow. The general public apparently thinks: *Goodness, the water will be a metre higher by tomorrow.* People come up with the weirdest solutions, such as moving en masse to the higher grounds in the eastern part of the country. That can't be done. What about Tata Steel/Hoogovens and the petrochemical industry near Rotterdam? Seventy five percent of the Gross National Product is earned in the lowest-lying part of the country, several metres below sea level. *The Delta Committee* has estimated the value that needs to be protected by the Dutch government. It amounts to several hundreds of billions of euros. Can such a risk be insured at all? And if so, at what cost? Our studies showed that insurance premiums would be so high that effective protection against high water would turn out a lot cheaper: € 1.2 billion per year, less than 0.2‰ of the GNP. Nobody can insure his own house against fire and storm damage for less than 0.2‰. Why shouldn't we all jointly invest this relatively small amount to protect ourselves and our capital, keep our feet dry and supply ourselves with fresh water?'

1968

Cone testing at sea

—
—

Fugro's friction cone penetrometer and inclinometer were operational on time to carry out CPTs in the seabed. A gas blow-out had taken place on one of Shell's oil rigs and its owner wanted tests done to check the density of the sand on which the rig had been built. Shell's regular supplier McClelland wasn't interested; the CPTs meant nothing to it, let alone how to perform them. Virtually no-one had experience with CPTs in the seabed and Fugro seized this opportunity to demonstrate Dutch enterprise. Herman Zuidberg's ingenuity and perseverance helped to usher in a glorious period in which Fugro acquired a strong position in the field of offshore geotechnics.

Fugro's relationship with Heerema became more close-knit. Heerema had the ships and did the drilling; Fugro originally just did the geotechnical work. Fugro provided operators, mechanical engineers, electronics engineers. There were engineers who understood the soil layers, carried out tests and made calculations. But they did more than that: they used their eyes and ears on board and studied Heerema's drilling technique and learned from it. Heerema watched as Fugro slowly but surely took over the role of main contractor and in turn tried to take over Fugro's geotechnical department. Fugro however wished to remain independent. Heerema was the contractor and provided the infrastructure so that Fugro could set to work. The oil and gas industry on Curaçao provided constant work, which justified setting up

>

Change and movement

'Everyone has to eat. You can't hold back the African refugees. We have implemented the *Schengen rules* in Europe to eliminate internal border controls, based on Friedman's philosophy: rely on economic forces as much as possible, because that will create prosperity for everybody; the market doesn't make mistakes and will correct itself. Unfortunately the banking crisis proved different!

'As a result of climate change, the important agricultural production regions in the world will suffer from droughts. Production losses in Africa are estimated to run up to 10 to 15%, and the population there will double within the next fifty years while the situation is already catastrophic in some areas. It's not just about good seeds, but also about good governance that promotes investments. A hectare of farmland in Brazil yields on average ten times as much as in Nigeria.

'Climate change will intensify the spread of diseases. Bluetongue has been endemic in the Netherlands for a number of years – before then the disease never made it past the Alps. We will have to deal with insects and fungi that couldn't have survived here in the past. Beeches and other tree species will disappear, and others will take their places, with different birds on their branches. It's all changing; everything is on the move.'

1968

>

a branch there. The same happened in Suriname, prompted by the construction of Zanderij airport and projects for the local bauxite industry. Although the branches in Willemstad and Paramaribo were nothing special, they did give Fugro the image of a multinational company. This was very important for oil companies who wanted others to do the geotechnical work.

Onshore geotechnics in the Netherlands had long been a regional activity. The clients liked to communicate with contractors who spoke their dialect and were familiar with the local geology from personal experience. This is why Fugro divided the Netherlands into regions each with its own office. The most important of these was the head office in Leidschendam: this was where more than half the orders were fulfilled.

The entire organisation was geared to speed: get an order one week, execute it the next. There was rarely more than three weeks' work in the portfolio.

A temporary building was erected on Veurse Achterweg for the Geodesy and Project Measurement departments.

—

And student protests in Paris led worldwide to *the sweet revolution.*

Mekong Delta, Vietnam

500 pounder, traced by Fugro near Paris, France

MEASURING THE MODERN WAY

The days of manually filled-out measuring reports and daily and weekly cone penetrationa test reports are almost over. These days, measuring tools are inserted into the ground, put into wireless communication with our recording stations and subsequently with the client through the internet. Clients can instantaneously monitor on their screens what is happening in the field and can keep track of the measurements real-time. They demand automatically generated data, which they can examine themselves. That way a building contractor monitors his own process, and a client can monitor progress.

The demand for locating unexploded Second World War ordnance is rising explosively. To this end, Fugro performs cone penetration tests using modern magnetometers that detect metal. In Paris, Fugro investigated the presence of unexploded bombs on a military site along the *Boulevard Périférique*. During the Second World War, Renault's and Citroën's automobile factories were located here, and they were the targets of Allied bombers. Statistics suggest that three more unexploded five-hundred pounders must still be present somewhere in these grounds. That's what you call booming business.

2027

COMMUNICATION METHODS

TIM DUNNE
FUGRO WEST,
USA

By 2027 communication methods will have evolved such that staff will carry one hand held device to cover all forms of communication, i.e. no longer will a laptop, *Blackberry*, *IPad*, *Kindle* etc all be carried around. They will have been replaced by one low cost A5 size device. The device will also have the ability and resolution to be used for the equivalent of *Skype*/Video Conferencing, and have voice recognition built in. This form of Skype/Video Conferencing communication will become more prevalent as staff in certain positions become more home based.

POSITIONING

Rob Luijnenburg, global service line manager at Fugro Survey, stresses the importance of more accurate offshore positioning; Jackson Chang, managing director of Fugro Subsea Services in Singapore, talks about the strategic positioning of operational companies in Fugro's network.

'When the oil and gas industry's production activities moved offshore', Rob explains, 'they started in shallow water with drilling platforms on legs standing on the sea floor. As the water in which we had to work became deeper, the number of challenges grew. We could no longer use the same platform design, so production facilities were increasingly placed on the sea floor and the produced oil or gas transported through pipelines to shore or to existing platforms. Fugro Subsea Services assists in the installation, inspection, maintenance and repairs of these facilities, and in dismantling once production from a field has ceased. In deep water, beyond where divers can work, we are using remotely controlled equipment, which critically depends on very accurate positioning.

One aspect of present-day technical developments is that more and more basic knowledge, expertise and intelligence are *pre-packaged* in tools, software and systems. Twenty years ago, offshore positioning with an accuracy of five metres was difficult, and required specialists to achieve. Whoever wants to know their position these days only needs to hold up their mobile phone. Tools are becoming smaller, and more powerful. You can do more things now without having to think about them. When you park your car, the number of beeps tells you how much space there is left to the next bumper – even the business of reversing is moving forward.'

Filtering and selecting

'After the first nautical map was published in the 16th century, basically not a lot changed for four hundred years; a cartographer recorded information on a sheet of paper and sold it to someone who needed it for his job. After four centuries of peace and quiet, the discipline changed completely within two decades. Everybody can now download a profusion of information through *Google Earth* and view it on the screen of their own PC, smartphone or *iPad*. Wherever you are, you can find an answer to virtually any question. This profusion is accompanied by new challenges. Bridal couples needn't

fear that there won't be enough photographs of the most beautiful day of their lives: all their friends and relatives will send them their digital pictures. And there they are: a young couple at a computer screen with a mind-numbing quantity of hundreds of photographs. They don't get around to making them into an album. This characterises general technological progress: the challenge is not just in the gathering but also in the filtering, making a choice. What selection captures the essence, and shows the real thing? And then it comes to interpreting the data – this can greatly affect the end result. Users of digital nautical maps know little about the underlying measurements. They can zoom in on their screen onto a particular location on the map where the water depth is indicated. They then assume that that spot is exactly so deep, when in reality the depth mentioned is usually an average of the shallowest depth measured so as to prevent ships running aground. Electronic nautical maps are designed to show safe depths, not necessarily all depths. What's more, the sea floor changes all the time, in any case near the shore; just think of the positions of the tidal channels in the Dutch
Wadden Sea moving about under the influence of waves and currents. Technological advances are amazing and many people can't keep up. Because new tools contain ever more knowledge and GPS receivers are even built into the smallest mobile phones, few realise the meaning of the numbers on their screen. They think these are accurate down to half a metre – as suggested by the number zero or five behind the decimal point – but in reality they can find themselves way off the mark. In a sense, the young engineers who join Fugro are also starting anew; they arrive with different technical and intellectual baggage than in the past. That's why *the Fugro Academy* was originally established, where Fugro staff can take all sorts of training and refresher courses.'

Onshore is different

'Positioning is not an end product but a tool. Oil companies request as accurate an indication as possible as to where they should place and anchor their facilities on the sea floor. To gather and unearth the necessary data, a number of consecutive measurements is required. A chain is as strong as its weakest link, and the links in an offshore survey comprise positioning, the effects of salinity and temperature on the acoustic signals we use to survey the subsurface, and the hardness of the ground surface. By accurately adding potential errors in measurements, you can obtain an indication of the potential error in, for instance, a position at a water depth of 2,500 metres. In order to obtain a final result that is as dependable as possible, most clients will request the best tools for each step, i.e. the best satellite positioning at sea level, the best acoustic underwater equipment, the best echo sounder etc. Some building companies that were accustomed to building onshore wind turbines believed that they could directly apply their experience and

1969

Collaboration with Cesco

—
—

Fugro was increasingly expanding as an engineering company for soil mechanics and geodesy and wanted to be known as such, but it kept the name Fugro. This autonomous expansion necessitated a new investment, on an adjacent industrial site, even though the existing site was not being used to the full. There were thoughts about a merger with Cesco, who did offshore geophysical investigations with acoustic systems. The two companies had already worked together on offshore operations and shared an office in Singapore. Ideas for a joint air-mapping department with KLM Aerocarto came to nothing.

Fugro's boffins were constantly experimenting with the *Sea Bull* and other appliances for offshore CPT work, but underwater technology proved a hard nut to crack. They had to get used to the utterly different scale and translating theory into practical solutions needed a great deal of thought. It required specific knowledge, an understanding of the factors at play in open water and more money than the research budgets would allow.

Fugro wanted to have as much in-house technology as possible and keep its hard-earned know-how and sophisticated working methods to itself, so as to be able to build up a good competitive position. It was prepared to stick its neck out and distinguish itself by doing more experimental investigations.

—

And Neil Armstrong's first step on the moon signified a giant leap for mankind.

systems offshore. They were in for a rude awakening. Offshore surveying is a specialist job and an entirely new world for those who come from the shore. Fugro knows a thing or two about it: we also started onshore and learned by hard earned experience when we started to do soil investigations in the North Sea and the Gulf of Mexico.'

Remote control

'Remote control will become increasingly important. Not only for ROVs (Remotely Operated Vehicles) and AUVs (Autonomous Underwater Vehicles), but also in operations support. Our Leidschendam employees follow 24/7, real time on their screens what is happening on a floating production facility offshore Gabon, for example. All the instrumentation systems on board are also installed in our control room. The captain on board is responsible for production – not for positioning. We are continually taking measurements and making sure the platform remains in the right spot. If it doesn't, we immediately get in touch or sound an alarm. We use the same routine to supervise less experienced staff members moving a drilling platform. There is no room for mistakes; a platform costs half a million dollars a day. We look over their shoulders from a distance at critical moments and, if necessary, assist them.'

Future for AUVs

An AUV is a self-propelled, unmanned submarine that moves autonomously. It is powered by batteries and can go anywhere. It maps the seabed and gathers information such as the location of wreck. Twenty years ago, operations in 500-metre-deep water were virtually unthinkable – these places were practically beyond reach. These days, AUVs gather data at water depths of over three kilometres. The equipment is becoming increasingly intelligent and the technology will have been updated completely within ten years. Demand for fossil fuels is sufficiently large to justify major capital investments. Offshore surveying for oil and gas exploration in the Arctic is a hot item. Scientists carrying out surveys under the Arctic ice cap also use on AUVs.

'Oil and gas exploration on the open seas is done with modern seismic vessels, towing twelve-kilometre-long cables. If these vessels sail through floating ice, they keep losing their cables. So we needed to come up with another idea, because there was hardly any existing technology. Equipment developed by the defence industry falls under military secrecy. Anyway, the slow-moving military development processes and private enterprise's drive for profit often results in products being available on the commercial market sooner. This happened in the *Gulf War:* the US government developed its own GPS equipment, but it wasn't ready when the war started: so soldiers were equipped with standard commercial receivers, off the shelf.'

2027

CONSEQUENCES OF
CLIMATE CHANGE

RALF TRAPPHOFF
FUGRO CONSULT,
GERMANY

Height and safety of dam and flood protection measures at coasts will enforce innovative geotechnical solutions; geotechnical monitoring will be essential for estuarine areas; due to sea level rise flood protection measures at deltas and rivers request flood risk evaluation procedures/ methodes for public and private clients (i.e. EU directive); climate change will also lead to more drought areas – drinking water supply, water for mining processes and agriculture will be a challenge for our water management group.

Check on ROV manipulator

Launching an AUV

Integrating knowledge

Foreseeing a rapid growth in the market for survey and ROVs, Fugro acquired Thales Geosolutions in 2003, including its specialist know-how of this high-tech equipment. Then the group focused vigorously on the design and production of these vehicles.

As Jackson Chang says: 'Our people have been successful in developing subsea technology further, and will continue to be so for many years to come. Fugro is now a leading manufacturer in this field. But our assignment is not only technological, but also commercial. Fugro Subsea Services is a profit-driven business, not a scientific institute. The quality of our basic hardware probably differs little from that of other providers, but we can make the difference because of the integrated Fugro network, including its state-of-the-art geotechnical systems. We build and maintain ROVs exclusively for our sister companies – we guard our technology like *the Crown Jewels* – and continually try to keep abreast of the technology developed by our sister companies to be able to apply and exchange know-how. Because of a growing demand, we may have to double our current production of around nine ROVs per year. That requires flexibility of our electro-technical, mechanical and software specialists and the same applies to the organisation in which they are working together. As a manager, I'm continually trying to make them aware of what the future may have in store. It would be great if the company could grow into a breeding ground for young Fugro talents.

'And I believe this is where the challenge lies for the entire group: our first priority is that Fugro meets its shareholders' expectations by making a profit, but there should also be constant attention to specialist trends, to research and development, and to the company's image as a source of inspiration for young people. Fugro can also distinguish itself worldwide by contributing to solutions for environmental issues and training new generations of engineers.'

Strategic positioning

So, positioning, in many different senses, plays an important part in Fugro's successful history, its present-day existence and its future. Strategic positioning requires a totally different *global positioning system* to that in Fugro employees' cars for finding the most attractive (or fastest) route to work and the GPS our offshore experts use to find the best places for anchoring drilling platforms.

Which position will Fugro aspire in a world where surprising and bewildering developments are happening and will continue to happen simultaneously in so many areas? There's plenty going on in the geopolitical balance of power, climate change, demographic developments and energy supply. What technology, fields and activities will the company focus on

---

2027

TRANSITION FROM FOSSIL TO RENEWABLE ENERGY

BERND JEUKEN
FUGRO-OSAE, GERMANY

No doubt, the ratio will shift towards non-fossil energy, but we will use more and more energy all the same. So within such short lapse of time, I don't expect much of a regress to fossil energy, and Fugro will continue to play an even stronger role in exploration of these resources. Nevertheless, musing 15 years ahead, I would give hydrogen fuel cell technology the key breakthrough on its way to become a major source of power.

But Alas! This is old news, from Jules Verne's 1874 novel *The Mysterious Island*, where protagonist Cyrus Smith predicts: "Water is the coal of the future" and will be used to power everything [...] by using electricity to break water down into its component elements [...] hydrogen and oxygen [...] which are then used to provide power".

in the medium to long term? What visions and ideas exist, internally and externally, and which are relevant and have prospects? What perspectives are technically challenging and sufficiently profitable? What is the best form of organisation for the group with its many global operating companies?

Rob: 'Obviously, one activity is more profitable than another, but the size of this company makes it possible for some activities to be profitable thanks to the networking synergies within the group. Without the links between all these companies, some activities would hold little or no interest. The whole is greater than the sum of its parts. The group's size and geographical spread account for much of its strength.'

2027

CONSEQUENCES
OF CLIMATE CHANGE

MARK SINCLAIR
FUGRO LADS CORPORATION,
AUSTRALIA

Climate change and rising sea levels are dramatically increasing the requirement and frequency for surveys to support many vulnerable coastal communities. Coastal zone management, including habitat mapping, inundation modeling and nautical charting for safe navigation are placing greater demands on the information needs of decision makers. Fugro LADS is playing an important role in developing, building and operating Fugro's own Airborne LiDAR Bathymetry systems that safely and efficiently collect depth, reflectance and imagery data in the coastal zone. Fugro LADS is rising to the challenge and assisting governments, communities and commercial organizations better manage these threatened near shore environments.

*Satelite disc for
high accuracy
positioning*

*Gyro Calibration,
Gulf of Thailand*

*Satelite positioning
for survey work,
Oman*

WORLD WATER ISSUES

In the Netherlands we may be tempted to think that flood risk is the world's most important water issue, but this is probably not true for the whole world. Water has a wide range of functions and all of them may involve problems and risks. As engineering has a lot to offer in all of these cases, it is worth our while to consider the most prominent issues.

Water as a condition for living

Worldwide probably the most important function of water is its importance to life. Availability, accessibility and good quality of water are crucial to all life on earth. Recent studies have shown that water scarcity is driven primarily by demographic processes, more so than by climate change. In densely populated areas, safe recirculation via the minor urban and the major hydrological cycle is therefore vitally important. This raises engineering issues such as sewage networks, waste water treatment, water quality assurance, water supply systems, water storage, reservoir operation, etc.

Water as a threat

Water can be a threat in different ways. Storm surges, floods, dambreak surges involve the risk of loss of people's lives, livestock, material property and infrastructures, as well as severe societal and economic disruption. The example of New Orleans, where the economy five years after *Katrina* has recovered to only 50% of its original size, shows how intrusive floods can be. Waterborne diseases may lead to epidemics, waterborne pollutants to loss of lives and habitat. Engineering can help reducing the former risks via flood protection works and sediment management measures (many rivers are lying above the surrounding land due to poor sediment management), the latter by measures guaranteeing a good water quality.

Huib de Vriend is Director Science of Deltares. The mission of this institute is to acquire the knowledge needed for sustainable living and working in low-lying deltaic areas. It does so by applied research, by transforming knowledge into practically usable products, expertise and services and by testing these in specialist advisory projects. Prof. de Vriend is a civil engineer by training and received his PhD from Delft University of Technology. From this position, he acts as director of the Ecoshape Foundation, which coordinates the national innovation programme *Building with Nature*. This programme is executed by a broad consortium of government institutions, academia, applied research organisations, consultants and engineering contractors. Huib de Vriend is a member of the thinktank on flood safety of the Netherlands Ministry of Transport, Public Works and Water Management.

Water as an opportunity and carrier of functions

Water provides for a variety of opportunities to increase human wellbeing. International trade depends to a large extent on transport over sea and inland waters, water is a most popular object of recreation, and many people like living on waterfronts. Engineering works, such as harbours, access-channels, navigable rivers, bank and coastal protection works, as well as bridges, tunnels and aquaducts are necessary to facilitate this.
The functions carried by water are many. Water provides for food (fisheries, aquaculture, irrigation) and energy (algae), but it also plays a crucial role as a carrier of waterborne transport, of recreation on, in and under water and of the natural environment. Moreover, it has important regulatory functions, for instance in relation to urban heat islands. The need for engineering works to enable these functions is obvious in urban environments. In more natural environments, sustainability, impact reduction and compensation measures are important aspects of human activities, requiring clever engineering based on thorough knowledge of the environmental system's functioning. The concept of *Building with Nature* attempts to create win-win situations for economy and nature in case of hydraulic engineering infrastructure development, by designing the infrastructure in such a way, that the forces of nature contribute to its realization and at the same time create new opportunities for nature. In some cases, this approach turns out to be cheaper in the long run than traditional engineering.

Water as a carrier of energy

Hydropower is a well-known way to turn the potential or kinetic energy of water into other, more utile forms of energy. Large engineering works, such as dams and reservoirs, but also tidal energy plants, have been built to exploit this. Nowadays, reservoir maintenance and dam removal are becoming increasingly important. Water, however, also has a large heat capacity, which means that it is a good medium to provide for temporary heat storage and withdrawal. Central heating in houses makes use of this principle, and so does the cooling of power plants by water. Recently new technology for heat storage and withdrawal in and from groundwater has been developed. Here, too, good engineering is the key to exploitation.

Water as a 'carrier' of land

Usually, people take a stable height of the land for granted, without realizing that this land surface is partly carried by water and/or gas. Only when large amount of groundwater or gas are withdrawn from the subsoil, they are confronted with this, usually only some time after the act.
A dramatic example is the city of Jakarta, which faces some 10 centimetres

1970

On into the world

—

—

Fugro opened branches in the Netherlands, in Eindhoven and Arnhem. In those times of mergers, expansion and collaboration Fugro maintained close contact with Heidemij (now Arcadis), Nederhorst United and the Research Department of the University of Florida. Two American engineers from California had heard of Fugro's state-of-the-art CPT techniques and made the trip to Leidschendam. They presented a plan to join with Fugro in a new office for soil mechanics and geology in the US. As a result, Fugro Inc. was founded in Long Beach, CA. A modern CPT truck was shipped to the States to introduce the Dutch CPT methods in that country.

—

And Japan made major inroads on the world market with cars and televisions.

per year subsidence due to groundwater withdrawal. This creates not only an increasing flood risk, it also wrecks the water management system (sewage and water supply networks, storm water discharge, etc.) and may even destabilize the subsoil (cf. the Groningen earthquakes, due to gas extraction). Reducing these risks requires clever and adaptable engineering, since these processes tend to continue for many years, once they have been initiated.

Water as an access to scarce resources

Many important resources are buried under water, are concentrated on the ocean floor, or are moving in the ocean water column. Others, like wind energy, are more available at open sea than on land. In many sea-bordering countries, this has led to a flourishing offshore industry, putting special demands on engineering skills, to enable working in extreme environments, to guarantee stability and safety of structures, to minimise environmental risks, etc.

All these issues require clever engineering, making optimum use of the properties and the dynamics of the environmental and governance systems one is working in. The basis of such engineering is a good insight into the functioning of those systems and the capacity to predict how they will respond to the envisaged intervention. For the environmental system, data and predictive models, preferably mutually integrated, are often indispensable tools. Bringing this technology further requires an intense and interactive cooperation between academic research, applied research, product development and practical application, plus room (physical as well as administrative) for experimenting, launching customers and sometimes even new legislation and procedures to make innovative solutions possible. If properly managed and financed, the collaboration between private sector, government and knowledge institutes initiated in the Dutch *topsectorenbeleid* (prime sectors policy) can be the basis of such an integrated approach.

Water barrier, Algeria

Flip-Map survey,
Kinderdijk,
The Netherlands

1971

Capturing the essence

—

The head office moved to the new premises in Leidschendam. By now Fugro had a staff of some 200 in the Netherlands and several dozen in the branches in the US, Singapore and the Caribbean.
The demand for offshore CPTs was growing by leaps and bounds. Fugro's technology was ready in time for a large job off the Scottish coast – far offshore, almost on the open ocean. Herman Zuidberg and company thought hard about the basic principle of cone penetration testing at sea and brought together all the components. The result was christened the *Sea Calf*; this cone penetrometer rig had a 2.5 ton thrust capacity and after a few months' development as much as 7.5 tons. Equipped with a self-developed cone penetration technique, the *Sea Calf* could perform tests at what were then spectacular water depths of 150 metres and establish how dense or hard the soil was below the seabed. One CPT a week was still pretty slow going but they finally captured the essence. The Americans didn't believe in it but European oil companies were convinced.

—

And Willy Brandt, Federal Chancellor of West Germany, knelt before the Warsaw Ghetto Uprising memorial as a symbol of the then-new policy of détente between East and West.

▲

*Drilling for water in the
Middle East*

◄

*River floodings
near Cuijk,
The Netherlands*

WATER IS BECOMING MORE IMPORTANT

Fugro's Water Services business line combines the expertise of Fugro Consult in Berlin, Fugro West in the US, and Fugro GeoServices in the Netherlands. It addresses water defence and flood control or, conversely, drought relief, water resources management and the management of urban water and sewage systems.

In the coming decade, Fugro will focus more on the growing challenges created by climate change. Drinking water and irrigation water are becoming scarcer and water shortages create tension and even conflict in some areas.

In terms of percentages, the Water Services business line may not contribute much to Fugro's overall financial results as yet – particularly when compared to the oil and gas industry – but the appeal of Water Services is that operating companies from all our divisions are joining forces. Fugro Airborne, for example, has until now been active in ore exploration, but its sensitive equipment has already been used in planes for searching for underground water resources in Florida, California and Australia and imaging these resources.

In many countries, water is free – you simply dig a well and *Bob's your uncle* – but the significance of water as a resource is on the increase in ever more places. That means business and for a commercial company such as Fugro, the trick is to manifest itself in that field. Special hardware is required for the search for water and a lot of money is involved in measuring, registration, water management and the efficient use of water resources. In the coming years, Fugro will step up its efforts in this field and become more proactive. A pilot meeting with potential clients organised by Fugro in England was very successful and immediately resulted in new commissions. This development is inspiring other operating companies to become involved in water as well.

2027

COMMUNICATION METHODS

GREGORY PALEOLOG
FUGRO AIRBORNE SURVEYS
TORONTO, CANADA

The telephone will still be dominant. E-mail will be used and will become indistinguishable from text and other web-based messaging services. Secure web networking/meeting systems with text, voice, and imaging will become effective and pervasive for most group communication and discussion uses.

SAFETY AS AN EXPORT PRODUCT

Martin van der Meer is a technical manager at Fugro's Water Services business line, the worldwide network for expertise and business development in the field of water. His colleagues in Leidschendam mainly consider water from a geohydrological point of view and focus on groundwater and the exploration thereof. The Nieuwegein branch office, where Martin is working, focuses on combating flooding with dykes and other constructions.

Fugro traditionally carried out all the soil investigations required by dyke builders, learned all the ins and outs of the subject and later also presented itself as an adviser. 'In 2012, we are a focal support point for Fugro offices in other countries, and are increasingly called in by national government authorities. *Hurricane Katrina* was the trigger in 2005. In the wake of this disaster, several US Fugro operating companies were involved in mitigation projects. Authorities from all over the world grew interested and allocated budgets. Fugro could apply the Dutch expertise and skills in flood control.'

Dutch networks

There is a worldwide trend of people moving into deltas, where the economy thrives. They don't realise that rising sea level, soft soils and subsidence make deltas unsafe places – until nature strikes. Floods occur increasingly frequently, also as a result of climate change. 'Interest in the Dutch expertise on deltas is growing. This knowledge is vested in a network of universities, government institutions and companies. An important initiative, the Netherlands Water Partnership (NWP), unites Dutch water expertise and promotes cooperation in what is now known as *the golden triangle,* previously referred to as the KGB model (Knowledge, Government and Business). Governments – responsible for protecting both countries and their populations – usually take the initiative; knowledge institutes devise ways to intervene in the system and businesses translate these into solutions. This type of network fosters decisiveness. Dutch companies may be competitors in their own country, but abroad, their consortia present a united front in solving water-related challenges. There, they support each other. Similar consortia arise in knowledge development, e.g. *Building with Nature, IJkdijk* and *Flood Control 2015*. Fugro helped formulate proposals for the *Flood Control* programme. The Dutch government endorses the notion that it makes sense to pool the available knowledge and focus on practical problems. These trends result in government authorities from other countries calling in our assistance and wishing to share knowledge. The Netherlands regularly receives missions visiting the *Delta Works* project in Zeeland and the *Maeslantkering*, the storm surge barrier in the Nieuwe Waterweg between Rotterdam and Hook of Holland. We take representatives of countries faced with flooding on tours of the works that are part of the national *Room for the River* project.

'The increased demand for services in the field of water has resulted in wide-spread rapid knowledge development. We are still seen as the experts, but new expertise is developed elsewhere in the world, at the project sites. Fugro's world-wide network enables us to anticipate this.'

Vietnam and the Netherlands

'The situation in Vietnam is particularly interesting; it is facing the same problems as the Netherlands. The Vietnamese government is developing long-term plans for building dykes and is considering the relationship between dyke systems and added economic value. They want to build dykes for protection but also, at the same time, create economic value; spatial planning is part of it. They asked the Netherlands for advice and Fugro participated in the missions. Our knowledge can help in redesigning river systems and protecting the country from floods. Dutch people first think of safety when they hear the word water. Safety is created at three levels: prevention, spatial planning *(Am I making the right investments at the right place?* Or: *Why did we all decide to live in this marsh?)* and contingency plans *(What should I do when things go wrong? And then how can I get to safety?)*. We are working out of our Vietnamese office, supported by our Hong Kong and Singapore companies.'

Decide now what to do then

'We can endlessly debate the causes of sea level rise, but we had better address the question of what should happen when the water level rises faster than expected and exceeds a certain limit. We still have the time. Once a scenario has been drawn up, we can sit back and wait and see if and when it needs to be implemented. In the meantime nothing would be done that would prevent that scenario from being implemented. Capital investment in our dykes will continue, if only to maintain the current level of safety – even in the Netherlands many dykes still fail to meet the agreed safety standards.

'In some countries, however, floods are an immediate problem. We are familiar with the floods in Bangladesh, but in Hungary, for instance, the water systems are now facing a surprisingly dangerous situation. Up to now, discharges from the various rivers neatly took turns, but as a result of climate change they now frequently discharge their water at the same time. And then things can happen fast. We had better stop believing that we know what will happen by extrapolating data from the past. These calculations no longer match the facts and the chances of extreme storms may be greater

1972

Employee participation and sharing knowledge
–
–

Advocacy planning, or bilateral decision-making, arrived in the Netherlands and the Works Councils Act *(Wet op de Ondernemingsraden)* came into effect. Even Fugro, a company with few office workers and many free spirits used to managing their own affairs in remote places, set up its own Works Council *(ondernemingsraad)*. This had to regularly act as referee between the Cesco and Fugro people – who were often at loggerheads – when a Works Council is meant to be an advisory body. Fugro was all for discipline, but there was no question of clocking in and out after flexible working hours were introduced. There was little point, since Fugro consisted almost entirely of field staff.

Joustra wanted to do something special for his people for the firm's tenth anniversary and decided to hold a symposium about cone penetration testing and drilling. No-one had ever done such a thing before, but this pioneer had the guts to hire the Congresgebouw conference centre in The Hague for the occasion. It was to be a

>

than calculated. *Katrina* was a wake up-call, not just for the US but for many other countries, including the Netherlands. The Japan disaster had the same effect: countries made choices. Data will always be needed to understand what is happening. So, we have to remain active in that field – the issue is too complex to tackle purely from a scientific perspective.'

Accumulating data sets

'Fugro built up a cast-iron position in the oil and gas industry, which requires technological expertise, skills and experience. By combining these specific measuring techniques with those of the water scene, Fugro can strengthen its position in both sectors, as well as in others, by developing data-processing methods and making them available. We accumulate and combine data sets. By applying automatic computing models, we don't have to do every calculation separately. We are experimenting with automatic input files to generate data, for instance for entire dyke-ring systems instead of single dyke sections. To compute a number of scenarios, we switch on the computer in the evening and, by the time we return to the office in the morning, the computer has done some 60,000 calculations and produced map presentations of them. By modelling the combined measuring data through data processing and data fusion in such a way that they yield more information we can add value and also offer our services on other markets. 'One of the challenges is that the attitudes of government authorities in other countries are usually not as aligned with respect to water issues as they are in the Netherlands, where views on safety hardly differ. In the Netherlands, we have no political debate about the necessity of dyke maintenance; people at most marginally disagree. Stable countries, where knowledge is secured in centres of excellence, can persevere with sustainable developments. After *Katrina*, the US authorities are, for instance, stepping up the safety inspections of dykes. When approaching government authorities in developing countries, you need to have a long-term view as well as smart ideas.'

Finding water from the air

'In places where water is scarce instead of abundant, we are engaged in exploring for subsurface fresh-water resources and water management. In the course of time, Fugro has gathered many data. Most of these were gathered in airborne projects – fresh water can be found rapidly and cheaply with airborne geophysical surveys. Equipment hung under an airplane or helicopter broadcasts signals and records the responses a bit later. That enables us to compose a three-dimensional image of the subsurface. The system is similar to an MRI scan. By varying the frequencies, we can change the depth range and record information down to a depth of sometimes as much as 800 metres. The deeper you want to get, the coarser the signal should be. There are different techniques. One is suitable for clay, another

1972

>

trade symposium for everyone involved in Fugro's field of activity, friend and foe alike, where dissenting colleagues could cross swords on electrical and mechanical cone penetration testing, discuss the pros and cons of smooth, constricted and mechanical friction cones, and argue in favour of continuous or discontinuous CPTs. Experts from the Netherlands and abroad addressed an audience of 525. Fugro showed off its new achievement: the direct calculation of the friction ratio, the basis for classifying the soil and drawing a drill profile. The proceedings from this symposium would long serve as a reference work. It was such a success that Joustra decided to repeat the symposium every five years.

By now it was clear that the mechanical CPT method didn't work at sea. This meant the definitive breakthrough of the electrical method, which from then on qualified as the world standard. Although the success of the electric cone was secured at sea, this was soon repeated back on land. The constricted cone was relegated to the glass cases displaying antiquated devices.

Fugro and Cesco seemed to complement each other well. Cesco did offshore surveying and shareholders Nederhorst (Fugro) and Heidemij (Cesco) decided that the next time the Leidschendam office was enlarged, it would take into account the fact that Cesco was also to be accommodated there.

Fugro performed many CPTs in The Wash on England's east coast to facilitate the construction of dykes and fresh-water basins.

—

And the Club of Rome sounded the alarm with the book *The Limits to Growth*.

▶

*Hurricane Katrina 2005,
USA*

▼

*Wavescan buoy,
Adriatic Sea*

for rock. Fugro discovered that these techniques are not only useful to explore for natural resources but also for fresh water.
'An airplane flies high and fast, but measures less accurately than a helicopter. Fugro companies in Australia and Canada specialise in it. Airborne measurements make it possible to map an area quickly and cheaply. Data are available within a month, whereas surface-based measurements would take three years. Combining the two methods yields the best results.'

Data for decision-making

'I foresee a continuing development, in combination with satellite data. Satellites have been orbiting the Earth since 1994, but we are only recently starting to understand the data, giving us the feeling that we can look into the past. This fascinating insight led to a new concept: gather data now – the applications will follow later. Fugro not only collects data when commissioned by other parties, but also of its own accord, in order to use them afterwards for purposes we don't know of at present. It's a kind of time travel.
'Data management and storage are becoming increasingly important, at all kinds of levels. The World Bank sometimes makes public access to data a condition for funding. The Rotterdam local authorities have their entire territory surveyed every year, on the assumption that someone may ask a question that can make use of survey data from five years ago. Three-dimensional models of the city and harbours can then display changes over time. Demand for information is growing as clients wish to base their designs and planned developments on facts. They expect to be able to combine our data, juxtapose them in layers, so to speak.'

Watch the whizz kids

'Thanks to the new methods, many more data are becoming available than the client originally requested. We are deliberating how we could offer that additional information and in that case how we should organise our operational management.
'Looking fifteen years into the future is difficult – fifteen years ago, nobody foresaw that we can now point a mobile phone at an object and instantly receive relevant information. A university in California is running a fascinating project. While you walk through a cave wearing a special helmet, a computer projects data seen from your own perspective onto your small screen. You are more or less walking within the data set. That is more than 3D: you are actually part of it! A sort of hologram. This technique makes it easier to interpret, add and model. These fantastic and surprising new developments are happening at the speed of light. For Fugro it's not only interesting but also important to keep track of knowledge centres and university whizz kids. These youngsters will bring about technological breakthroughs. They won't be guided according to a plan, they just *make* things.'

2027

CONSEQUENCES
OF CLIMATE CHANGE

TERRY MCCONNELL
FUGRO AIRBORNE SURVEYS,
CANADA

Rising global temperatures will increasingly result in more water being released from storage in sea ice, glaciers, ice sheets and permafrost. This newly mobile water will change sea levels in coastal areas around the world. It will also power increasingly destructive weather systems; resulting in larger storm surges at seaside locations, and rain water flooding at inland areas. Mapping surface topography is essential to understanding relative water flow channels and low, flood prone, areas. But so too is understanding the gravitational forces which *pull* water one way or the other over the topographical surface. The *Geoid* is an irregular, equipotential gravitational surface that essentially represents *mean sea level* as it would exist if all points of the globe were covered by water. Irregularities exist in this *geoid* due to local variations in the earth's density. These variations in density result in a *geoid* surface that undulates by as much as 190 metres from the smooth ellipsoidal surface that is mapped out when you use a GPS system for height measurement.
Knowing which areas are most prone to flood waters and sea level changes is becoming increasingly important to stakeholders as varied as governments, insurance companies, engineering firms and individuals. For the reasons discussed herein, Fugro will in the future include in contracts to accurately map the topography an optional service to accurately measure and calculate the underlying gravitational *geoid*.

FLOOD CONTROL 2100

All over the world, flood protection requires better, more effective and faster solutions. Flood Control 2015 is a Dutch public-private collaborative programme by the Dutch government (50%) and businesses and institutions (50%) whose focus is to better protect the Netherlands against water. The knowledge gathered here can be exported and the modular packages can be used all over the world.

The Netherlands owes its name and part of its fame to its low-lying location in the Rhine, Scheldt and Meuse delta; cows graze six metres or more below sea level in large parts of this country. The inhabitants of the Low Countries have had to deal with water and flooding from time immemorial, and have combated water in their struggle for survival and to protect home and property. Setting a loyal, supportive and clear policy was a public priority: protection against and control of water flows, control of the polders' surface-water and ground-water levels, drinking-water supplies and the processing, purification and discharge of rainwater and sewages. For centuries this management rested with the regional water boards, polder boards and dyke reeves, and later also with Rijkswaterstaat, a department of the Ministry of Infrastructure and the Environment. They have critical responsibilities, and therefore great power.

Global social consequences

Dutch hydraulic engineers have invented and developed impressive defence works, and as a result they didn't only keep their feet dry but also built up a wealth of expertise and experience. Their growing expertise in water management can be regarded as a positive side effect of sea-level rise, coastal erosion and flooding.

Fugro decided to go with the flow and conceived solutions to mitigate the consequences of high water levels for river deltas, storage and water management; and in the process developed standard procedures for a

> ## 2027
> ### NEW GEOGRAPHIC AREAS
>
> **DAVID LOWE**
> FUGRO ROADWARE, CANADA
>
> Brazil and India for providing services. China is already a good products market for us but has been difficult to provide services as our clients are government agencies. Russia too has quite restrictive practices and will likely start to grow as a products market. The African nations are starting to show interest in our services and we expect this to continue over the coming years.

▸
Afsluitdijk barrier (32 kilometres), The Netherlands

global analysis of these phenomena. The challenge is to prevent damage to buildings and infrastructure, but the safety of people and animals comes first. Ninety per cent of the world's population lives less than five metres above sea level.

Geologists know that sea level may eventually rise as much as six metres higher than the level at the time of Fugro's fiftieth anniversary in 2012. There is scientific proof that, 120,000 years ago, sea level was actually six metres higher. Experts expect that the expansion of the ocean water alone, as a result of a higher temperature, will result in a 30-centimetre rise. They no longer debate whether sea level is rising but the rate and extent of that rise and the underlying causes. Is this rise purely caused by natural processes? Or can it be attributed to human actions? Or is it a combination of factors?

Even a rise of just a few decimetres will have dramatic consequences for a large proportion of the world's population. Think of famines, mass migration and refugee troubles; the global consequences of a rise in sea level should not be underestimated.

Integrated monitoring and management systems

Timely measures and adequate crisis management can prevent disastrous consequences, such as the flood caused by the 1953 storm surge in the low-lying parts of the Netherlands. Flood Control 2015's integrated forecasting systems ensure that better information reaches the right place faster. This will not only increase safety in case of unexpected floods, but also prove useful under normal conditions; a better day-to-day management of water-defence systems will give us protection that is easier to understand, faster and, in the long term, cheaper. The programme focuses on safer dykes and especially on innovative solutions for better and more comprehensive systems that consider dykes, decision-makers and their environment in a fully integrated manner.

2027

FUGRO TECHNOLOGY

JIM MANN
FUGRO SUBSEA SERVICES,
UK

The level of business generated by Fugro from the offshore oil and gas (energy) sector will drive us to provide clients with faster, better, safer and cheaper services that deliver added value. The latter two demands (safer and cheaper) will drive the technologies used within that principle sector to require much less human intervention and into technology to place the human in the loop purely in a supervisory capacity. Given the importance of the offshore energy sector; to not only Fugro but the large majority of our clients; then subsea technologies as a whole are likely to predominate.

▶

Geotechnical inspection
of dikes, New Orleans,
USA

Implementation of global know-how

A consortium of stakeholders and knowledge institutes is taking part in the programme. In addition to Fugro (one of the initiators), Arcadis, HKV Lijn in Water, ITC, Deltares, IBM and Stichting IJkdijk are on board. Dyke managers also play an important role: the developed expertise is applied more or less directly in their dyke-ring systems and they and other safety experts are members of the external sounding board group.

Fugro is developing applications to match its own research with Flood Control 2015's objectives. Fugro's global network in the field of data management, geohazard management systems, real-time monitoring and geophysics is very useful in this respect.

In developing software modules to evaluate the strengths of dykes, Dutch Fugro GeoServices is collaborating with Fugro Consultants Inc. (VS). Fugro GEOS (UK) supplies technology to improve the measuring and forecasting of water levels, waves and currents. Fugro NPA (UK) is responsible for mapping dyke failures with satellite data and is contributing to developing a Global Flood Observatory.

Many other countries are interested in our Dutch knowledge and experience. Fugro, Haskoning and HKV are jointly working on a *Storm and Levee Strength Forecasting System* in New Orleans, as part of the *Levee Information Management System*. In Indonesia, Fugro is involved in developing Jakarta's *Water Information Management System*.

High water in 2100

Rising sea level and increasing river discharges require that further advances be made. The Dutch government provides research grants for a number of sectors in which the Netherlands excels. For the water sector, the partners in Flood Control 2015 are now developing plans for Flood Control 2100.

2027
STAFF RECRUITMENT AND THEIR MOBILITY

MELINDA ROBINSON
FUGRO CONSULTANTS, USA

Staff mobility will be a core value and a foundation for future managers and executives. A leadership development program will continually identify a group comprised of the top 1-2% of Fugro employees. The group will be immersed in purposeful project, geographic and cross-disciplinary assignments. Accompanied by active mentoring, they will gain a thorough understanding of Fugro's operations and business functions; accrue global experience; master the management of complex projects and profitable business units; and consistently perform according to the company's Golden Rules. This cadre of trained professionals will possess multi-cultural/multi-country experience and the eagerness to assume increasing levels of responsibility – thereby comprising Fugro's future leadership team.

CYCLES

If tomorrow's weather forecast says *storm,* someone invariably remarks that it's clear that our climate is changing. People have no perception of time; or that the Earth is 4.5 billion years old and how long that is; and that, during the Ice Ages, the sea level was 120 metres lower than at present and that all that water was stored in glaciers. Glaciers will melt. People passing through the Netherlands 20,000 years ago would have seen one such melting glacier. Just as well it did melt, or there would have been no Fugro.

People think in short cycles, but our habitat is characterised by very long cycles. It is true; the climate is changing – as proven by the Earth's 4.5-billion-year history. The expanding world population may have a minor influence on this change – seven billion people burn up an awful lot of oil and gas – and CO_2-reducing measures and offshore wind farms may slow down global warming somewhat. Anyway, wind farms mean business for Fugro just like oil and gas production.

▲
Icebergs in the Ross Sea, Antarctica

◄
Offshore operations, North Slope, Alaska

◄◄
Wind farm in the Baltic Sea

THE CLIMATE
ALWAYS CHANGES

Ever since Salomon saw two-billion-year-old rocks in Suriname and the entire geological column in the Colombian countryside, he has been fascinated by geological time. These experiences made him realise even more that the human species had only just arrived on the scene, and barely witnessed any of the great things the Earth is capable of. Time was not only the theme of his inaugural lecture in Wageningen *(Yesterday, today was tomorrow),* but also of his book *De menselijke maat* (translated and published as *The Human Scale*), describing the Earth in ten million years' time. Kroonenberg explains the huge public interest in his book by pointing out that he puts the climate issue into perspective.

Geological time

Salomon is, however, mainly concerned about the general public's limited understanding of the phenomenon time, in a geological sense. He was trying to find a vehicle to make laymen aware of geological time. People who have heard or read *Yesterday, today was tomorrow* are aware of the fact that the climate *always* changes. And this has gone on much, much longer than *from time immemorial* – mankind has only been around a mere 150,000 years. Kroonenberg's many publications, lectures and talks – whether scientific or popular – focus on geological time. He regularly criticises Al Gore's film *An Inconvenient Truth.*

'Gore's film has made climate change into a hot item all over the world. Many people accept his theory with open arms, but many others dispute the message that human activities and the associated CO_2 emissions are the cause of the present-day climate change. Al Gore presented his film in 2006, the year after *Katrina*. But 2006 was almost as warm as 2005, and yet there were far fewer hurricanes. Some people believe that hurricanes go with cold weather, rather than hot weather. A paper, published in 2007, shows that the numerous hurricanes in 2005 were not caused by warm seawater, but by unusual wind patterns over the Gulf of Mexico. The 2007 report of the Intergovernmental Panel on Climate Change (IPPC) couldn't establish a

Salomon Kroonenberg graduated in Physical Geography at the University of Amsterdam. He subsequently worked as a geologist-petrologist for the Suriname Geological and Mining Service, and he also obtained his PhD during that time. He was a Professor at the Universities of Amsterdam and Wageningen, and taught at the Centro Interamericano de Fotointerpretación in Bogotá, Colombia and at University College in Swaziland. Until September 2009, he was working as a Full Professor of Geology at the Civil Engineering and Geosciences Faculty of Delft University of Technology. He is a prolific author. His book *De menselijke maat* (2006) has sold 30,000 copies. As a result of this publication he is frequently called a *climate sceptic,* but he prefers to be called a *climate relativist.*

link between average global temperature and the frequency of storms – at the most a link with the storms' intensity.'

A convenient lie

'In his effort to blame carbon dioxide emissions for all changes in climate (according to Salomon *a convenient lie*) Gore refers to the Aral Sea drying up. He doesn't mention that a medieval mausoleum was found on the dry lake floor. The Aral Sea dried up as many as three times previously in the past 10,000 years, as a result of natural causes. The film shows melting glaciers all around the world, but doesn't talk about the forests, dating from Roman times, that are now appearing from under those retreating Alpine glaciers. Evidently, the glaciers have previously retreated that far as a result of natural causes. The climate would have been stable for the past 11,000 years, but 11,000 years ago Gore's own city of Washington D.C. was located at the edge of a melting ice cap. And during those 11,000 years, sea level rose as much as fifty metres, a result of natural causes. Gore suggests that fluctuations in CO_2 concentrations caused the ice ages, while it is exactly the other way around: ice ages are caused by *Milankoviç cycles* (a measure of the intensity and variation in solar radiation on Earth) – carbon dioxide *follows*.

'Gore's presentations disregard all other natural processes, all the delayed reactions, all the feedback mechanisms, all the non-linear elements – leading everyone to believe that carbon dioxide is the only culprit. No wonder people are becoming worried and believe climate change is their own fault.'

Solar activity and other uncertainties

'Part of the scaremongering can be attributed to the IPCC. The climate seems to have become warmer between 1976 and 1998. The IPCC's Fourth Assessment Report (2007) states that this is probably due to increased greenhouse-gas emissions. But a certain degree of uncertainty has to be taken into account, as this conclusion is based on papers that were published in "last week's" *Nature*. Little is yet known about the roles of water vapour, clouds and especially solar variations. Variations in solar activity show striking correlations with the climate on Earth, and we shouldn't ignore the possibility of other, as yet unknown, feedback mechanisms. Danish meteorologist Svensmark showed a direct correlation between low cloud cover, cosmic ray intensity and solar activity. It may be crucial. 'But even if the past global warming was largely manmade, the motto still applies: *Past results are no guarantee for the future*. Those who believe that mankind determines the future climate will be disappointed; climate and carbon dioxide concentrations fail to show a one-to-one correlation. Trend breaks are the rule rather than the exception, and are due to volcanic eruptions, variations in solar activity, and feedback mechanisms we don't yet know. All this will be published in a paper in "next week's" *Nature*.'

1973

Operational in more and more fields

—

Fugro split the Soil Mechanics department into two sections: Overseas and EEG (the Dutch initials for European Economic Community). Fugro Inc in Long Beach now had a staff of fifty and was doing well. It took the audacious step of opening an office (Fugro Gulf) in Houston, the home base of arch-rival McClelland. There was a lot of work to be done in Hongkong so Fugro opened an office there too. Closer to home, expansion was the order of the day: the third Dutch branch office opened its doors in the city of Groningen. This was where Fugro had performed thousands of CPTs in 1964 after the discovery of the natural gas field at nearby Slochteren.

The laboratory in Leidschendam put equipment for dynamic triaxial tests into use. This equipment could imitate the effects of varying loads on dyke bodies, calculate the repetitive load on oil rigs brought by wind and wave action, and simulate the behaviour of the ground during earthquakes.

Fugro had written various software programs and installed its first computer, which could calculate more reliably and much faster than the engineers.

OPEC turned off the oil tap, petrol was rationed and the Netherlands became acquainted with car-free Sundays.

>

Hand-built dykes and toy islands

What measures should people take? 'Chiefly: adjust, do things that will definitely help. If sea level rises, we should raise the dykes, or build floating houses. No one has ever said that mankind is entitled to a constant sea level. Coast dwellers run as many risks as people who live at the foot of a volcano. Dykes first need to be built in the most susceptible regions. Not in the Netherlands, one of the best-protected countries in the world. Farmers in Bangladesh are still building their own dykes by hand, while Dutch engineers are constructing palm-tree-shaped artificial islands off the coast of the United Arab Emirates. If the farmers on the slopes of Mount Kilimanjaro don't have enough water because the glaciers are melting, we could desalinise sea water and pump it up. We build pipelines for oil and gas across all the continents – why not for water?'

Future demand for carbon dioxide

'Energy policy and climate policy are completely different matters. If the global climate cools once again for thirty years, as happened between 1940 and 1970, we can choose between two alternatives. If we keep saying, as we are doing at present, that the climate mustn't change, then we'll have to burn more fossil fuels (assuming we still believe that carbon dioxide is the dominant factor). But that means our energy resources will be exhausted even sooner, while the worst cold may be yet to come. The alternative is to keep conserving energy and accept climate change. As long as it keeps getting warmer, energy policy and climate policy seem to align well. But when it gets colder, they will counteract each other.

'Storing CO_2 underground, to get rid of it, is nonsense: to produce the energy required to store the CO_2 emitted by four power plants, we would have to build a fifth power plant. CO_2 storage costs extra energy and therefore isn't the way to go. Once the next ice age is upon us, people will say: *What can possibly have possessed those twenty-first century people to put carbon dioxide into the ground? Now we need it again! How can we get it out?'*

Nothing new under the sun

'All the disasters we fear at the moment have already occurred sometime in the past. Even worse ones – and as a result of natural causes. The Earth has seen it all. We, the people, are looking through a tiny keyhole into time, and we think that everything is happening for the first time and will never happen again, as long as we behave. People who like Al Gore say *We might lose the earth,* only see the Earth as a lucky dip, for mankind to benefit from. These people don't realise that everything, including the recent global warming is just business as usual as far as the Earth is concerned. When people say the Earth is going to the dogs, they don't mean Earth,

1973

>

Exploitation of the West's energy sources gathered momentum, bringing about the substantial development of geotechnics in the North Sea. Half the turnover of the drilling vessels of the major offshore concern Heerema came from Fugro's activities. Fugro had developed a swell compensator so as to be able to operate in deeper waters. Heerema wanted an exclusive contract for Fugro's expertise but Joustra was having none of it. The working relationship between Fugro and Heerema had something of an uneasy 'armed peace'; at times Heerema could be quite arrogant which was something the Frisian Joustra and company could have done without.

The combination of consultancy and investigation by a single company was nothing like as established abroad as it was in the Netherlands. This gave Fugro a head start in many places. Fugro worked unceasingly on increasing its fame as a geotechnical specialist. A well thought-out publicity policy and a willingness to pass on some of the expertise it had developed were contributing factors. This openness cultivated a great deal of goodwill worldwide.

In England Fugro performed eighty CPTs in connection with a forthcoming new airfield. This was a tricky business, as it was to be laid out on military grounds that had been used for target practice for 150 years and were littered with unexploded bombs and grenades.

—

And OPEC declared an oil embargo, ushering in the first oil crisis.

but themselves, mankind. This petty, anthropocentric world view fails to realise that to the Earth, mankind is no more than a skin of paint on the pinnacle-knob of the Eiffel Tower, as Mark Twain remarked.'

Salomon Kroonenberg doesn't consider himself a climate sceptic, but rather a climate relativist: he agrees that climate is changing, but doubts that mankind is the chief perpetrator. 'It has been established that human activity has emitted more CO_2 into the atmosphere than there has been for a long time, but the impact on nature is less certain, as is nature's reaction. Who knows how the oceans will react to a higher atmospheric CO_2 concentration? Or how plants will react? The uncertainty stems from the multitude of signals that justify doubts about the net effect. Politicians believe it is necessary to reduce CO_2 emissions in order to save the climate (or win the next election), but there isn't really much to worry about. I'm not convinced that the Earth will become a few degrees warmer, let alone that that warming will result in accelerated further warming, as the ice melts and methane is released by melting tundra's, as the IPPC claims.' According to Salomon, we had better prepare for future cooling rather than for warming; the variations in solar activity correspond much better with the twentieth-century climate fluctuations than do variations in CO_2 concentration.

Snowball Earth

Climate change is particularly noticeable at Spitsbergen. Some mussel species, for instance, which were last present there six thousand years ago, are now returning.

Spitsbergen has a fascinating climate history. The notion of *Snowball Earth* was coined there, when the British geologist W. Brian Harland discovered traces of 600-million-year-old glaciations. Similar traces have also been found on other continents. Harland claims that there were worldwide glaciations in those days. American geologists developed his hypothesis further into *Snowball Earth* – the assumption that the entire Earth was covered in ice, from the poles to the equator.

The present-day climate change is nothing new. That is the crux of Kroonenberg's story: it is indeed getting warmer, but not for the first time, and neither is the change excessive, in comparison with other periods since humans roamed the Earth. 'The recent eruption of the Eyafjallajökull volcano on Iceland kicked up a lot of dust. Every time that volcano erupted before during the past thousand years, its huge neighbour Katla also became active. When I mentioned this fact in current affairs programmes, I scared many people out of their wits. People see me as the ultimate authority on geological matters, but what I told them wasn't sensational – at all events nothing new.'

1974

Fugro and Cesco go offshore together
—

—

It was decided that Cesco, whose strong points were hydrography, marine geophysics and the mapping of obstacles on the seabed, should merge worldwide with Fugro as Fugro-Cesco International (FCI). Cesco had far more offshore experience and had its own ships, including the *Bison* which was specially built for seabed surveying using sound waves. FCI was an instant success.

In Houston Fugro chartered its own ship, prosaically named *Fugro I*. In Curaçao business was flagging and so Fugro closed the office on that island. In Dubai by contrast there was plenty of geotechnical work and the next branch of Fugro was established there. The differences between Cesco and Fugro were soon apparent. Cesco's board of directors consisted primarily of geologists and officers from the navy or merchant navy, whereas Fugro's directors were largely graduate engineers from the Technical University of Delft and technical college, many of whom had served as officers with the Corps of Engineers. The palpable differences in mentality between navy and army had an effect on the working atmosphere and on productivity. For the first time in eight years the figures failed to show the annual doubling of the operating result, but this was partly caused by the declining economy. There were endless reorganisations in Leidschendam. The technicians of Fugro-Cesco, unconcerned by the organisational ups and downs, developed

Heaven and hell

Salomon strongly supports reducing fossil-fuel consumption, but because these resources are finite, not to reduce CO_2 emissions. He advocates paying more attention to the interior of the Earth. His new book *Why Hell Stinks of Sulphur* not only deals with the physical underground but also with mythology and human perception. Why is the ground beneath us terrifying and what is above us blissful? Why do lovers look up at the moon and those who are punished down at the ground? And he considers our interventions in the subsurface – such as mining, constructing tunnels and underground storage – as *Hell in the making*.

Salomon Kroonenberg not only puts climate change into perspective, but also his own authority – he doesn't like power. But he does want to be influential. He especially enjoys his independence, and audiences that listen seriously to what he has to say.

1974

> a cone penetration technique that enabled a thrust capacity of ten tons in deep water. There were now three *Sea Calves* with a thrust capacity of 20 tons, two of which were reserved by Shell. The price was of no consequence – the oil companies were up to their eyes in work.

Fugro opened a branch in Ickenham (UK), from where it could compete with McClelland in the North Sea. British members of staff polished up the Dutch contingent's English since oil companies wanted their reports in that language only. If McClelland's reports were standardised, Fugro started each report with a blank page to force itself to stay focused. The top brass of Fugro-Cesco retired to a hotel for several days to learn the basic principles of a new concept: marketing. This year's turnover was € 30 million, 50% of which came from the US.

—

And Richard Nixon was forced to step down as US President as a result of the *Watergate* scandal.

2027

TRANSITION FROM FOSSIL
TO RENEWABLE ENERGY

BIGHNA N NAYAK
FUGRO SURVEY,
INDIA

India will continue to be a big user of fossil fuel for next 15 years. Consumption will move to coal and gas. As fossil fuel becomes more expensive, India will look at bio gas and solar energy.

North Slope, Alaska

Jebal Shams,
Hajar mountains,
Oman

Joshua Tree National Park,
California, USA

RUDOLF
DAS '12

MONSTERS OF THE DEEP

This is not a prehistoric deep-sea monster, but a Remotely Operated Vehicle (ROV), as pictured by futurologist and artist Rudolf Das. The ROV is carrying out mining investigations on the ocean floor at a depth of five kilometres.

It is pitch dark down there, so many adjustable lamps are required.
Because of the immense water pressure, most of the vehicle should be filled with water – only a tiny part, notably the control electronics and electro hydraulic power pack, needs to remain dry.

The deeper the water, the greater the challenge of positioning accuracy of the vehicle on the seabed. The vehicle is propelled by two huge spiral thrusters.

This ROV is churning up the sea floor in front of the vehicle and collecting valuable research samples; one of the three hydraulic manipulators picks them up and deposits them inside.

LEGEND

1   Manipulator for large items
2   Two manipulators for small items
3   Inlet with conveyor belt
4   Twin vertical sampling drills
5   Rotating central TV camera
6   Rotating screws in ring mantles, with
     TV cameras above the lamps
7   Dry compartments of the vehicle
     (e.g. for the electric motors)
8   Twin spiral screws for propulsion on
     the sea floor
9   Central part with umbilical connection
10   Dome to make spherically packed samples
     float upwards
11   Hydraulic spud pole secures the vehicle
     and acts as a pivot point
12   Central lighting with TV overview

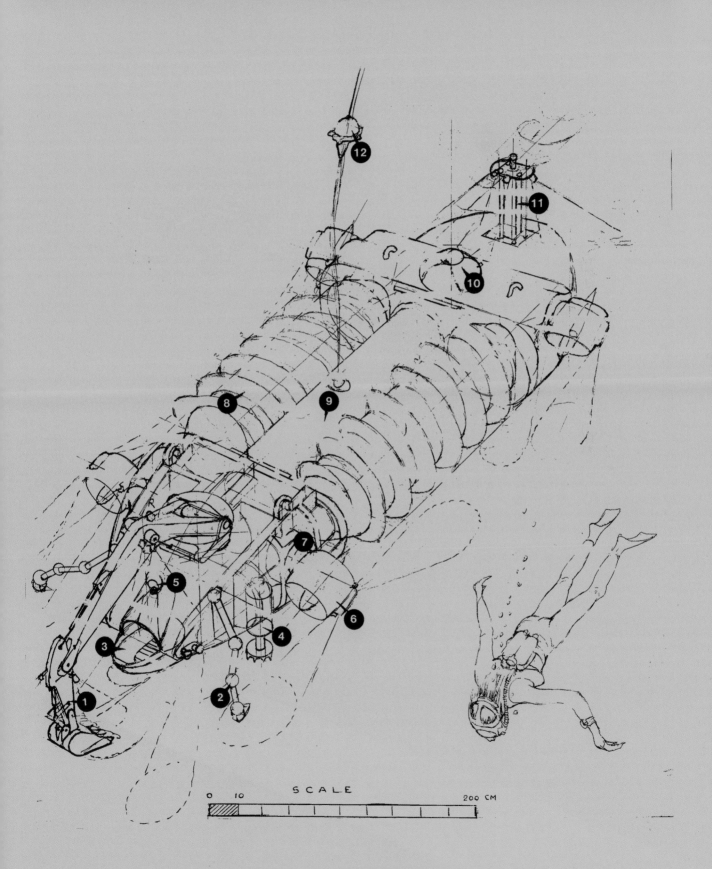

SCALE

0   10   200 CM

III

EARTH UNLIMITED

PEOPLE

THE EXPANDING CIRCLE
OF ETHICAL RESPONSIBILITY

'If you ask an engineer for a philosophical vision, the reply will generally be a stony silence. It's good to link technology with philosophy because they have a lot to offer one another. Technology can change the world, and ethics helps us think about what kind of world we want to live in. Technical companies like DHV, Arcadis, Fugro and Philips are already working hard to couple technology with a vision for the future.'

Responsible innovation

Some five years ago, Van den Hoven inaugurated a research programme on ethics and technology for the Netherlands Organisation for Scientific Research (NWO) and several Dutch ministries. The programme had a budget of 13 million euros for the humanities and ethics.

'The theme of the programme is *Responsible Innovation: Ethical and Societal Exploration of Science and Technology,* but it's also known by the abbreviation *MVI.* It addresses issues of technological developments that are likely to have a significant impact on the individual and on society. On the one hand it relates to new technologies such as IT, nanotechnology, biotechnology and neuroscience, and on the other to technological systems in transition such as energy, transportation, agriculture and hydrology.

'The programme aims to stimulate socially responsible innovation by expanding research into societal and ethical aspects of science and technology. This takes place in an international collaboration among technological scientists, and among researchers into the societal context and normative questions.

'In order to attract a subsidy, social and behavioural scientists, economists, jurists, ethicists and technologists must find a way to cooperate. It is an interesting combination, in my opinion.' Van den Hoven, together with the NWO, is currently focusing on socially responsible innovation in the *top sectors* – those branches of industry in which the Netherlands has the strongest position internationally.

Jeroen van den Hoven is Professor of Moral Philosophy at Delft University of Technology and Scientific Director of the Centre for Ethics and Technology of 3TU, the three Dutch universities of technology. He has published extensively on topics concerning ethics and information technology, he provides consultancy to the European Commission, and he has acted as an adviser to the Dutch government on several matters, among them the redesign of the population registration system. 'Moral considerations could once again become the mainspring of our behaviour ten years from now', he says.

Social sustainability

'The European Commission is developing its own long-term research programme, as published for example in the report *Horizon 2020,* with a call for ideas on socially relevant innovation. The main topic is *value-sensitive innovation* or the coupling of moral and socioeconomic values with business innovation and functional requirements. The developers must be able to defend the functions of an innovation where they conflict with other values. At TU Delft, ethicists collaborate with economists and econometricians to improve the precision of this weighing-up process. The French President Nicolas Sarkozy invited Amartya Sen and other winners of the Nobel Prize for Economics to characterise the Gross National Product in a wider social and moral context. A treatise on this subject must take in issues such as circumstances in the disadvantaged suburbs of large cities, neglected maintenance of the infrastructure, and the demographic distribution of prosperity and economic growth. Are the costs, benefits and risks fairly distributed? And how do people feel about it? The GNP may have risen compared to last year but the way the increased prosperity is shared may be less than fair. Can this be justified? Sustainability is not just about the environment but also about social conditions. The London riots of mid-2011 were to some extent a symptom of neglected societal maintenance. The maintenance backlog emerges more quickly and intensely at times of crisis. Issues of this kind deserve our attention, and we can express our ideas about them in some way or another in the things we make. We must present social institutions, organisations and systems such as transport, health care, communications infrastructure, education, markets, the financial sector, governance, legislation and compliance in a lively way that will strongly stimulate people to do the right thing. The way these systems are designed influences human behaviour. In analyses and legal proceedings on train crashes, the standard reaction used to be that it was the driver's fault because he rode through a red light. Yes, he should have seen that stop signal, but nowadays we realise that the designers of safety systems bear part of the responsibility. If the signalling system is inappropriately designed or installed, it is little wonder that a train driver could miss the stop sign, especially when a low sun is shining in his eyes. The same applies to the designer of a train timetable: a poor design can lead to excessive speeds and congestion. We look at the design from the outside in, but you also have to see a design in the light of the moral values and social aspects that we consider important. In short, engineers and designers must integrate moral values and social wishes into their development processes. That is what we mean by *value sensitive design.* Without a broad social relevance and acceptance by the client and users, later modifications could make the product too expensive and barely implementable. That is the main idea behind socially responsible business and innovation.'

1975

Parents in trouble

—
—

Fugro-Cesco wanted to operate in the market segment that placed the highest demands on quality – the average return was higher there. A market share of at least 20% was needed to ensure that clients would neither ignore Fugro nor try to impose their will on it. The land departments Geodesy and Roads were having a difficult time, although Fugro was successfully using a small mobile TV camera to inspect the insides of sewers. Geology and Hydrography by contrast were doing well; Fugro enlarged the grounds in Leidschendam with another 3000 m^2. The parent companies Heidemij and Nederhorst had had a bad year, bringing in less than 4% of the work. Nederhorst even appealed to the government for financial help. The office in England gave Fugro-Cesco direct access to the former British colonies and in November the German branch got off the ground in Bremen. It was now possible to directly enter recorded data into the computer. This produced a CPT log and calculated the friction ratio. It meant less drilling, with an enormous cut in costs for the client.

—

And in Helsinki 35 countries worked towards easing East-West relationships by signing the Final Act of the Conference on Security and Cooperation in Europe.

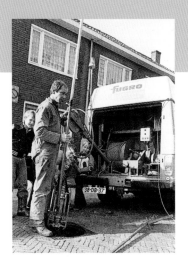

Things that matter

'Enlightenment thinking continues to play a significant part in Western society. Peter Singer, a philosopher at Princeton University, described an aspect of it as *the expanding circle*. We have abolished slavery and child labour and we have given women the vote. Even animals have gained rights. You don't feed medieval manuscripts through a paper shredder, and you don't fell a 500-year-old oak tree without authorisation. There is an expanding circle of things that matter to us, Singer explains, of things that have a moral status which we must take into account. The idea that we might want to reverse those achievements is inconceivable. How far would the world have to sink to seriously consider raising a business case for slavery again? Its abolition is irreversible because we have realised that we are all human and that as such we have an absolute worth that must be universally respected. That is what *Enlightenment* means. That is the foundation of our ideas on universal human rights and democracy. Some pretty sound empirical research has indicated that countries prosper more in step with their level of democracy, transparency and accountability. 'Brussels also believes that engineers must learn to think along these lines so that they can embed ethical values into what they make from the outset. This notion could well become a precept for thinking about innovation in Europe for the decade ahead. It's a characteristic EU outlook, because Europe is considered synonymous with human rights and societal values. Something like this is also gaining credence elsewhere in the world. The Chinese understand that they need to add different values to their technology. They are building new high speed railways, dams and highways at a breakneck speed. The road accident statistics are rising shockingly and the country seems to be bursting at the seams. I went there to speak about 3TU, the collaboration between the three Dutch universities of technology with regard to ethics and technology. Two weeks later, I heard that five large Chinese universities had already decided to collaborate on this theme. China has long swept the ethical component under the carpet, but ethics is now on the agenda – in part due to actions spurred by the Chinese versions of the new media. Public protests are in principle forbidden there, so the activists refer to such demonstrations euphemistically as *going for a walk*. Not long ago, ten thousand people went for a walk at the same time and succeeded in blocking construction of a new chemical plant in the modern, rapidly growing port of Dalian. That's new there.'

Visionaries wanted

'Ethics is about restraining yourself from doing things because you care about the public interest and the individual interests, needs and rights of others. The next generation of engineers must be trained to work with restraints and requirements of this kind.

2027

CONSEQUENCES
OF CLIMATE CHANGE

ARIS LUBBES
FUGRO N.V.,
THE NETHERLANDS

The Offshore Survey Division will I think not be much affected by sea level rise. I do not believe that services provided to the Offshore Oil and Gas sector will be affected by a 20 centimetres increase in water depth. The effect of the melting ice caps will in my mind be much bigger. As the Arctic areas are only sparsely understood and surveyed, there will be an increased call for survey services in Arctic regions. Oil companies will increasingly call for under ice studies in anticipation of further withdrawal of the ice caps and also in anticipation of summer seasons as they will wish to reserve the (ice free) summer for heavy installation work and not for engineering studies and survey.

*High Speed Railway,
The Netherlands*

*Cone testing near
Geertruidenberg,
The Netherlands*

'The project to redesign the personal records database used by Dutch municipalities wasn't just a question of information technology. We started with a system architecture study. What, we wondered, should its main characteristics be? What difficulties had to be overcome? Who must be allowed access to the data, and how could we assure privacy protection? Later, we asked IBM, Atos Origin, Getronics and similar companies to think along with us by way of a reality check. The people needed for developing the new system not only have to be excellent computer scientists with a knowledge of security, but they must have a feeling for the changing relationship between government and the public. They must be able to exchange ideas with ministers and senior civil servants about the role of public administration. We are trying to train the current generation of students at Delft, Eindhoven and Twente, the best of whom will some day find there way into the top echelons of the business world, in these skills. Our efforts are meeting with more and more success because the students are growing up in a world where current events are a normal matter for discussion. People rarely pause to reflect about what they are doing until practical problems arise. They aren't inclined to ponder deeply while they can still function by routine. But once things grind to a halt, a different mechanism is set in train. That's when you start thinking: wait a minute, you realise, we'll have to devise something new because our long-cherished assumptions are no longer valid.'

The role of business

'A movement has started in ethics in which it's no longer considered getting your hands dirty if you design stimulus structures, in the same way as you design roads, bridges and other infrastructure. We term the new outlook *motivating morality* or *incentivising ethics*. For example, the bonus system for business leaders has generally failed to deliver the expected results. Control mechanisms are largely lacking, and we must redesign stimulus structures of that kind differently so that those involved respond with the desired behaviour. The government has also directly intervened, for example in banning naked short selling. It's easier to talk down a share price by spreading rumours than it is to make the price rise. That is asymmetrical. Once the mechanism is exposed and it is democratically agreed that a certain behaviour is wrong or undesired, you can decide that naked short selling is inadmissible and you can try to design new infrastructural frameworks. But our socio-technical systems are dynamic and complex. It is questionable whether we can modify the thoughts and actions of people in time to save this planet from self-destruction; we have left it a bit late, haven't we? The younger generation must grow up internalising this awareness, and they must design organisations, institutions and technologies accordingly. Processes of this kind could easily take decades.'

1976

Learning the hard way
—

Developments on the social front saw more and more signs of disgruntled employees at Fugro. Absence through illness increased and the turnover of staff rose to 20%; most complaints could be traced back to the bad work climate. Investigations launched by the Works Council revealed that the management conducted an opaque policy, failed to meet its promises and had a communication problem. Joustra admitted that the management was more interested in the technical side than in the staff.

Fugro was painfully aware that McClelland was earning a fortune in Saudi Arabia. 'We can do that too!' It set up an office in Jeddah, with the intention of laying a pipeline from the Red Sea to the Persian Gulf. A big offshore survey job was coming up in Yanbu in connection with the forthcoming construction of harbours and piers. This different world took a bit of getting used to. Overwork and beginners' mistakes gave Fugro-Cesco a loss of Ð 600,000 in 1976 but then things improved for Saudi Fugro. The prospects were good and certainly much better than in Singapore, where the offices of P.T. Cesco Indonesia had to close down. The Americans ruled the roost in the Middle East, East Asia and the Gulf of Mexico, but the Fugro cone drove McClelland's share of the North Sea market down to 40%. In Houston, Fugro Gulf Inc celebrated a record depth in the Gulf of Mexico where they took soil samples from well over 300 metres below the seabed in waters 600 metres deep.

Fertile soil for ethics

'We must learn about behaviour and socio-economic mechanisms in order to prevent negative effects. I will mention two well-known examples. Arms races have perverse effects and have destroyed societies through the idea that *we* must be better than *them*. You encounter arms races of this kind in all kinds of places, for example in cosmetic surgery. If everyone in my department has a face lift, I will look rather decrepit by comparison at age 53, so I have no choice but to play along. There are cultures where neck rings are an indication of status; the more rings, the higher the status. The wearers end up deformed but status is paramount. Competitive practices of this kind are not in the general interest because they often lead to waste and destruction. Another example is known as *the tragedy of the commons*. If every fishing boat on the North Sea tries to catch as much herring as possible, there will be nothing to fish for next year. Tragedies of this kind are encountered all over the world, in relation both to the environment and climate, and to the *common pool resources* studied by the Nobel Prize winner Elinor Ostrom. A growing ethical awareness has to find fertile soil and be widely accepted. The business community has a part to play in it too.'

Responsibility

An enterprise like Fugro operates worldwide and has to deal with many different cultures. How much should you adapt your behaviour to those differences? What is permissible short of renouncing either your ethics or your self-interest? 'A small player carries small responsibilities', Van den Hoven explains. 'Those with deep pockets have large responsibilities. That is an axiom of the allocation of responsibility, and even judges take this standpoint in their sentencing. Big players have the responsibility to change the parameters of the system when necessary and to change their own dealings. They can't shrug their shoulders and say *That's the way the system is, and if I don't go along with it someone else will take my place*. Companies must think seriously about their social responsibility. Some companies do in fact have their own ethics departments, but, with all respect, those departments are rarely manned by suitable people. Besides, they often have too little space and opportunity to think critically and independently. There must be confidence in those who take a stand to support such values. I am convinced that companies and society will be none the worse for taking a serious approach to ethics.

'Value-sensitive design makes it possible to integrate ethics into research and development, product development and operational activities. As long as there are people who do not have what they deserve, we must actualise economic growth and greater prosperity to provide jobs for as many people as possible. At the same time, we must spare the environment – a major societal problem. Anyone who succeeds in finding a smart solution to that can claim to have innovated responsibly. Someone who focuses on

1976

>
The tens of millions of dollars Fugro earned worldwide with technical ingenuity and enthusiasm flew out of the money-box as fast as they arrived due to organisational difficulties and lack of financial expertise. The shareholders Nederhorst and Heidemij had to pull out all the stops to keep their own heads above water and left Fugro-Cesco to its own devices.

—

And China mourned the loss first of Prime Minister Zhou Enlai and then of the Great Helmsman himself, Mao Zedong.

2027   ORGANISATIONAL DEVELOPMENT

PAT POWER
FUGRO GEOCONSULTING,
UK

In 2027 Fugro will be a knowledge-led business in which our experience, expertise and technology is deployed to quantify the natural environment and minimise the risks it poses to our client's projects. This will enable safer and more cost-effective delivery of these projects, within which we will be perceived as a strategic partner and not just a vendor of services. We will be renowned for our *FINESSE (Fugro Integrated Earth Science Solutions & Expertise)*.

values and calls attention to this dilemma instead of sweeping it under the carpet, allows himself a chance of innovating. But you will have to think up something clever if you want to grow without polluting. All Europe looked on with dismay in the 1960s when the forerunners of *The Greens* in Germany chained themselves to the factory gates. They confronted the politicians with the true dilemma and created the necessity for innovation. Germany is now the market leader in environmental technology. It's the contradictions between important socioeconomic values that give rise to the real innovations: we can only opt for one or the other, but we don't know how. A car that parks itself automatically is not perhaps particularly interesting as an innovation. There's no constraint on the design of a new toaster in the light of these challenges. In ideal circumstances you can permit yourself the latest model of coffee maker, but when the world is burning it's time to devote effort to more important things. The essence of value-sensitive design is to make various values explicit. By so doing you give yourself a chance to design interesting things and hence to shape the world in a way that lets you satisfy ethical criteria too.'

The fight to attract talent

'Delft University of Technology has an honours track for students who score an average of 80% or more at Masters level. The majority of them not only study a difficult discipline like Aerospatial Engineering, but also take ancillary subjects such as Econometrics. What is more, they run marathons and play the violin beautifully. It's not a good idea to have too many people like this in your vicinity because it can get depressing! They also follow philosophy courses, go to lectures on ethics, ponder issues of responsibility and devise clever solutions for global problems. They are ambitious and highly motivated, and they have their hearts in the right place. Industry is fighting to attract these young people. But companies must themselves create an environment in which they can flourish. Jut as the universities compete to attract talented school-leavers, the recruiting (and keeping) of the top talent among graduates is crucial for companies like Fugro. It will succeed only if the company offers a fruitful, inspiring environment with good stimulus structures.'

Collective wisdom

'It's not only ethically commendable to engage in socially responsible business and innovation – it's necessary and unavoidable. We have landed ourselves with institutions and mechanisms that don't always tend in the right direction. In wartime, innovations abound, unemployment sinks to zero and the dividends rise. We need great minds to solve the peculiarities of our systems, but they can no longer do it all alone. We need collective wisdom or crowd sourcing. It's something we have to organise and institutionalise so that a movement develops. Philosophers from British,

1977

Shareholders wanted
—
—

Fugro Inc in Long Beach by now covered North and South America (together with its daughter Fugro Gulf in Houston); Fugro-Cesco Leidschendam serviced Europe and Asia. These were far and away the most important operating companies of the parent FCI and the only operational companies able to act on their own initiative. FCI itself regularly approached the bank for loans and was on the lookout for a third shareholder to help reduce interest charges. The Rotterdam-based Smit International, famous for its salvage operations, considered taking a 30% share. Nederhorst and Heidemij would then each come to be owner for 30%. The five members of the board - Joustra, Van Overeem, De Ruiter, Smith and Schoustra – would get the remaining 10%.

Rising costs were beginning to afflict Fugro-Cesco. Those of Research & Development had doubled in two years and Marine Survey braced itself for heavy losses. Could the merger with the offshore Cesco be described as a success? The management discussed the possible sale of the *Bison*, Fugro's colossally expensive survey vessel, and there was even a threat of the

American and Australian universities and from our 3TU, ethicists who are occupied with this matter, have joined forces. Some five hundred of them, leading players from all over the world, are collaborating with the Institute for Global Justice, an initiative of the Mayor of The Hague, Mr. Van Aartsen. He would like to bring all the institutions of international law together in his city. My message to him is make sure you also become the world's ethical capital, because jurisdiction which isn't rooted in a widely supported moral justification cannot provide guidance and lacks authority. You first have to agree what is ethically desirable or undesirable, and then codify it juridically. The Netherlands, and The Hague in particular, could occupy a special place in the international arena where people can ponder such issues as climate treaties, the sharing of scarce drinking water, the accumulating burden of space junk, exploration and exploitation of the earth's seabed and of other planets, internet governance, safety at sea, restrictions on research into deadly viruses, and the use of robots and drones in modern warfare. Provide a neutral place with authority and know-how, where we can exchange ideas multilaterally about these matters.'

The theme of the century

'What Europeans identify as being of value differs less and less from what the Chinese or Brazilians care about. Ideas about this are coming closer together under the umbrella of the Universal Declaration of Human Rights. Some people still experience difficulty with this kind of egalitarianism, but it will happen one day. The abolition of cultural differences is a question of time. Western cultures, too, needed time to develop. Communications technology is the mainspring of this development. Once people see how well people live in other countries, they demand to know on what basis this right is denied them – and rightly so.' That is where the interest in global justice comes from and it's the theme around which this century turns.
'The European Union and the US ought to conduct big science by concentrating thousands of top scientists worldwide around a specific issue. The EU Chairman José Manuel Barroso champions the formation of a European Institute of Technology, on the model of America's MIT. Governments can only tackle major issues successfully by pulling open all the stops together with the business world. And, by definition, it's an international affair.'

Cone testing near the International Financial Centre, Hongkong

1977

> entire department being closed down. Smit International considered the risks too great and withdrew as a possible shareholder. The threat of unpleasant measures only made the already poor working atmosphere worse. The company was unable to avoid a drastic reorganisation. Although the management and the Works Council were in agreement on the need for cutbacks and greater efficiency, differences of opinion caused emotions to run high. All this failed to prevent Fugro's president and chief executive office Joustra from organising a second symposium, but he had to make mention in his Christmas message of the first serious setbacks in his company since it was founded. He trusted that they had passed rock bottom but for most the message didn't sound particularly convincing.

—

And Israel's prime minister Menachim Begin made peace with President Sadat of Egypt.

LIABILITY CLAIMS AS CULTURE CHANGES

B usiness liability is playing an increasingly prominent part in the organisation. A project priced at 5,000 euros can land you in a liability claim for 100,000 euros – for example if a building suffers damage due to faulty foundation recommendations. But Fugro cannot accept limitless liability and tries to restrict it through our corporate terms of business.

Many Dutch companies in the same industrial sector have modelled their own delivery conditions on ours, so these have effectively become industry-standard terms. Large clients, on the other hand, insist on their own terms of purchase thereby easily giving rise to conflicts. Often it is a matter of negotiation, but in the end the customer is always right. The knowledge that, as a heavyweight player, we are necessarily well insured makes some clients all too quick to submit a claim. This kind of behaviour has brought about a change of business culture in Fugro. Liability claims always land on the desk of the Board, and they have delegated their processing to Louis de Quelerij. Among other things, he has organised workshops to train all the company's consultants and make them aware of the risks. 'It takes a bit of legal knowledge but it's not all that complicated. I've been doing it for twenty years, and I've seen, evaluated and processed dozens of claims. We work with regular lawyers, who have helped us shape our strategy. I draft the responses, and the external legal adviser tightens them up.'

Often it's not how you think

The number of claims is rising and it seems to be a general trend. Subcontractors and clients have grown smarter than they used to be, and you have to watch your P's and Q's. Some subcontractors find it more lucrative to snuffle out the weak spots in a contract than to devise a smarter working method that will cut their operating costs. They use lawyers as a way of making money. Louis served on the Building Council (Regieraad

---

2027

NEW GEOGRAPHIC AREAS

JOHN LAZARUS
GEOSPATIAL SOLUTIONS,
AUSTRALIA

We will follow our clients. Supply and demand dynamics will cause our clients to work in more and more remote and hostile environments. I am not so sure that there will be a clearly defined new geographic territory apart from the Arctic circle. In general I believe there will be changes to technology that will allow resource extraction from known reserves that are currently too expensive or difficult to extract. Deeper water oil and gas, deep water mining etc.
In addition some of the current less politically stable regions will have become more mature (Central Asia, parts of Africa) allowing greater interest in investing in natural resource extraction.

Bouw) for several years, is well versed in road and waterway construction, and acted as an arbitrator and expert in contract negotiations. 'Every case is different. I have learned a lot about legal priority. What counts as legally binding is often quite different from what your feelings tell you or from what you think. Your own terms of delivery, for example, only prevail if you state explicitly in your tender that you reject the client's terms of purchase. You have to know things like that. Fugro has learned from experience and the Board has now made that a mandatory stipulation. Sometimes you agree a compensation, sometimes you raise the price to cover the risk and sometimes you simply fail to agree.

'Tightly calculated prices are good for the client but don't earn us a cent – and we can still be sued if something goes wrong. This makes it unattractive to shave too much off the contract price. We may be willing to carry the risk, but then we also want to share in the cost savings and the client is generally not too keen on that. Still, it can be quite interesting to go that way as people are already doing in the US. It means that suppliers and clients operate more like partners.'

FUGRO IS NEVER BORING

'Fugro has grown rapidly through its numerous acquisitions combined with the agility of an autonomous but decentralised organisation. Three reasons for acquiring another company are: (1) a specific desired technology, (2) better geographic spread, or (3) a well proven company whose major shareholders are at the point of retirement. The growth rate for Fugro has averaged about 15% per annum over the last twenty years. Most people don't realise that only a third of that growth has been the result of acquisitions. Actually, two thirds of it has been organic growth.'

Utilising intrinsic value

'Fugro's decentralised structure, small company attitude in a large company environment, has made it easy for Fugro to absorb acquisitions into the organisation and allow the new entities to grow along with the company. But what is next step in the overall development of the company's business and business model? What direction do we see ourselves taking over the next ten years with the new organisation and how do we extract the full value of the company? Fugro is likely to increase the rate of acquisitions in the future but with a different philosophy. We excel in niche markets but we will have to start thinking more laterally and force our operating companies to look outside of their current capabilities. Fugro will have to leverage its huge intrinsic value of technology, experience, knowledge and skill. Merging some of the smaller operating companies into larger units will free some senior management time necessary to build a stronger organisation. We need to focus on the values and strengths that made us successful in the past and apply them now to our present day situation. As an organisation we must be more aggressive and not accept anything less.'

Mutual synergy

'The new management style should create a horizontal approach to reveal opportunities that were previously invisible. The new management has

Scott Rainey holds a BSCE and MSCE from the University of Texas Arlington. He joined the Fugro Houston office in 1981. His tenure with the company and the experience he gained during that time will help him define Fugro's path to sustain the company's growth and guide it successfully through the next decade. Traditionally, Fugro was lead by a single CEO; however, a new leadership structure and management style has been implemented. What some might consider to be a slightly dictatorial approach toward management is about to make way for management by a board.

a challenge to create new synergies across the company. We will have to make decisions of where to build, what to keep and where to divest. We can become stronger if managers realise the necessity of expanding outside their day-to-day expertise. A new class of managers will be necessary in the next ten years in order to achieve our goals. We have to foster a group that is driven by the necessity to succeed, that has unlimited energy and are afraid of nothing. There is nothing that this group can't achieve! The decentralised structure will continue but we will allow our managers to have the autonomy and authority to fully demonstrate their potential and competences to manage our business both regionally and globally. There will be no *stopping short* of greatness. They must learn to win big and not to be afraid to fail. They have been successful in the past with autonomous thinking but now have to also learn to work as a group. Fugro has been building our capabilities since the early 90's and no other company has amassed comparable geoscience capabilities whether operating in the air, land or sea. These assets have been distributed globally but, unfortunately, only a few within the organisation actually have a complete overview of the vast capabilities that the group has to offer. This is a deficiency within a decentralised system which we now hope to change. In the past, local managing directors have had unlimited latitude in growing their business but gave little thought to how it would impact the organisation as a whole. It will be senior management's responsibility to change this culture and encourage more synergy within the entire organisation.

'Determining the way forward in the next ten years will be a real challenge. It is essential to keep experienced staff that will be able to lead us through our ever changing markets and clients. Changes are always difficult but more so in a large corporation like Fugro who in the past determined its success by the performance of each individual operating company.

'It's a major challenge for Fugro to function as a single company with a single voice, but facing this type of challenge is what keeps our staff motivated and competitive. Fugro is never boring – never! I look forward to watching the company exceed its accomplishments of the past ten years.'

Grow or shrink?

'Fugro continues the learning process. I know a lot more now about how companies operate and the reasons for its success and failures. There were times when four acquisitions were on my desk at one time. Keeping your eyes open and paying attention is a shared attribute of both Gert-Jan Kramer and Klaas Wester. Both have the uncanny capability to devour information and comprehend the important message. Surprisingly, a number of the senior management also possess the same skill set. Both Gert-Jan and Klaas share the same vision for Fugro. Gert-Jan expected 150% effort from us every day and forced you to deliver. Klaas, on the other hand, had a more subtle approach but achieved the same results. Their similar

1978

A new approach
—
—

When a large order from India for Marine Survey failed to materialise, it meant the end of this department. Osiris, a subsidiary of BosKalis, took over all activities as well as the name Cesco, the *Sonia* trademark and a share of the staff. Some remained with Fugro, others left for pastures new. Even the *Bison*, then bobbing idly alongside the quay in Dubai, passed to Osiris. The sale meant that FCI had to change quite a few names. FCI remained FCI, but now stood for Fugro Consultants International. Fugro-Cesco became Fugro Ingenieursbureau, engineering company for geotechnics and geodesy. The former holding company for the companies in the Middle East became Fugro (International). The group commissioned the Rotterdam business economist Haselhoff to take a critical look at the company. After his investigation, he concluded that Fugro-Cesco had based its prices too much on actual costs and hours instead of on the possibilities held out by the market. Market-oriented salesmanship and engineering technology would have to join forces. The management needed to formulate objectives (management by objectives); it was only to intervene when things threatened to go wrong (management by exception). Fugro relied on technical professionalism, not on professional management. For those with ears to hear, this meant: 'The management is not listening, not delegating, and making its own decisions.' The top lacked philosophical quality. Employees were living on the edge of protest and that could deal the company a fatal blow. The great merit of Haselhoff's report was that all reproaches and suggestions of the past few years were now available, neatly compiled

>

thought process resulted in an underlying understanding and culturally created a strong bond with management. If anyone was underperforming, they would be responsible for solving their own problems which taught this group how to become *problem solvers*. This approach promoted teamwork and accelerated performance.

'The number of managers has increased sharply due to acquisitions. Now this new group will have to figure out the formula to capitalize on Fugro's underlying intrinsic value. They recognize that changes are inevitable and now have to pilot Fugro successfully through all these changes. Fugro has a solid foundation but its strengths lie in its people.

'As a senior staff member, I look back in amazement at what has been accomplished and wonder what it is that has driven us to become the company we are today but also what the future brings. We are moving into a new era for the organisation with a regional management structure and entrusting a new group of management to drive the company forward. How will the Fugro family react to these new changes? What will prevent us from reaching an equivalent increase in the financial results? What will stand in our way of growing our workforce from 14,000 to 28,000? Or will it shrink instead? I can't wait to see!'

Quick decisions are best

'I have just joined the Board of Directors with responsibility for the Onshore and Offshore Geotechnical Division. It's my job to determine how I can fit the pieces of the puzzle together to foster synergy within the two groups. Should I spend my time on the companies that are doing well or on those that aren't? Most managers devote their time and effort to those that aren't performing well, but in my view, it makes more sense to concentrate on those that are doing well. Fugro has always given the less successful operating companies the benefit of the doubt and hard decisions took a long time. Quick and calculated decision making is good for a corporation and will be a necessity in the future.

'However, the million dollar question is how to determine the right direction in order to steer the company into a profitable future. Opportunities force choices which can be a combination of acquisitions, organic growth or divestment; all of which mandate tough decisions. Where do we invest and should we pour all our profits into any one area? Or should we refill the war chest and continue on our acquisition path looking at the larger companies to expand beyond our present capabilities but in related businesses? Historically, we have often performed better than others by investing in ourselves. So there's a lot to be said for how we invest our money going forward. Say what you will, even though we are turning fifty, we are still a growing and maturing company entering a crucial period.'

Geotechnical vessel
Fugro Explorer

1978

> and of an authoritative value. The economist advised Fugro to invest in improving the existing technology and not in widening the range of products on offer; the outside world was particularly impressed by Fugro's technical know-how. (In 1978 Fugro's expertise was enlisted at some fifty claim cases because of subsided buildings and other damages.)
After Marine Survey was dropped, the two remaining divisions, Geodesy and Geotechnics, were made autonomous with their own profit centres. Everyone set to work in good spirits. The government had decided to have the Netherlands mapped in detail and Fugro was happy to get in on the act. It had installed a new computer with astounding software; the Interactive Graphic System (IGS) allowed you to make calculations, digitalisations, automatic drawings and designs, and store maps. It enabled Fugro to communicate effortlessly with municipalities, utility companies and other institutions working with IGS.
For Joustra, the conclusion at the close of this shocking year was clear: the Rotterdam economist had saved the company. Fugro and Cesco had some common ground but the people and their mentalities failed to match.
Fugro's Bremen branch landed an order from ICI in Wilhelmshafen that included 165 CPTs for the construction of a jetty.
—
And the Netherlands' plans to play the World Cup in Argentina were the subject of fierce discussion and protest.

▲

Geo Caribbean

◄

*Deployment of
seismic equipment*

SEISMIC PALACES

'**W**orking in the offshore world is far from easy,' Rob Luijnenburg says. 'Fugro too expects a lot from us. Some employees spend a lot of their time on long-distance flights, and that usually means a lot of hanging around in departure lounges.

We expect them to be ready to set off at a snap of the fingers – typically the same evening – and to visit countries where the conditions are less than comfortable. This can upset family life considerably. But there are always people who are glad to do it.
'The disappearance of Holland's traditional seafaring culture means we are taking on more and more Poles, Hungarians, Indians and Chinese employees. They are good at their work and less inclined to complain about disagreeable situations. Of course, we also take considerable effort to keep the conditions on board our ships as pleasant as possible. Our seismic fleet spends long periods at sea. The new ships are small waterborne palaces and are practically up to luxury cruiser standard. They offer ample space and comfort for each crew member. The cabin dimensions are partly determined by the collective labour agreement, but we go a step further in our onboard amenities. We demand a lot from our people but we offer a lot in exchange: an onboard internet café, a swimming pool and a gym. The facilities wouldn't be out of place in a mid-sized city. So it's a different story from whiling away the evening playing rounds of whist with three crewmates on a ramshackle little boat somewhere off Africa. The Dutch are sentimental about conditions like that because they fostered good cheer and camaraderie. Nowadays, everyone disappears into his cabin to watch his personal large-screen TV. Probably it is less good for team spirit than the old-fashioned card games because it is harder for everyone to get acquainted with one another. But team integration is important. People have to function together on the poop deck like a well-oiled machine.'

2027

FUGRO TECHNOLOGY

RAY WOOD
FUGRO CONSULTANTS,
USA

From the perspective of the onshore geotechnical business line, Fugro will continue to be at the forefront of the development of remote sensing (satellite imagery) and non-intrusive investigation techniques (engineering geophysics) to significantly reduce the inherent uncertainties and hence geotechnical risk associated with the characterisation of sites for engineering analysis and development. The integration of these technologies into the site characteri-sation process means that more information can be gathered more quickly and at less expense than with the conventional approach and the reduced uncertainty allows deep foundations and other geotechnical works to be delivered much more cost effectively and with less risk to project schedules.

FAITHFUL TO THE OIL AND GAS INDUSTRY

'There are so many activities required: exploration, development, production, drilling, decommissioning etc. We provide a whole range of services for different stages in the 25-years' plus production lifespan of an oil field. We have a balanced portfolio in the oil and gas area, but we have also been able to transfer the technology to the rapidly growing renewable energy market. The latter industry has grown significantly in recent years, partly due to subsidies granted by governments out of a professed concern for the environment. The reduced attractiveness of nuclear power following the disaster in Japan in spring 2011 has meant that fossil fuels will continue to be important. The world's need for energy is increasing daily and for the while a good part of that need will have to be met by oil and gas.'

The growth policy that Fugro has followed over many years has helped to spread the business risk, but the oil and gas industry still forms the lion's share of our client portfolio. 'It's impossible to ignore the importance of the oil and gas industry', says **Jim Sommerville, Chief Operating Officer of Fugro Subsea Services. 'It makes more business sense to offer a wide range of services in this industry than to focus exclusively on new fields of activity.'**

Remotely Operated Vehicles

'Divers are able to work at depths of up to some 300 metres. At greater depths, the pressure and risks are too high. When exploration for oil and gas moved from land to offshore and then to deep sea, remotely operated vehicles (ROVs) became necessary to do the work at greater dephts. An operator (pilot) controls the ROV remotely from the mother ship with a joystick using video monitors and acoustic scanning devices to visualize what is happening. The pilot uses other control systems to operate manipulator arms and specially designed underwater tools.

'Fugro Subsea Services has a worldwide fleet of about 150 ROVs, most of which operate in North Sea, Brazil, Asia and the Middle East. They vary from less than 50 kilogram to 4,000 kilogram in weight and in length from less than 1 metre to over 3 metres. Some are permanently installed on specialist vessels or drilling rigs, while others are moved between vessels or production platforms on a project basis. The lighter-weight ROVs are used mainly for inspection purposes while the larger *work class* ROVs can be used conduct complex underwater tasks. Depending on their specifications, standard ROVs can operate at depths down to 3,000 metres. They can open,

ROV controlpanel on board Fugro Saltire

Work class ROV with tracked skid system

1979

Sand in the machine: Jeddah closes down

—

—

Fugro were not back on top yet. The new organisation with its various profit centres was the cause of some confusion. In setting up a new department, Visual Inspection (VI), the management went so far as to reject Haselhoff's advice not to invest in widening the range of products. VI was a poor achiever. Fugro was having an equally difficult time financially in the US, but there the feeling of solidarity within FCI was shown to be improving.

In Leidschendam the management started organising hearings that were greatly appreciated. People wanted to be better informed; for this the directors had to leave their ivory towers.

The first quarter of 1979 showed such a massive loss that Fugro was forced to take back funds from the American and English companies. The big financial leak was in Saudi Arabia. The building construction market there was deteriorating and Fugro had to deliver for knockdown prices, although arch-rival McClelland had fifty men working in the offshore. The board of directors decided to end the Arabian dream and lock the door in Jeddah for good.

The Saudi Arabian government commissioned Saudi Fugro Ltd to carry out 75 drillings in the sacred rock of Mecca for a forthcoming storm water tunnel that was to protect the holy city against floods.

—

And in Iran, the spiritual leader Ayatollah Khomeini took over secular power.

check and replace valves, record images, retrieve components to bring to the surface and collect data. A standard ROV is a bit like a farm tractor which can be fitted with all kinds of accessories for various purposes. The increasing drive to deeper water exploration and production is paralleled by a demand for more and better ROVs. They are therefore subject to continual development and enhancement. Most ROV components need to be replaced every few years to the extent that after 5 to 7 years many ROV's will have been virtually rebuilt.'

Four kilometres beneath the sea

Successive takeovers of companies that utilise ROVs have gradually given Fugro ownership of many kinds of ROV. When development of Fugro's subsea business expanded along with growth of the market, Fugro decided that in future it would design and build its work class ROVs (roughly half the total fleet) itself. The new models would be equipped with new systems and new technology, and their development would be the task of an internal team of specialists. The integration of data recording and data management technology from the Survey Division resulted in a system that is unique to Fugro.

'Standard ROVs can work to a depth of approximately 3,000 metres but Fugro has operated systems down to 4,000 metres, thereby meeting demands from the oil and gas companies for work at a greater depth. Fugro's internally designed work class ROV combines innovations in hydraulics, electronics and control systems. ROVs are full of high technology components and their maintenance and repair is hugely important. All the components must withstand the extreme water pressure at the intended operational depth. A specialist team is working on further development of the technology for the next generation of ROVs at Fugro's own factory in Singapore. The designed depth for an ROV dictates the dimensions and quality of its components. Some components are interchangeable, but, as we go deeper and introduce increased capability, new systems need to be developed.

'After special training, someone with a suitable technical background is able to operate an ROV. The pilot has to cope with limited visibility and currents, and has to monitor what he is doing up to three kilometres below him on 2D screens and sonar displays. It takes years of experience to operate an ROV well. Once the ROV has reached its working destination, the pilot can switch to a dynamic positioning mode, a system that automatically stabilises the position of the ROV so that the pilot can concentrate on required tasks such as manipulating subsea equipment or taking measurements.'

1980

The pioneer has reached his limit

—

There was a great deal of commotion nationwide concerning the possible takeover of parent company Nederhorst by the Dutch energy giant OGEM, which was itself in a financially precarious state. The last thing Fugro was looking for was a weak parent; that behemoth was all about trade and no part of Fugro's world of technology. As for Heidemij, it wanted to trade in its 50%, so that the whole FCI share package would come on the market.

External adviser Haselhoff had remained involved in the discussions about the best organisational structure. He felt it would be better to have one top executive; one of the two managing directors would have to go. A preference for centralism over federalism was beginning to show. A committee set up by the Works Council held meetings where staff members could express their views about the way things were going and about the future. It was felt that the Offshore, Financial and Economic Affairs and Marketing departments should be managed centrally. And that it would be better if the local branches operated independently, each with a Dutch manager at the helm; the Dutch operational company in fact had to take over FCI's role of holding company. The management showed willing and organised an internal information day. Those present were informed that Fugro Inc would be sold to the local management, Fugro Gulf was to come under the direct supervision of FCI and the X-Ray Technical Service had

>

Training and simulation

'ROVs are popular with young engineers. ROVs are leading edge technology. The younger generation are used to game consoles, and an ROV seems to them like the ultimate video game hardware. However, we take great care in being highly selective for new pilots. Those chosen for training must have a sound electrical, electronic or mechanical engineering background as well as computer skills. Many of them come straight from college or university, but others have had experience in the navy or air force where they are well trained in maintaining advanced equipment. Ex-forces operators are also accustomed to working far away from home for long periods. We cooperate with several universities, and our own *Fugro Academy* is putting more and more effort into providing internal training courses for subsea engineering. Simulation is becoming a regular part of ROV training. The potential risk and the costs involved in ROV work are huge, so every effort must be taken to avoid errors. The trainees learn to control the vehicles using our own simulation software. The software simulates the effects of buoyancy changes, weight distribution, currents and wave motion so as to realistically reproduce the experience of working on seabed structures. In the past, engineers had to decide in advance what they would need to solve a specific client problem, and then go to sea to try out their proposed solution. It worked? Great. It didn't work? Oh well, back to the drawing board! Modern simulators allow us to incorporate all kinds of physical properties and environmental variables into the model, and then investigate the effectiveness of a proposed solution. This saves a lot of time and money. If something doesn't work, we can quickly reconfigure the tool or ROV for the next attempt.

Simulation is also very effective as a way of convincing clients that we can provide a solution to their problems. Once we have demonstrated that we can solve their particular problem in the simulator, the client is more likely to hire us to do the job for real. The technology of simulation has advanced considerably in recent years and is the main reason Fugro acquired General Robotics, which specializes in this area.

A new simulation module is added to the software for each new Fugro built ROV added to our fleet. The onshore engineers can prepare a simulation for replacing specific components whenever necessary. On board the mother ship, the engineer can load a disk with the appropriate subsea model, and the pilot can practice before attempting the actual task.'

Growing business

One of the challenges faced by Fugro Subsea Services is keeping up with the growth in the subsea market. The recession has caused delays in the execution of projects here and there, and it has reduced the growth rate of this work a little. As soon as the market picks up again, there will be a bow wave of projects that require catching-up. 'Then you have to find the

2027

TRANSITION FROM FOSSIL
TO RENEWABLE ENERGY

PHIL MEADEN
FUGRO SURVEY,
UK

The transition will remain work in progress as new hydrocarbon resources are discovered in underexplored regions such as the Arctic and South Atlantic and a high oil price driven by strong energy demand continues to drive exploration in mature basins such as the North Sea. However renewables will be key part of the energy mix with UK and Germany having 20% of domestic electricity supply obtained from renewable sources; offshore wind will gain most attention with each nation having built capacity of 8,000+ turbines each. Wave power will mature later in the period to provide a reliable additional renewable offshore energy source.

Seabed sampling with a Remotely Operated Vehicle

right people and hardware. When business takes off resources become scarce. In Brazil, some 850 Fugro employees are active in Survey and the Subsea Services field, but only five of them are non-Brazilian. The Brazilian government sets high requirements on local content. The state oil company Petrobras offers attractive long-term contracts but the requirement to have a high local content places restrictions on foreign companies and drives how we need to operate there. Petrobras has set extremely aggressive growth plans for the next 5 to 10 years and the industry will find it difficult to meet both these growth plans and the local content requirements. There are still too few Brazilian ships available and foreign owners can enter the market but increasingly over time companies must commission new vessels from Brazilian shipbuilders – as Fugro has just done.'

Mining the sea

Fossil fuel extraction is not the only application for Fugro's ROVs. They are also used for such things as inspecting undersea cables and installation work for offshore windmill farms. Seaborne mineral prospecting is also a growing market. Fugro helps by charting the seabed and extracting samples from it on behalf of the mining industry. Most of this work has taken place so far in the South Pacific, where submarine volcanoes disgorge deposits containing of copper, gold and other valuable minerals.

1980

> taken over Visual Inspection. The atmosphere was tense, not least because of the way the management fielded questions from the floor. The Works Council refused to approve the 1979 balance sheet, as there were too many items that were unclear and not enough information. Fugro still had just under € 3 million due from its foreign offices with a loss of € 275,000 in annual interest. In the autumn, the management presented Fugro's new organisational and policy structure. These made provision for a Fugro Management Committee and policy committees for Land Work, Sea Work and Finances.

—

And in the Chinese city of Xi'an the discovery of the *Terra Cotta Army* gave the world an Eighth Wonder.

2027

FUGRO TECHNOLOGY

GRANT AITCHISON
FUGRO SUBSEA SERVICES, UK

Fugro will be extremely active in subsea robotics and intervention, inspection and repair technology due to the vital importance in subsea oil and gas, and renewables infrastructure management and maintenance. Hard to highlight a specific single technology which will enable this – it is more of an application and development of what we have now to even greater extremes.

REGIONALISATION AFTER GLOBALISATION

–
–
–

'We no longer live in a time when a Western-based oil company could fly in fifty men to get the oil out of the ground. Countries like Angola, Nigeria and Ghana insist that you contribute to local development in your specialist area. *The Fugro Academy* helps by training local people, for example in Angola. There are rules for the minimum number of local people that a foreign company must employ. The employing company must do more than pay a wage: it must transfer knowledge. Companies respond by making their production processes more socially responsible. Nestlé had to find a reliable source of coffee, and they trained local planters, raised the output level and implemented guaranteed purchase quotas. The wide surroundings benefit from a socially sustainable production process. Fugro is following this path too. We are currently engaged in setting up local operations in which we employ local staff trained by us. When the local business is established, we will no longer need to fly in specialised engineers and managers.

'We maintain contacts with African universities. We support the University of Angola with equipment and with visiting lectures – this is the ideal way to do business in the future. The time will come when Africa is the only place where we can still find personnel, so it's in our own interest.'

Towards a smaller scale

Barely forty years ago, the large oil multinationals owned rights to some 80% of global oil resources. 'The situation has changed totally', Luijnenburg says. 'Now 80% of the world's oil reserves belong to national governments. State oil companies aim to maximise their profits, but above all they strive to support the country's development. Norway's Statoil, established as a 100% state-owned corporation in 1976, pursues the goal of making Norwegian society the best in the world in all respects. Although more than 40% of Statoil has since been privatised, its original goal remains practically unchanged. The Brazilian state oil company Petrobras is somewhat similar in that is 40% is owned by the national government while the remainder

The recent development of Africa is fascinating. A knowledge and understanding of the circumstances is vital to Western companies that aim to operate there. There is a heavy burden of local legislation laid down by a somewhat fickle political process. Fugro has established procedures for passing on information, in particular about security and regulations.
'Stability is crucial to our work and the events associated with elections can hinder us severely', **Rob Luijnenburg** explains.

▲
*GEOTEM survey system
installed on a
CASA 212 plane*

▶
*Fugro did soil investigation
for the Burj al-Arab hotel,
Dubai*

belongs to private investors and is traded on the stock exchange. Petrobras sets the national agenda. The company insists that foreign companies employ Brazilian workers and buy Brazilian products. They erect trade barriers and set limits for the number of expatriate foreigners who work there. Even ships have to be built locally if you want to do business there. This trend of localised development is supported by the national politics. 'The large oil multinationals employ uniform working methods worldwide and use English as their corporate language. People fly from continent to continent, and to that extent the traffic of people and goods is free. This is about to change, however. There's a rising trend towards regionalisation as opposed to globalisation and it's likely to accelerate, led by the oil multinationals. Developing countries take advantage of their oil wealth to conduct local and regional politics. These are trends to which we must react appropriately.'

2027

ORGANISATIONAL DEVELOPMENT

TOM HAMILTON
FUGRO GEOSERVICES,
USA

By 2027, Fugro will have fully developed into a more traditional corporate structure with the flat, entrepreneurial model being fully abandoned (*Navy out; Army in!*). This will evolve from overall growth and expanding requirements for mature HR, HSE, IT, marketing and risk management policies that can no longer be effectively met by small operating companies with limited resources. The substructure of the corporation will remain as large divisions (i.e. Geoscience, Engineering and Survey + *one more*). The next organisational level will be business-line based. Similar to the present Seismic Imaging, Geoteam and GEOS models, these units will grouped regionally for administrative purposes.

▸
*Fli-Map survey
in Ghana*

◂◂
*The Fugro Odyssey in
Rio de Janeiro, Brazil*

◂
*Monitoring the
construction of the
Shenzhen Western Corridor
bridge in Hongkong*

CONSERVATIVELY PROGRESSIVE UPSCALING

Paul van Riel, Chief Operating Officer of Onshore Geotechnics, sees ample opportunities for new developments in his division, which has a worldwide workforce of some four thousand. Before he is prepared to pour time, money and energy into new ventures, however, he would like to finish building up a globally consistent network of existing activities.

'Onshore Geotechnics can trace its ancestry back to Fugro's original business, that of building foundations. Laboratory studies and soil analysis have long been part of our armoury and we use them all over the world. But we are far from globally active in road surface studies, coastal water studies, engineering geophysics or geomonitoring. It's better to pursue our organic growth paths first; these alone should be enough to yield a doubling of our revenues in the next five years. Scaling up activities you are good at is easier than starting up completely new ones however attractive they may seem.

'Take engineering geophysics, for example. The discipline is better developed in Europe than it is in the US, and American engineers are keen to make headway with it. Their European counterparts believe in knowledge-sharing and are keen to spend a few years working abroad. It can be a good career step if you have the chance to work in the US for a while, for example. You learn from the experience because the American market is just a bit different in makeup compared to ours.

'A push towards a worldwide distribution of effort is partly a response to the demands of our clients. The major oil companies and clients in the mining and construction industries expect a company as large as ours to provide its whole package of services anywhere in the world. This is why I would like to develop our present scope of activities so that we can offer them wherever they are called for, rather than thinking about diversifying the range. This outlook is a progressive as well as a conservative one. We know our discipline, the systems and the rates to charge. Scaling up our activities is a spearhead.'

Positive energy

'Our capacity to take on large projects is a mainstay of our competitiveness. Fugro's organisation has long been such that each operating company is largely autonomous. A setup of this kind makes it hard to be efficient when a large project is involved. When I first started working in Onshore

Geotechnics, the division included five operating companies in the US – all of them in the South and West; nobody was interested in the East or the North. So we set up a single organisation with a single executive team to decide which activities and locations made sense for us and what the priorities were. This type of organisation is better at identifying potential large projects and can do more than a number of separate, smaller organisations, regardless of how well they cooperate. In other areas, too, we are increasing our responsiveness by upscaling. We try to stimulate people to make progress.

'These change processes demand a lot from the senior management of the subsidiaries involved. I regard it as one of Fugro's core values that operating company managers realise that the group as a whole can achieve goals that are impossible for the individual components. They understand that the ship can only have one captain. The process costs time and energy, but it is positive energy: you are acting constructively and setting things that were at a standstill in motion. It is attractive and motivating for all those involved.'

Local challenges

In the development of this style of organisation, local circumstances are part of the mix. At this point in time it is easier to find highly qualified people in the Far East than in Africa. 'A worldwide player like Fugro has to view these aspects globally, and in doing so has to cope with two awkward factors: the fact that developments are much faster in one country than they are in another, and, above all, the requirements regarding local content: in certain countries, you can only operate if a certain percentage of the personnel is sourced locally – as much as 90% in some cases. This is a challenge where there is a lack of adequately qualified human resources, but once you succeed you have established a cast-iron competitive position that makes it almost impossible for other companies to get a foothold in that country. In Nigeria, for example, we achieved our position through blood, sweat and tears. The branch is under completely Nigerian management, and they are people who know the local market like the backs of their hands. Had the local regulations been more permissive we might have been able to do a lot more, but now we are profitable there because Fugro is one of the few companies to have made the grade.

'As I mentioned, differences in the pace of development can be a significant factor. High-tech began in Western Europe, but the educational system here is showing the strain and the number of graduating engineers is declining. Meanwhile universities in countries such as India and China are turning out more and more graduates, and this is a factor in the success of companies located there. You deal with people very differently in China compared to in the Netherlands, and the same applies to India, the Middle East, other European countries and the US. Local systems are shaped by the political culture and its history. Europe and the US are increasingly protectionist.

1981

Up to its neck

—
—

In the first quarter of 1981 Fugro showed a loss of € 230,000. The group kept busy, despite the bad state of the construction market, although the management had to consider where the Dutch soil mechanics market was heading. The market in East Asia was strong, but things were less rosy in Dubai and the UK. Fugro Gulf in Houston had incurred a debt of € 450,000; the branch in New Orleans had closed down. At home the competition in the geotechnics market was stifling. The receivables from affiliated companies had increased further; half of Fugro's debts had been incurred in England and America. In one year, salary costs had risen by 77% in Houston, where the loss was as high as € 1.6 million. The Works Council spoke of mismanagement, in view of the fact that the Fugro top let this situation drag on so that the entire organisation suffered the direct consequences.

During the 1970s the environment had become an important social issue. Fugro joined forces with Alcontrol to carry out environmental research into soil samples.

An investment company, Caland Holdings International, bought up the block of Nederhorst shares.

—

And in the US, former film star Ronald Reagan moved into the White House.

Their notion that non-Western people must just adapt to the Western way of doing things and to the Western mentality is no longer tenable. Young academics from other regions are looking elsewhere for their opportunities. It's essential to appoint local management, and developing an empathy for that is an interesting challenge. Indian managers have tried to explain to me how things happen there. They can tell you ten times and you can absorb everything they say but you still can't quite get a grip on it. I have worked all over the world and I always found it fascinating, but I never really understood how the systems worked in certain countries. As a Westerner, I just didn't have the find-tuned feeling for it.'

Loyalty as a universal core value

'All the same, certain human core values apply regardless of cultural differences. Loyalty is one such value; one person may have it, another may not. And then there's openness and honesty. For an Indian, a Chinese or even an English employee, it's almost impossible to say to the boss, *I have to admit things are not going all that well here*. Americans feel uncomfortable in that situation too, but the Dutch are relatively at ease about saying what's on their mind.

'If you succeed in finding talented managers around the world who embody some of these core values, you can function extremely well. The senior management must be able to make the selection themselves. What good is a psychological assessment of someone from India, for example, if you don't know his or her character or cultural background? There's naturally a clear preference for people who have been part of the system for some while and have grown along with it. That's what makes Fugro tick. Hardly anyone can believe that, somewhere in a small upstairs office suite, we are capable of running a multinational corporation with a workforce of fourteen thousand.'

1982

Touch and go for Fugro

—

—

The alarming financial state of Fugro Gulf in Houston forced FCI to take Fugro Gulf's land activities division under its wing. The offshore market continued to slump. Fugro Gulf retreated first to a single floor of the building and then to a single room. Once boasting 140 employees, the company was stripped right back to a handful of office people and just five engineers who licked stamps and watered the plants. From this position the company could start slowly building things up again. McClelland was stronger than Fugro in the Gulf of Mexico, but Fugro was more highly regarded internationally.

Fugro returned to Saudi Arabia through a joint venture with Ramzi Geotechnics (25%) but the renewed activity there only lasted a year. A third symposium was held to celebrate Fugro's twentieth year and Joustra was interviewed for the occasion. He spoke in guarded terms about the difficult times Fugro was going through. 'You have to take the facts for what they are, like them or not. ... Of course people are more important than the company, but you should keep a close eye on that combination, because if the people no longer want to do their best for the company, there's no more company and no more people either.'

—

And in France the TGV *(Train à Grande Vitesse)* got you from Paris to Lyon in two and a half hours.

THE DEMAND FOR AUTHORITATIVE ENGINEERS

—
—
—

Nowhere in the world is the idea that engineers are introverted and surly so deeply rooted as in the Netherlands, where the status of engineers has declined. 'Nowadays it's lawyers who call the shots. Engineers with inspiring ideas – such as those that led to the *Delta Works* – used to have a significant say in the running of the Netherlands. People listened to them; they were indispensable for the design, execution and control of major projects. Now that a new underground metro line is being built through the middle of Amsterdam, nobody accepts the possibility of things going wrong, which means that the risks being taken are gigantic. In the offshore industry, similarly, nothing may be allowed to go wrong. People who are totally immersed in the discipline are needed in these situations. The Dutch government has placed itself entirely at the mercy of commercial consortiums for large infrastructure projects. They can see the technical problems ahead but tend not to propose solutions for them out of fear of being held liable. They prefer to wait for the extra business that results when the problems finally have to be resolved. This modus operandi has given engineers and their discipline a poor standing in the news media. The situation has changed considerably since the completion of the East Scheldt *Storm Surge Barrier* when all Holland beamed with pride at the achievement.'

Ambition is a good motivator

'Most of Fugro's employees are not amenable to a manager without a technical background. The manager must be able to judge how well a project is doing. In a takeover, the Fugro management must be capable of evaluating the technical substance – it's not only the financial data that matter. Fugro has always been a technically-oriented company, and the management comes almost entirely from within its own ranks.

'Large engineering consultancies in the Netherlands are generally short of specialists with depth of knowledge in their own disciplines. Most of them work as policy advisers to the government and have their own little plans to worry about. I'm convinced that the demand for specialist engineers is going to rise.

Practically everyone in Fugro has some kind of technical background, ranging from low-level to high. **Maarten Smits** is a manager through and through, but he speaks the language of engineers and understands what drives them. He considers this an advantage compared to managers whose profession is management pure and simple.

Groundwater monitoring
in a standpipe below
pavement

Tunnel
monitoring

'Many technical people know about nothing outside their own particular little patch. Fugro is in the process of integrating its subsidiaries. Among the advantages, the diversity of activities within the group will be more widely known and the staff will be better deployable in project after project. None of our competitors is as well supplied with logistics and technology as we are. Fugro can bring together lots of equipment in a flash and transport it anywhere in the world. This is what makes Fugro stand out. There is no question of us holding a monopoly onshore, but our ambition is an effective motivator to keep developing and to stay ahead of the crowd.

'This outlook ought to spur good technical people to come to work for Fugro and to stay. We are not interested in taking over small cone penetration operators in order to boost our market share. We prefer to aim for superior measuring technologies and equipment that are beyond the reach of others: satellites, aircraft, helicopters and the survey vehicles that can collect data as they drive.'

Fugro employs magicians

Fugro is going to survey 50,000 miles of the Californian road network by radar. The roads are in a poor condition and no one knows how thick the hardened surfaces are. 'Among our activities in the US, we carried out airborne geophysical surveys on the levees. A helicopter with a torpedo-like pod suspended beneath it flies at a height of fifty metres along the dyke. The levee managers assume that we immediately have a total picture of everything, but the work is fraught with technical problems. They see it as a kind of magic; they imagine they can call on Fugro for a quick job and have the data by next week.

'We don't like to disabuse them of this image, but it means we have to deliver the goods! It would be perfect if we could build a vast database for our own reference. After all, *Google Earth* will tell you a huge amount about the earth's surface. Wouldn't it be marvellous if Fugro were known as the company with a worldwide knowledge of what lies under the surface? This is a business model we would love to work on in quiet periods, although the permissions needed would make it far from simple. Besides, we rarely have quiet periods.'

The Chinese are coming

'People in the Netherlands seem to be afraid that the Chinese are going to take over the work. It's quite plausible, for example, that a bank could finance roads and other infrastructure and hire Chinese contractors to build them. Taking this to its logical conclusion, Dutch engineers will be completely superfluous. Data processing is now extensively farmed out to India and China so why shouldn't the Chinese be capable of taking over our major construction projects? Maybe it's reassuring that the Dutch subsoil is very distinct so specialists are needed here. Similarly, some of the world's top-flight earthquake experts work for Fugro in Oakland. They all graduated

2027 TRANSITION FROM FOSSIL TO RENEWABLE ENERGY

IDAR HORSTAD C.S.
FUGRO MULTI CLIENT SERVICES, NORWAY

The main challenge for any other energy than fossil fuel is the low weight, easy transportation and low cost for oil and gas in particular. It is hard to see that we within the next two decades will have a source of energy that is relatively stable and easy to transport, of which only 1 kilogram will be able to take a 1,000 kilogram car 20 kilometres. The question will be for how long can we continue to waste this source of energy the way we have done the past 100 years. We have to accept and get used to higher energy cost and short term solar, wind and thermal will be the most important contributors but gradually wave/tidal and hydro power (where possible) will become more important. Towards the end of the period, fusion energy and thorium might be on the door step.

from Berkeley University and have higher degrees, but none of them is an American; they come from India, Pakistan, Spain, Portugal, Columbia and so on. I think this is because Americans are no longer keen on spending ten years studying difficult subjects and doing mathematics that makes their brains hurt. The US too has a shortage of people who can do things that are difficult.'

How do you test a tunnel?

By current criteria, the *Transbay Tube* under San Francisco Bay, built in the 1960s, is not earthquake-resistant. A million people travel through the metro tunnel every day, so the catastrophic consequences of a severe earthquake would be unimaginable. Fugro has analysed the tunnel tube, taking into account known earthquake effects, the instability of the soil in which it is submerged and the stiffness of the tube structure. 'In our discipline, this counts as a top job. How will the tunnel move? Will it survive undamaged? Does the government need to do something about it and if so what and how quickly? These are important public questions. The local population receives intermittent reminders that they live in an earthquake-prone zone, but most Americans feel no need to know anything more about it even though they own lives and personal safety are at stake.

'The most difficult part is interpreting the data and calculating what will happen. You have to make assumptions such as about the present condition of the tunnel, which consists of a concrete tube with a steel shell. It is impossible to measure how much of the steel has been lost to corrosion. Random samples tell us little about the tunnel as a whole. Medical technology is much more advanced. It has become a simple matter to make a 3D film of an unborn baby, but we can see hardly anything of a structure buried underground. Besides, there are only a few tunnels but there are billions of people, and people are more inclined to pay attention and spend money on their health than on the condition of an invisible tunnel. Maybe it's also something to do with scale. A tunnel is a big, massive object and the technical investigation requires a far higher energy input than medical imaging does. So you could say that however advanced Fugro's technology is, it doesn't amount to anything compared to medical technology. Maybe we can learn something from the medical scientists, and in fifteen years time we will have the technology to make a scan of whatever is below the soil surface. It would be interesting to make a start on this development.'

Probabilities

Statistics has an important part to play in earthquake studies. 'Probability theory, to be more precise. What is the likelihood that the next tremor will be stronger than the last one, and what are the chances that the next storm surge will be higher than the last one? Besides, what is publicly acceptable?' 'Wave heights and rising sea levels are reasonably measurable and capable of being extrapolated. But the subsoil of a dyke has never been analysed at

1983

Changing of the guard

—
—

Rounds of bilateral talks with staff alternated with consultative meetings, trade unions and works councils exacted ever-higher wages, but the financial economic situation worsened and FCI's future looked bleak. Nederhorst's administrators sold their FCI shares just in time to IHC Caland. The confrontation between the body that thought it had the power (the Workers Council) and the body that had that power (the new Supervisory Board) signified a rude and cold awakening for the Works Council. The Supervisory Board decided to save the moribund FCI and recruited civil engineer Gert-Jan Kramer to take over managing the company from Joustra and De Ruiter. Kramer had spent years working for dredging companies and built up international experience there. It was particularly painful for founder and pioneer Joustra to have to step down. According to Joustra, it all began to go wrong when Fugro took over Cesco. The legal struggle around Joustra's departure went on for years, but he later admitted that Kramer had made the company a great success.

Fugro earned a small fortune doing survey work for laying out the road between Muscat and Dubai, but it was slow going since large projects were supervised from Leidschendam. Things were particularly messy in the US, where the offshore and onshore divisions Fugro Gulf and Geogulf were shut down. Ten of the original 140 employees remained to salvage what they could in a new company called Fugro Inter.

>

Pavement survey in the USA

Cone testing and drilling
at NASA, USA

this level, so we are less certain of the risks. Incidents make us wiser. When an incident happens once every ten years, most people experience it several times in their life and it finds a place in their collective memory. But no one has any concept of the likelihood of a storm surge flood in the Netherlands (1 in 10,000). They think, *Oh, that can happen only once in 10,000 years, and maybe there will be 100,000 casualties,* so they don't lose any sleep about it. But that is not how things really work: it means that every year there's a one in ten thousand chance that 100,000 people will be drowned. In the US, people define a critical water level as one that occurs once in 100 years. Once that level has been reached, they think it will be another 100 years before it happens again. That is far from accurate, but it indicates the popular understanding of the statistics. Americans take a different view of risks like these to the Dutch, and what's more they think that anything can be insured. 'The only thing you can be certain of about regarding the next earthquake is that it will happen. For Tokyo, it is already 100 years too late, I have heard. The next earthquake will hit the city some day and I prefer not to think what the consequences might be. How much is a human life worth? Ethical questions are not usually a strong point among engineers.

'Fugro has always been a fairly anonymous company which goes about its business without raising a lot of dust. In Australia, we were in the process of assessing the probable consequences of a flood when it actually happened. We were asked not to say anything about it publicly; Fugro doesn't like being associated with a catastrophe. We prefer to talk about areas that are still dry. The salinification of ground water in the Netherlands is a similar topic. The drinking water we get from the dunes is saltier than ever. Fugro knows a lot about it but prefers to work behind the scenes. Even when we have a promising solution, we don't get involved in the discussions because we don't wish to be seen as a special interest organisation.'

Passing the hat round for stronger levees

'The Dutch national budget for dyke reinforcement is already set as far ahead as 2020. Californians, on the other hand, may have to pass the hat round when something goes wrong. First of all there has to be a referendum on the investment of ten billion dollars for reinforcing the levees. Given sufficient support, Congress will debate the plan, although the Democrats and Republicans are bound to disagree so the decision will be postponed. Finally, when the delay becomes intolerable, they must raise money on the financial markets and issue obligations to finance the projects. It is incredible considering the potentially serious consequences of a levee breach to the state economy. No one seems to realise that the worst could happen tomorrow. The *Sacramento-San Joaquin Delta* is a vulnerable agricultural region. If a levee breach occurs there, the brackish water will destroy the lemon and avocado orchards that mean so much to California's prosperous agriculture.'

1983

>

Dual management didn't work and the Supervisory Board had been malfunctioning for years. Fugro's equity capital should have been some seven times what it was. Things were looking grim. Fugro made its living from technology and was still highly regarded internationally on this front, but technology without good management leads to bankruptcy.

Kramer wanted to spread the risks and show off the results of Geotechnics and Geodesy individually in two private companies with limited liability. 'The offshore department financed the onshore department after it had first been able to develop with onshore profits.' He put an end to employee participation which had got completely out of hand, since why should a Dutch works council have anything to say about investments in Asia? The local managements breathed a sigh of relief: they had finally received objective answers from the holding company. New systems were introduced to relate operational companies and financial reporting. Each director had to report what he needed to run his company.

It was largely thanks to Singapore, which had been doing very well for years, that Fugro was able to finish this tempestuous year with a negligible loss. Its equity capital was in the black, if only just; priority number one was to improve this situation. Fugro now had to work 'like hell' to earn its keep. The time for talking was over.

Kramer supported the few who were still working in Houston and those in Alaska who sought to gather geophysical, geochemical and geotechnical data on the off chance to sell to oil companies – pure speculation and sheer hard work. McClelland was squeezed out of this area and Fugro managed to keep going there for several seasons. Fugro might well have entered its final hour if not for this audacious and lucrative investment.

—

And the American geneticist James Gusella mapped a human gene for the first time – a milestone in genetics.

STAYING ON THE MOVE

Mark Weber has been the managing director of the Fugro Robertson Group of Companies, which includes the world's largest geological consultantancy, since 2011. The group of companies also supplies products and services in the areas of satellite imagery, marine geochemistry and seismic data. It has branches in Europe, the US and China. But matters are not likely to end there, considering the rising demand for geoscience services in Brazil, India and other developing countries.

Fugro Robertson's full range of products and services comprises no less than seventy-five categories delivered often on an integrated basis from a mix of twenty-four different business units. To aid in staffing these business units in a very competitive market for geoscientists Robertson has developed a unique *Graduate Training Programme*. 'We invite 18 recent graduates (most often from Master's level studies) that are selected from nearly four hundred applicants to spend three intensive weeks at our establishment in Llandudno, North Wales. The training programme delivered by the same industry experts who conduct state-of-the-art geologic and geophysical services for the world's leading oil and gas companies. It's a first rate opportunity for the graduates. They do practical work six days a week on both an individual and team basis using real world maps, well logs, seismic sections, geologic samples, satellite imagery, reports and other information. Their training occurs both in the office and in the field, and they are required present their results to their peers and to Fugro Robertson staff. Then we offer jobs to those that have performed well and left he impression that they will be a good fit on our team. During the *Graduate Training Programme* they have become acclimatised to the mountains of Snowdonia, made new friends and explored the vicinity. This increases the likelihood that they will accept our job offer and stay with us a long time. We aren't a wealthy oil company with a spectacular head office, but they will find many highly recognized industry experts and a wide variety of diverse and interesting people working here in a fascinating and growing organisation.'

Cultural identity
'The Fugro Robertson Group is involved in a wide variety of projects entrusted to us by clients from all over the world. Our staff profile looks a bit like the United Nations and reflects the wide diversity of our client base with many nationalities and a high concentration of Masters and PhD level scientists that are industry experts in their specialized fields. We aim to

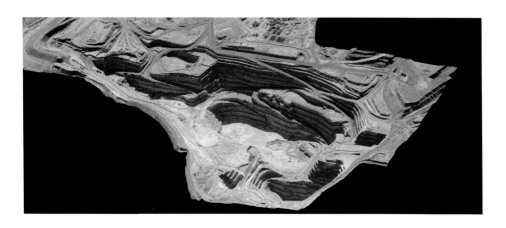

▲
Site investigation from
jack-up platforms along
the coast of India

◄
An airborne mapping
survey of one of Australia's
largest open-cast gold
mines to determine the
extent of the excavations

grow globally. While 90% of our 300 staff are currently located in Europe we can be increasingly successful through strategic expansion to other centers of oil and gas activities including Houston and possibly India and Brazil. A big advantage of being part of Fugro is that the Robertson Group of Companies already has sister Fugro companies located in all of the locations we are likely to expand. This brings a wealth of knowledge we will use to leverage our continued growth.'

Change is the only constant

'We work in an ever changing industry. Rapidly changing client needs and technologies create a dynamic work environment that requires us – if we are to continue to be a market leader – to remain flexible and open to change. A good example of this is the recent shale gas revolution. Ten years ago exploration and production for natural gas in shale formations was relatively unheard of but now countries including the US, China and India are in process of rapidly increasing their exploitation of shale gas as a key resource that can provide a higher degree of energy independence, not to mention jobs for their citizens, which is favorable to spending large amounts of money with overseas producers of oil. Fugro is aiming to be a key player in shale gas including the Robertson Group's development of *RoqSCAN*, a well site based electron microscope and rock library that provides near real-time mineralogical information that can be used to stear the drilling and optimize the costly, and environmentally sensitive, fracking of the shale required to extract the gas. We are also working on new algorithms that will enable our clients to better estimate the economic value of their shale gas prospects. Over time these tools and others we will develop will dove tail with an increasingly wide variety of products and services being developed

2027

ORGANISATIONAL DEVELOPMENT

CYRIL CHAN
FUGRO GEOTECHNICAL
SERVICES, HONGKONG

With the continued growth for the company in terms of turnover, number of employees and geographic spread, we anticipate a move from the traditional model of multiple individual opcos reporting by business line direct to the Netherlands to higher regional consolidation, with three to four major regional centres (for example Fugro Asia, Fugro Europe, Fugro Americas) responsible for overseeing the activities of all opcos in their respective regions.

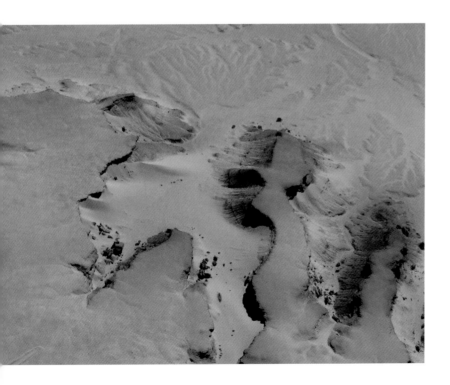

by other Fugro companies for shale gas, and other *unconventional* energy sources including shale oil and coal bed methane.
'We have to stay on your feet because nothing stays the same for ever. I recently heard an interesting statistic: *Half of the jobs on the planet that 25 year olds do nowadays didn't even exist when they were born.* Change is the only constant. 25 years ago there was almost no exploration being conducted in deep water, greater than 2,000 feet, but evolutions in technology – including those provided by Fugro to enable our clients to reduce their risk – have resulted in a revolution in deep water exploration and production with deep water accounting for about 50% of all global discoveries since 2006. Production from deep water discoveries is anticipated to more than double over the next 20 years and for this to occur Fugro and other companies will need to continue to provide innovative solutions to increasingly difficult conditions found in the Arctic, in complex sub-salt fields in Brazil, and ever increasing water depths. The technical developments are awesome, for example the geologic side Robertson's unique deformable plate tectonic models and paleo-geography (topography, temperature, rainfall, and drainage) prediction tools enable oil and gas companies to correlate current discoveries with the earth's crustal evolution of over millions of years. This provides a competitive advantage for finding and developing new discoveries in the future. On the geophysical side gravitational sensing acquired from aircraft and surface ships is becoming increasingly precise and Fugro is a leader in this technology. There is ongoing development of more compact gravity sensors which can be mounted in AUVs so they can work closer to the geologic source which will further increase resolution. We integrate the gravity sensor output with other data including seismic, and the result is high-value information for the client, obtained in a safe and environment-friendly way.
'Hydrothermal energy extraction is anticipated to grow at a faster rate than oil or gas over the next 15 years and yet it is an area that few companies including Fugro have historically taken significant interest in. However, this is changing as fossil fuel prices continue rising and funding for clean renewable energies are increasing. The Fugro Robertson Group through our satellite sensor technologies, and Fugro as a whole, are well placed from both a technology perspective and geographic spread to play an significant role in the development of hydrothermal energy.

Smart

'The Fugro Robertson Group's data resources, people and equipment can also be valuable for our colleagues in other Fugro companies so we put a great deal of emphasis on finding and cultivating synergistic leverages. Fugro's Geoscience Division is unique in that no other company in the world offers as wide a range of geoscience techniques. In order to derive maximum value from this unique position we are increasingly utilizing the wealth

1984

First make some money

—
—

Fugro grew and became more structured. The critical phase seemed to be behind it. In the US the break-even point was approaching quickly. Even England was making a profit after three disastrous years with no reorganisation. According to the new expansion strategy, Fugro was to open two new offices every year with a built-in start-up loss of two years at the most. Japan and Canada got the ball rolling.
The offshore safety regulations became more stringent, making it difficult for the landlubbers to spend some months at sea as they had done, a change being as good as a rest.
From then on Fugro was to be a single entity of independent branches whose managing directors would enjoy a reasonable degree of freedom. Basically they were partners in a joint venture and had to keep to the *Golden Rules*, the internal rules of conduct that dictated how Fugro companies were to deal with the market and with each other. During the Managers Meeting the managers could thrash out issues together. Mistakes were to be made known and discussed, as this would make the community strong. This way, Fugro could exert great pressure on the market and it would be difficult to compete with Fugro. FCI became the shareholder of all the subsidiaries. The buildings of Fugro were transferred to a Real Estate limited liability company. The five most important offices abroad were now Singapore, Hongkong, Dubai, England and Houston.
The shareholders of IHC Caland and Heidemij

>

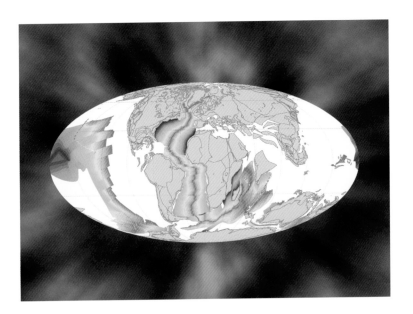

>

wanted to sell 30% of the company and each keep 35% themselves. The top twenty managers demonstrated their long-term commitment by taking an interest in the company and what was still left of bad feelings disappeared in one fell swoop. Later the employees were also given the opportunity of buying shares.

—

And the world's largest hydroelectric power plant went into operation in the Rio Paraná between Brazil and Paraguay.

The study of plate tectonics and the climate in the distant past is of considerable assistance when it comes to searching for new oil and gas fields

of geologic information obtained over 50 years of business as the *glue* for integrated multi-disciplinary geophysical/geologic interpretations. 'Clients see Fugro's logo and think that it's a single company, although in practice they have to deal with various Fugro marketing departments. Sometimes I arrive at a client's premises and see from the visiting book on the reception desk that a Fugro colleague has been there before me. One client asked me, *Couldn't we do this more efficiently? This is the second time in two days that I've had a meeting with someone from Fugro.* This is an area where Fugro can improve the services provided to our clients, but it is not an easy fix given that there is such a wide variety of technical offerings across each of the Fugro operational companies, let alone across Fugro's three divisions. What both the client and Fugro want is the most efficient path to get the *right* mix of our respective technical and commercial people talking to each other as early as possible.

'Fugro's growth increasingly presents Group-wide challenges. The decentralised organisation of Fugro is part of the success, but here too there are drawbacks as well as benefits. We have successful competitors who benefit from having a more integrated or coordinated structure. Fugro has, and is investing increasing time and effort to improve in this regard including the development of the *GOLD* database, cross-divisional marketing groups, and increasing amounts of inter-operational company education which makes more of our 14,000 employees aware of the vast array of offerings available from Fugro.

'Fugro tries to strike a balance between short-term and long-term thinking: winning and filling orders, and at the same time investing in development.'

Fighting leakage

'To make the best of our opportunities, we have to be on our guard against a gradual leakage, an accumulation of avoidable but unplanned incidents that reduce profit, from the moment that someone sees the possibility of an order to completion of a project. Every part of the process is susceptible to leakage. If we fail to interpret tender specifications properly because they are unclear, errors can find their way into our bid. Later corrections are always expensive. Things can also go wrong in the planning of project management. For example, a ship and its crew might be ready to set sail but have to waste time waiting for a component to clear customs because someone didn't allow for the fact that the customs procedures take a week to complete. Leakage and the quality of project management are factors in our reputation among clients and in the work satisfaction of our staff. Leaks can be prevented by having the *right* well trained and experienced people in the right positions, good communications and common sense. Our business demands a lot of energy and needs people who take the attitude that every hour must be well spent, 24 hours a day. We don't want to leave it to chance whether things go well or not.'

1985

Restructuring

—

—

Within Geotechnics, a distinction was now made between Onshore and Offshore. Onshore work was more a matter of routine, with many clients, small projects and plenty of competition; offshore work had fewer clients, bigger projects and complicated contracts. This held out the promise of a greater share of the market. This difference in markets was the reason for distinguishing between two operational companies in the Netherlands: Fugro Ingenieursbureau (Engineering Company) for the onshore market and Fugro Geotechnical Engineers for the offshore market and for near and onshore activities worldwide.

In the mid '80s all kinds of pollution scandals were rocking the Netherlands. Rubbish dumps were found to be full of illegally dumped chemical waste and needed cleaning up. Fugro began an Environment department. The environment was a hot topic and there was fierce competition.

In view of the reviving economy, the management predicted a much better result than had originally been expected. The windfall profit went partly towards a thorough renovation of the head office, with the laboratory as priority number one. A large offshore job in India saw a number of Indians working temporarily in Leidschendam to learn how to operate Fugro's machinery. Fugro for its part dispensed with unprofitable offices in Belgium and Malaysia.

—

And Robert Ballard discovered the wreck of the *Titanic*, which had sunk in 1912.

R&D IN ONSHORE GEOTECHNICS

Fugro's R&D will inevitably become a worldwide activity, according to Paul van Riel. The R for Research will remain a largely American and European business for a while, but the D for Development could just as easily take place in Hongkong or Singapore. There are simply more people graduating in technical subjects there, among other things on account of the status of technical professions.

Norway, well endowed as it is with universities, is just about the only country in Europe where engineers still enjoys some prestige in society. The Norwegian government expends considerable funds on R&D, and follows a strategy for industry that cultivates respect for people who graduate in engineering. In Holland, by contrast, people tend to look down on engineers as though they were bicycle repairers.

Fossilised standards

Companies active in oil and gas technology have to innovate to survive. Oil companies and service providers like Fugro invest substantial sums in development. 'Onshore Geotechnics has a different dynamic', says Paul van Riel. 'People here spend less on R&D. Fugro is a favourable exception, though. We continually work to improve on the cone penetrometer although there is little impetus from the market; people aren't asking for a better technology. This is due to the outdated regulations, the conservatism of building contractors and fossilised standards. Someone who builds according to the standards must perform the requisite measurements and compile the data according to the same standards, even if they are no longer appropriate. Until the national or international standards are modernised there can be no advance in the technology. All the innovation is aimed at safer and more efficient working. Fortunately there are new areas of work such as tracing environmental pollution. Modern techniques enable us

2027

EFFECTS OF
GEOPOLITICAL DEVELOPMENTS

CYRIL CHAN
FUGRO GEOTECHNICAL
SERVICES, SINGAPORE

In the next 15 to 20 years, we expect continued dynamic growth in the economies in China and South East Asia, which will eclipse the old world economies. The future is in this region!
This growth will require sustained massive investments in infrastructure for both transportation (including rail, roads, bridges and ports) and energy (with a large component of renewable including wind, geothermal and hydro). The growth will also result in a hunger for resources, resulting in growth in the mining and minerals sector. These are all areas in which Fugro can contribute in many ways.

Pipelines,
Oman

to profile the hydrocarbon pollution in an area. The results of the survey
are unusable for legal proceedings because they require ground samples.
However, the techniques do help us decide where to extract the samples.
'All the same, Onshore Geotechnics is not a dull business. There is plenty
of development, especially in the efficient processing of the data. We
are already implementing data entry in the survey vehicle itself, which
simplifies project management. Our improved archiving of the collected
data may also be regarded as an investment. If something is up years later,
we can quickly retrieve whatever we need. We recently launched a service in
England to archive the data from large projects. Our clients understand how
useful this is and are prepared to pay for our online data hosting facilities.
'Seacore's *walking* jackup platform is another innovation. The platform can
move under its own power so towing is unnecessary. It's a spectacular piece
of engineering.'

Opportunities all over the world

Currently some seven hundred people work in onshore geotechnics in Hongkong. The numbers are growing too in Vietnam, Australia and India. 'We have always been well represented in the Middle East. As to Western Europe, we are strong in the UK, the Netherlands, Germany and France. We have offices in Austria and Hungary. Our position in North America is substantial, and a few years ago Brazil joined our activities in the Americas. Nigeria has a fairly large establishment – mining is doing well in Western Africa. Oil has been struck onshore in Uganda, prompting investigations in Kenya and Tanzania as well.

'Onshore Geotechnics has opportunities to grasp in Africa although the local politics sometimes make life difficult. Security is high on our list of priorities in Africa. Fugro is the only company in the world to have the people and other resources needed to function in onshore geotechnics regardless of the location or the size of the project. We are no strangers to difficult situations and neither jungles nor rugged mountain terrain can put us off. They make a project more difficult but also more interesting.'

Brazil

Brazil has been opening up a new geological area offshore in recent years, striking oil in one location after another. The Brazilian oil reserves are gigantic but it is a big country in the throes of development. Its oil industry is comparable to that of the North Sea in the 1960s and 1970s. Fugro's focus is chiefly on offshore developments. The country is well organised and its governance is comparable to Western standards. The revenue from the oil and mining industries benefits the country instead of disappearing into the pockets of a few wealthy families. Brazil's economy is burgeoning and the demand for the services of Onshore Geotechnics will rise accordingly. Hosting *the World Cup* in 2014 and *the Olympics* in 2016 will boost the growth (and Fugro is keen to help with these projects). The work must be done well and Brazil is likely to succeed in doing so, considering the large number of well-educated Brazilians.

2027

TRANSITION FROM FOSSIL
TO RENEWABLE ENERGY

SANTANU MOITRA
FUGRO GEOTECH,
INDIA

So far as India is concerned fossil fuel will still be the major source of energy. However nuclear energy, hydropower, wind, solar and tidal powers will be other major sources of energy. It is expected that in the next 15 years the exploration of oil, gas, coal etc will subsequently reduce. We expect nuclear, solar and probably hydrogen to be the leading sources of energy by 2027.

▶
Cone testing in Hongkong (1), Germany (2, 3), USA (4) and Russia (5)

1

2

3

5

IN SITU JOINS THE PARADE

Suddenly there is a fax from Fugro. You've heard of them. Who hasn't in this business? They want to talk to you. It hasn't escaped them that Brazil is one of the places to be at the moment. OK, you think, it can't do any harm to talk to them can it? Let them try to persuade you into a joint venture – you can always say no. After all, it's your company. Your partner is not at all keen on the idea. There is no time and so much to do. You crumple the fax and toss it into the waste bin. But the idea won't leave you alone. There is a nagging thought that you might be passing up a golden opportunity. Fugro operates worldwide, its services are sought everywhere, it has fantastic laboratories and a wide network of contacts in the oil and gas industry. A few days pass by until you raise the subject again, and this time you manage to persuade your partner. The guys from Fugro come along and make their intentions clear straight away: forget about a joint venture, they are interested only in a complete takeover. You gulp with astonishment and ask for time to think. Don't take too long, they say.

Growing and growing better

The above is roughly what happened to Luiz Antoniutti as a prelude to Fugro taking over his company In Situ in 2008. 'I'm ambitious, I have my goals and I want to do things better. The call from Fugro was indeed a golden opportunity. The Fugro Group is never far away. They follow what you are doing closely and keep you busy. In Situ was ready for the next stage, to operate on a larger scale, and needed some kind of injection to grow in size and above all to grow better – because I have to admit, there is a lot that could be improved.

'As to why Fugro chose us rather than someone else: there are few geotech companies who work all over the country. The relative youth of our team must have been a factor too. There is one comparable company but the average age there is much higher. Experience counts for a lot but if you're ambitious and want to build a future, a young, energetic staff is better than people nearing retirement.'

Just imagine, you have graduated in geotechnology and you are now the enthusiastic manager of a successful company in your chosen field. Your firm is recognised for its high quality onshore geotechnical services in one of the world's leading developing economies. Your laboratory for soil analysis is well equipped. You have been successful in approaching financiers who extend credit to promising small companies, because you intend to expand. Besides onshore site investigations, you intend to offer data collection and database management. It's still onshore work, but the nearshore market has undeniable attractions for you now that huge oil and gas reserves have been coming onstream not far from the coast. You have close connections with the country's best universities where internationally reputed scientists stimulate your ambitions and present themselves as your partners. What more could you ask? The firm is flourishing and everything is going your way. You started exactly at the right time with exactly the right contacts. Luck is smiling on you!

2027

TRANSITION FROM FOSSIL
TO RENEWABLE ENERGY

MARK WEBER
FUGRO ROBERTSON GROUP,
UK

Renewable energy sources including
solar, hydro-electric, geothermal and
wind will have the greatest rate of
increase over the next 15 years, but
will remain behind oil and gas and
coal as the leading energy sources
in 2027. Developed countries like
Denmark that have already made
large strides toward cleaner energies
will lead the world in renewable
usage in 2027. However, economics
will continue to be the key driver for
the mix of energy sources consumed
on a global basis. The relevantly
inexpensive abundance of oil, gas and
coal combined with the exceptionally
large cost to build infrastructure
capable of capturing and distributing
renewable on a large scale basis will
necessitate that the transition to
renewables is slow but steady.

Recruiting well-trained personnel is difficult in the rapidly growing Brazilian economy. Everyone is hunting for the best people. 'Now that we're part of the Fugro brand, we can offer candidates a challenging career. The people we need are special. They have to be geoengineers who like travelling and are also available for lab work. The shortage of people and equipment is sometimes a hindrance to business. We can't yet take on too many projects at once. We feel we are planning things boldly, but time and time again our forecasts prove too cautious. One peak follows another.'

Not all eggs in one basket

Most Brazilian laboratories are attached to universities. 'My dream was always to run the best, most modern laboratory in Brazil; and now it has come true. We were already in the middle of investment talks when Fugro turned up. Our company cultures are a good match. Fugro's lab is terrific with hundreds of machines, and now we can let ours grow too.'
Management at this level is new to Luiz. It is not his favourite pastime but it is part of the job. 'I prefer the operational side of things but now that I'm more a manager than a geoengineer I hardly ever think of my technical profession. Still, it's good to run a company whose technology I understand. That's more satisfying. Once I had it in mind to do a doctoral dissertation but I can forget that now. Instead I'm planning to take courses leading to an MBA so that I can prove my worth as a manager.'
In Situ has now set its sights on the nearshore business, which will mean collaborating with Seacore. 'Seacore is recognised globally as the bee's knees in their field. We see them as setting the standard of excellence and we'll strive to reach their technological level. In Situ is contributing more and more to projects for building foundations, and nearshore can also revive our old speciality, the lab analysis of ground samples. As for consultancy, we have room to develop. Brazilian business is finding it hard to keep up with the burgeoning market demand. There are great opportunities to be grasped. Through Fugro, we could import expertise from countries where the economy is over the hill or stagnating.
'The fast growth also sets some hard challenges. We have integrated Fugro's QHSE system, but because new people are continually coming to work for us it is difficult to maintain the quality and safety level. The theory is important, but how it's done in practice is even more so. We are advancing but there's still much to improve.'
In Situ is not putting all its eggs in one basket. 'Seventy per cent of Fugro's work is in the oil and gas industry. We try to keep that proportion under fifty per cent. We are also addressing diverse markets: the considerable Brazilian mining sector, infrastructure, and port and industrial facilities. This strategy is looking successful. Our revenue has doubled in the three years since Fugro acquired us, but I regard our growing self confidence as the primary benefit. We can now handle complex international projects, and we are self-assured and proud of it. For me personally, the Fugro takeover marked a fantastic turning point in my life.'

1986

As Fugro refurbishes, oil prices plummet
–
–

Without warning, oil prices collapsed and the world entered the third oil crisis. Three months later there was no work. The technological *tours de force* of the oil and gas industry were formidable but so were the costs. The price was no longer realistic. The offshore market in the North Sea collapsed. The expensive refurbishment in Leidschendam gave Fugro enormous cash problems – the mortgage had still to be taken out. And the added value of the onshore activities was not high enough to guarantee Fugro's survival.
According to Kramer Fugro only had a future if the company were to be less dependent on the oil and gas industry. The takeover of 50% of the De Waal engineering company confirmed the growth strategy, one that would continue for some years.
Fugro suffered a loss of several million euros in 1986; plans to introduce the company on the stock exchange were shelved. Shareholders had to help out so that employees' salaries could be paid and the Fugro top withdrew to consider survival strategies. Nothing was too crazy, including the unthinkable: joining forces with arch-rival McClelland. The American offshore giant was itself in serious trouble and on the lookout for a strong partner, as only a merger could save McClelland. Both companies suffered a loss of € 3 million that year.

–

And the greatest nuclear disaster of the 20th century took place in Chernobyl.

A PROCESS OF EVOLUTION

'The Group is in a process of evolution. CEO Gert-Jan Kramer was a passionate, enthusiastic leader. He was involved in all the main transactions that turned Fugro into a major player and was closely acquainted with all the managers, and often knew their partners. He put a lot of effort into maintaining contacts, thereby creating the confidence and transparency which are vital to a decentralised organisation. His concern for people in Fugro is still renowned, as you will learn if you talk to the managers who worked under him. His memory for small personal details was legendary. Kramer's successor, Klaas Wester, distanced himself a little bit more, but introduced more collaboration and consultation. The holding company took a more leading role with regards to safety, human resources and project management. Under the leadership of Gert-Jan Kramer and Klaas Wester, Fugro has grown from a firm operating mainly in the Netherlands into a globally respected player with a turnover of over 2.5 billion euros. They both deserve much praise for the development of this great company with a highly loyal workforce.'

Managed autonomy

'There seems to be a paradox between the old, horizontal style of organisation whose success depended partly on the autonomy of the operating companies, and the need felt by regional and local managers for guidelines and feedback. Now that further growth of the Group is anticipated, it is desirable to introduce a more collective decision process with more delegation of responsibilities. The goal is to continue operating in the same decentralised way, with Division Directors which have operational responsibility for the three divisions Geotechnics, Survey and Geoscience. Each Division has a number of senior managers who are responsible for the operating companies reporting to them. The senior managers form an additional layer of management but that doesn't necessarily hamper the speed of decision making. The new team will involve the managers more in the decision making process. Fugro is operating smoothly but if we continue

Arnold Steenbakker graduated in 1983 from Delft University in Civil Engineering, with a minor in Offshore Engineering. He took a job with Fluor, a large, globally operating engineering and construction firm whose projects include oil production platforms and refineries. Fugro now provides Fluor amongst other services, with site positioning and soil investigations, for example for offshore wind farms. In 2005, Arnold moved over to Fugro, where, after four years leading the Onshore Geotechnical business line, he became head of the Information Services part of the Geoscience Division. On 1 January 2012, he succeeded Klaas Wester as Chairman of the Board of Management of Fugro N.V.

on our present path we run the risk of missing opportunities, particularly when it comes to winning large projects involving multiple operating companies. We aim to adapt the organisation to the new demands and fortunately we have the time to do it in.

'In the area of safety, we have succeeded in establishing uniform procedures throughout the decentralised structure. Initiatives like that can better come from within the organisation – it's not a good idea to impose them from above. It takes a while to set the flywheel spinning, but less effort is needed once it is up to speed.'

Mobilising the organisation

'My passion is mobilising the organisation. I feel I am getting on top of things only when the chosen strategy and the framework are clear, and the processes and systems are well enough implemented that the organisation runs practically on its own steam. I had some excellent training at Fluor. After working as a civil engineer for two years, I was made responsible for project management, construction management and general management, abroad as well as here. It meant moving every two years to a different business unit, with different bosses and colleagues. All those different characters and methods were a source of inspiration to me and made me think about how one should do – and not should do – things. I learned a lot about strategy and vision development there, although it's no good dreaming up visions and strategies and do nothing about it. I also learned to motivate people at all levels and not to lose sight of details. Job rotation of that kind is not part of the culture in a decentralised organisation like Fugro. We intend to give future managers of Fugro a wider experience of the company by means of focused career guidance.'

People want clarity

'Fugro Onshore Geotechnics employs four thousand people in about thirty different locations. I did my best to visit all of them at least once a year. The interaction with the management team during the day and at dinner was important. That's how you sample the atmosphere and discover how the team members function together. The manager understands what I want, but does this filter through to his subordinates? I intend to keep doing this. I like to understand that we are getting across what the management team wants.'

'I am part of the team, with a portfolio to lead it. It is in this role I can contribute the most. Everyone can share ideas, but once a decision is taken with majority support then everyone has to go along with it. Anyone who doesn't agree and puts up passive resistance is out of place here. Some people are team players but for them playing is as far as it goes. Then nothing actually happens. I don't care for that.'

1987

The merger that proved to be a takeover
—

Many companies were up for sale because of the oil crisis. Fugro bought the remaining 50% of De Waal and 50% of Oserco, a formidable offshore competitor. Two other companies in the US and England were going for a song but Kramer had no time to get involved, owing to secret and difficult talks with McClelland. Fugro had a staff of 450, McClelland 550. Fugro's edge on McClelland in the North Sea was more significant than that of McClelland on Fugro in the Gulf of Mexico. McClelland had better contacts, but in the North Sea, where the work was more difficult than in the Gulf, BP and Shell felt attracted to Fugro's better technology. Fugro had solid internal and external shareholders, whereas McClelland was a centrally run family business. *Pater familias* Bramlette McClelland charged the managers of operational companies a management fee, which frustrated their enterprise. He had made his fortune in the sweltering heat of Saudi Arabia, whereas Fugro's big profits came from the bitter cold of Alaska, where a bold investment had paid off big time from day one. Fugro had beaten its major rival on its home territory and was able to start rebuilding the company in Houston, while McClelland was obliged to cancel its pension scheme so that millions of dollars flowed back into the company. Bye-bye pensions.

In October 1987, after a protracted investigation by accountants and lawyers, McClelland and Fugro merged into Fugro-

›

Concrete priorities

'Being a company operating globally, Fugro has to deal with different cultures, thinking and social backgrounds. I like to keep things simple and at a general level. When I speak to a group of staff members, I want to be certain that they have understood me by the time they go home. So I restrict myself to essentials: this is the problem we need to address. You can't cover everything for the next fifteen years, but it's possible to formulate a few spearhead issues for three years ahead. In that situation I avoid abstract matters like strategy and vision. Most people need to know what the concrete priorities are in their work and how they can contribute to achieving them.'

2027

EFFECTS OF
GEOPOLITICAL DEVELOPMENTS

TIM DUNNE
FUGRO WEST,
USA

For the Americas region the key geopolitical issues until 2027 will be driven by China's development and increasing competition for the materials and energy needed to grow and sustain our societies. While technological breakthroughs will change the mix of energy supply between hydrocarbon and renewables, the global demand for water, hydrocarbons, metals, and other basic resources will continue to grow, resulting in higher prices and increased demand for Fugro's expertise. Climate change will also create more need for our services. Together these will provide good opportunities for Fugro to prosper throughout the region, although we will have to deal effectively with the competitive pressure that will come to the region from China.

*Newfoundland,
Canada*

Performance and personal development

'Following the model of the introduction of the HSE policy, Fugro set up a *Global Human Resource Team* in 2009 tasked with formulating and implementing a number of initiatives focused on our employees. One of the most important of these has been the *Performance and Personal Development Process* launched in 2010. This stimulates dialogue between the employee and his or her superior by a discussion of performance goals at the start of the year, followed by an interim and a final evaluation. Also discussed are the needs of the employee for training or which project assignments are desired with regard to career development. Formalisation of this process gives members of staff more opportunity to extend their knowledge and experience, so that they can add more value to Fugro's activities on behalf of the clients.'

Combined services

'I have no concrete expectations about where Fugro will be fifteen years from now. What matters is to create an organisation that gets what it wants. We can no longer rely on everything just falling into our hands. We must put more effort into it if we are to differentiate from the crowd. Fugro will have to follow the major trends and developments carefully, and be prepared to anticipate on them quickly and effectively. This is a culture we need to develop further. The notion that everything will work out because we are the best, is our worst enemy. This attitude is unknown in emerging economies like China and India. We must continue to innovate and to reinvent ourselves. That gives us our best chance of outsmarting the growing competition – and that is what will count in the end.

'Fugro occupies a first-class position in the markets where we work, but let's not get too complacent about it. We must coordinate our services in a way that will help us capture a unique market position. We were unequalled in specific services ten years ago, but now we can excel by offering them in combination with other services. None of our competitors are at this same level. This is where our real opportunity lies, even though we can't rely on the advantage lasting forever. In a few markets, we have a strong position that will be difficult to improve as result of our current market share. There is an inevitable ceiling. We shall have to think hard about which new markets we want to enter. Fugro is currently active purely in data gathering, which has a relatively low risk profile. As soon as we venture into other territories this may change. We mustn't rush into things. Selective takeovers remain part of our growth strategy, along with the promising prospects for autonomous growth within the organisation as it is now.'

1987

> McClelland – the name McClelland was too valuable worldwide to dispense with. Then it transpired that a third of McClelland's share-holding employees had not been able to sell their shares back on leaving because McClelland had for years lacked the necessary funds. FCI reached for its chequebook and, with help from an investment company, paid them what they were due. This way, Fugro obtained not half but more than 66% of the shares and the merger became a takeover. At a stroke, Fugro had become the world's largest engineering consortium in geotechnics and the takeover had bought Fugro that market position. All in all Fugro now owned 85% of the geotechnical offshore market. Branch offices all over the world were merged. In Singapore Fugro's representatives arrived just in time to reanimate the branch there; the office was a shadow of its former self and the bank was about to withdraw its credit facilities.

The clients were less happy about Fugro-McClelland's extremely strong market position. The company promised not to fleece its clients but it did want a reasonable price for the high-quality Fugro technology. The oil companies and Fugro-McClelland had been too dependent on one another to part company. A client in Asia wanted to avoid Fugro monopolising the region and granted Fugro's man in Singapore – who had gone to work for a Malaysian competitor after being dismissed – an immense contract.

After a hair-raising and arduous year McClelland was in the bag. The Supervisory Board was still as sceptical as it was supportive and the banks were surprised that it had worked.

At the end of the year Neelie Smit-Kroes, Minister of Transport, Public Works and Water Management, opened the renovated and enlarged head office in Leidschendam. Spirits were high.

And *Black Monday* gave Wall Street and the world the biggest stock market crash since 1914.

GROWTH IN ONSHORE GEOTECHNICS

O nshore seismics is a very labour intensive activity. The requirement for local content – especially people – is strict, putting local seismic operators at a great advantage.

'It's hard to get a foothold', comments Paul van Riel. 'We are presently staying out of onshore seismics for oil and gas, but we are active in engineering seismics – that is, a lightweight version of onshore seismics for the oil and gas industry. In 2010, we purchased a small three-ton truck for mounting a vibration unit to generate seismic waves. It allows us to penetrate to a depth of one kilometre on land. We are using this unit to trace earthquake-prone active faults so as to collect vital information for deep foundations and explore for coal resources. These are often located at depths between 300 and 1,000 metres where they are visualisable using seismic techniques. The vehicle is located in the UK but can be deployed anywhere in Europe. It fits into a standard shipping container so it is easy to transport. The new equipment is yielding good results. We already have ample experience in using geophysical techniques for the building and construction market, and we continue developing.'

Small, but the biggest

An advantage of Fugro's geographical spread is that we can follow progress in the BRIC and other developing countries closely. Nigeria, with a population of 110 million and a vast oil and gas income, could advance quickly as long as the profits are reinvested locally. 'Things are warming up in Mexico too. Worldwide, there is a huge dynamism in onshore geotechnics. The hard part is to figure out where our activities could be profitable and to grasp the best opportunities.
'Fugro is a world leader in offshore geotechnics and offshore surveying; we have a major market share in geophysics and geology for oil, in gas and in mining. Fugro may well be the largest operator in onshore geotechnics, but globally we only represent a market share of a few per cent – there

2027

CONSEQUENCES OF CLIMATE CHANGE

DAVID LOWE
FUGRO ROADWARE, CANADA

Climate change is presenting some interesting opportunities for Fugro Roadware. Sea level rises and flash floods and storm surges have created greater demand for the data we collect and analyse about the coastal road systems. Understanding the geometry and relative altitude for the road ways is critical to flood defence. These opportunities are most likely to involve a fusion of high precision road survey data from various Fugro companies such as Earth Data and John Chance Land Survey.

▲
*Cone testing,
San Francisco, USA*

are countless local companies active in this area. Being the biggest gives us opportunities to expand. What countries have a lot going on? How do the markets function there? What consortiums of construction and mining companies are active there? Large clients have little time for small subcontractors. They need a reliable partner who delivers good results in time and regulates safety matters well. Fugro has a march on the competition, despite local subcontractors being potentially cheaper. 'Clients are also willing to pay extra for our large scale. Some countries have laws that require everything to take place through tenders. We automatically find ourselves up against smaller players. Sometimes a consortium of contractors realises that protecting local interests is not the only consideration and they opt to do an exclusive deal with Fugro. We prefer to work in countries where direct procurement is allowed; it is criteria such as these that make a country attractive to us. In Kazakhstan, large Western contractors and design groups are working for the mining industry. The political system is reasonably stable, so the lights are on green. Turkey is similar. Fugro has put down a fantastic visiting card in the form of our recent investigation for the *Izmit Bay Bridge* project. It's an obvious country for us to seek more work. As a way of establishing a long-term foothold, we took over a small but highly regarded engineering consultancy in mid 2011.'

UMWELT
GEOTECHNIK
ANALYTIK

fugro
BERLIN
030/93 651 352

2027

CONSEQUENCES
OF CLIMATE CHANGE

SVEN PLASMAN
FUGRO SINGAPORE

Having intelligent monitoring and
early warning systems integrated
into fully automated city systems
will become increasingly important
in the highly populated (delta) cities
in South East Asia. The consequence
will be that Fugro Waterservices
will become more and more actively
involved in finding solutions and
providing data and automated
warning systems in cities, like
Jakarta, Bangkok, Singapore and
Ho Chi Minh City.

Fugro is acting in its own interest when it undertakes the first project together with a selected local operator. It is a way of getting acquainted with the country. If the collaboration fares well, a takeover may result, giving the Group an excellent starting position for future contracts. 'We can gradually expand in this way. There's no point in trying to rush things because it also requires good management. There isn't an endless supply of capable managers, and we can't invest blindly. It's useless to jump the gun. You need a minimum capacity to continue focusing on the developments in a particular country. This places a natural brake on the rate of expansion.'

Earthquakes are predictable

The *Izmit Bay Bridge* project was a very spectacular one for Fugro. The bridge is required to span one of Europe's most active faults which triggers a severe tremor every thirty or forty years. The bridge will have to cope with geological displacements both vertically and horizontally, so the foundation must be designed accordingly. The bed of the bay descends to a considerable depth close to the coast. 'For our survey, we used ships in deep water, a platform close to the coast and trucks onshore. We conducted geological, geophysical and coring studies to identify the local depth and location of the fault. Our earthquake study gave us data on the frequency of catastrophic events and the size of fault slippage to be expected. We even looked at ancient Roman roads in our study, giving us a two thousand year reference span. Fugro can deduce details of past earthquakes from misalignments in these roads.

'Earthquakes follow a moderately predictable pattern. We did much research on the *Andreas Fault* in California. In the vicinity of San Francisco, a major seismic event can be expected once in two to three hundred years. There's no guarantee of when it will occur, but once you know the subsurface geology it's not too hard to predict what will happen when it does.'

2027

NEW GEOGRAPHIC AREAS

JORGE HILDENBRAND
FUGRO LASA GEOMAG,
BRAZIL

Emerging countries like China, India, Brazil, Russia, Indonesia and South Africa are improving life conditions for their populations by creating better infrastructure and making more food available. All these efforts demand natural resources, notably metallic minerals (iron, copper, zinc, nickel, etc), energy (oil and gas) and non-metallic minerals like those used for construction and to produce fertilizing (potassium and phosphate), which support their agriculture. So, definitively Fugro would be very active in the large countries (with large populations) like China, India, Russia, and Indonesia; in South American countries (mainly Brazil, Argentina, Peru and Colombia); and in the south of Africa (South Africa, Angola, Botswana and Namibia).

*Cone penetration tests
in open mine,
Germany*

*Port of Los Angeles,
USA*

*Cone testing in arctic
conditions (-25°C) for a
windmill park in Pestera,
Romenia*

2027

CONSEQUENCES OF
CLIMATE CHANGE

ED SAADE
FUGRO EARTHDATA,
USA

70% of the world's population lives
in coastal zone regions, requiring
massive cultural transition to
mitigate rising sea levels. Fugro has
conducted >$ 35M in coastal area
mapping studies along the US West
Coast since 2006, mostly driven by
concerns related to sealevel rise and
coastal flooding impacts. We expect
these types of programs to continue
nationwide and worldwide. We also
see the impact as severe weather
events with more damaging winds
and floods associate. An additional
growing demand will be for evaluation
of bio-mass measuring capabilities
which rely on the tools that we
operate.

MERGERS
RAISE THE CAPACITIES
OF ALL INVOLVED

—
—
—

'Californians and Texans make an interesting combination. In California, they start small and build up to something big, but in Texas everything is big from the outset – nothing is impossible. The combination of these cultures was fascinating, apart from understandable individual concerns about the change of name and about the absorption of personal provinces into a larger entity. Imposing the requirement to report to a manager in Houston is a painful blow to a Californian. I continually drove home the message that the merger was better for Fugro as a whole. The Dutch are more outspoken than the Americans; if they don't agree with something they'll have no hesitation in venting their opinion. The Americans – especially Californians – are more compliant. It's often not until much later that you discover they are really unwilling to go along with you. I learned to listen and to read between the lines in a very different way while I was in the US. At first sight it seems that Americans are candid, but they are much more polite than the Dutch.
'The difference in business culture between Fugro Ingenieursbureau and Fugro Inpark is much narrower. Both of them are Dutch companies with a focus on building. Fugro Ingenieursbureau is at home with old-fashioned drilling, and Fugro Inpark with old-fashioned land surveying. Surveying takes place nowadays from vehicles that drive along the road at 80 kilometres per hour taking photographs and making laser scans of the surroundings. Ground penetration testing has become a part of the larger field of project optimisation, and cone penetration companies have turned into geo-specialists with a wide range of activities.'
Despite the emotions, Maarten Smits found ample support for the merger. 'Some people naturally wonder what consequences a merger will have for their jobs, both before and during the process. However, they have no less reason to consider the potential personal consequences if the merger of these operating companies doesn't happen. The combination offers much wider opportunities, for example for individual staff members who would like develop their careers by spending a few years working abroad, as I did in the US.'

Maarten Smits returned to the Netherlands after working in the US on, among other things, the merger of Fugro West and William Lettis. Back home, his duties included guiding the merger of Fugro Ingenieursbureau with Fugro Inpark, and developing a scenario for the first five-year period of Fugro Geoservices as the new operating company was to be known. His American experience served him well even though the American mentality and culture differ sharply from the Dutch.

HSE AND CSR

Arnold Steenbakker was charged with the task of formulating and implementing Fugro N.V. policies for Corporate Social Responsibility and for Health, Safety and Environment.

Until late 2005, the Group lacked a coordinated policy towards Health, Safety and Environment (HSE). Increasingly strict standards in the oil and gas industry convinced the holding to take more leadership in this topic. Clients required tangible evidence of Fugro's safety policy. Increasing cooperation between the operating companies also made it necessary to create a uniform safety culture. It is not possible to work together on projects unless everyone adheres to the same standards.

'It was our duty to cultivate an awareness of HSE with the more then thirteen thousand Fugro employees in all the countries where we operate. A small team of Fugro safety experts developed a transparent, flexible management system that was consistent with the Group's decentralised structure. We presented the *Fugro HSE Management System* during the May 2006 Managers Meeting together with a DVD on safety. The operating companies reacted very good to it, and it was the start of a successful safety campaign.'

Safety always matters

With the aid of an external PR agency, the team came up with a neutrally styled figure called SAM, standing for *safety always matters*. Each member of staff received a SAM along with a letter from Klaas Wester. Posters with slogans on safety went up around and on the work floor. 'SAM has since appeared on all our communications about HSE. We started several follow-up campaigns such as the SAM postcards. Showing management commitment to safety helped raise the awareness of HSE on the work floor.' Eventually a team of eight HSE specialists, together with their Chief Operating Officer, implemented the policy in all Fugro's business lines. The campaign was successful: the 2010 Annual Report shows that the number of accidents had fallen by half despite a doubling in the total number of hours worked. 'We have been at it for six years now. An external survey of 1,500 employees held in 2010 indicated that employees regard safety as a Fugro core value. So our message had got across. Things like this matter to people who are considering a job with Fugro. Given a choice, they will opt for a company where safety receives ongoing attention. People prefer to go home from work in the same state as they arrived.'

Safety first

'The increasing importance our stakeholders attach to Corporate Social Responsibility made it necessary to communicate Fugro's activities and initiatives in this area better and more visibly. Fugro also had to take a number of concrete initiatives towards giving these policies more substance and gaining wider support for them.

'We had to perform a catch up exercise in communication about HSE and CSR, and we devoted a chapter of the Annual Report to these topics for the first time in 2006. Thousands of people work for Fugro on ships and aircraft, in extremely cold or extremely hot conditions. These are the people who bring Fugro's technology, equipment and expertise to our clients and hence determine our success. The policy is currently aimed at our people. It entails providing safe, healthy working conditions, maximising local content (for among other reasons to contribute to sustainable development in local communities and service providers) and cultivating continual individual development of staff through specific programmes and *Fugro Academy* courses.

'We consciously decided to give the initial priority to the S for Safety. Starting in 2010, the holding company also tackled the H for Health with its *Fit for the Job* campaign. The operating companies went along with this campaign enthusiastically and took various local initiatives that raised the profile of this aspect among the staff. The E for Environment overlaps with Corporate Social Responsibility, which people usually associate with reducing CO_2 emissions and pollution. A ten year old ship cannot match the latest fuel efficiency standards, but that's no reason to take it out of the fleet. Corporate Social Responsibility means we have to take account of the requirements of all the stakeholders, including the shareholders. They expect some yield on their investment. All new ships must comply with the current requirements for energy consumption and emissions. We also put energy saving into practice for office alterations, and our new company vehicles have to meet minimum standards.

'At Fugro we have long operated with local people wherever we go, and in my opinion that's an important aspect of CSR. Even when we had no obligations as regard to local content, Fugro put Nigerians in charge of the Nigerian business and let the Chinese run the Chinese business. Some thirteen hundred people work for Fugro in Brazil, and only a handful of them aren't Brazilian. In other words, Fugro has been involved in Corporate Social Responsibility for a long time without explicitly stating it.'

1988

Streamlining for further growth

—

Those who had been used to McClelland's *regime* had to adjust to all the space Fugro gave them. By getting the right know-how from the market and combining it, you could use relatively little energy to rapidly expand. This way of thinking meant a fundamental move away from the course Joustra took. The year 1988 was a year of consolidating, improving operational quality and streamlining software. The organisation was flattened in the US, with shorter lines of communication and profit centres close to the client. But golden opportunities were not to be turned down, such as in Asia with Fugro-McClelland Japan Inc., a new joint venture with a 45% interest for Fugro-McClelland. Fugro took over the Institute for Soil Mechanics and Foundation Technology (with a certified laboratory for quality checks), which covered the Benelux and the Ruhr. Fugro Geodesy and NHS (Netherlands Hydrographic Services) were disposed of. In England, Fugro was involved in research for big projects, such as the development of *Canary Wharf* and the *Channel Tunnel*.

—

And Benazir Bhutto came to power in Pakistan, as the first female head of government in an Islamic country.

REGIONAL THINKING IS GOOD

—
—
—

The senior management team of Onshore Geotechnics considered a number of scenarios as a basis for strategic planning. What is the state of the world? Where are we going? Everyone wrote down their outlook anonymously. The results were astonishing and encouraging.

Their vision was unanimous, with one exception (the manager concerned differed slightly in his opinion because of the situation in his region which was provoking an organisational reshuffle). The team as a whole anticipated a reversal of the globalisation process. The future would lie with regional concentration.

The work of Onshore Geotechnics has long been concentrated in specific countries and regions. By regionalising the organisation, Fugro is responding intuitively to the strength of regional governance. Local autonomy, a significant factor in Fugro's success, is turning into regional concentration. The scale differs from one region to another. Brazil is a country but it is actually a region. In Africa, you have to allow for the fact that Angola is different from Nigeria or Namibia. The difference is hard to distinguish from afar, but the way a development vision is implemented politically is not the same. Throughout Africa, they are engaged in nationalisation. It is taking place in Brazil too but with less compulsion, and in the Middle East things happen differently yet again. Regional thinking is good, but it is essential to define the regional borders. We cannot transfer the approach taken in Nigeria unchanged to Angola, even though the underlying causative forces are the same. Every government hopes to boost the prosperity of its own people.

Quite apart from Fugro's business interests, the geopolitical developments are interesting. Protectionism is becoming widespread. Europe is open to India, Russia, Brazil, China and other advancing countries, but they impose restrictions on Europe. A moment will come when Europe and the US decide they have had enough of it. The result will be the rise of aspirational

2027

ORGANISATIONAL DEVELOPMENT

ELISABETH NAIRN
STRATIGRAPHY & PETROLEUM LABORATORIES FUGRO ROBERTSON, UK

Fugro's current organisational structure is decentralised delivering a wide range of services in a variety of operating environments. Our services are provided in three divisions: geotechnical, survey and geoscience. The Fugro Robertson Group of Companies (FRGC) is a relatively new concept within Fugro where a number of previously individual geoscience operating companies are grouped together under one Managing Director to provide an extensive range of geoscience services on a more integrated and global basis. This relationship should be beneficial to all, allowing expansion of the businesses from only one location and optimising synergies within the group. I believe we will see more of this organisational format in Fugro in the future.

Fugro offices in India (1),
China (2), United Arab
Emirates (3)

communities. Europe might split into a northern and a southern region.
The southern states of the US could join forces, followed by the western and
eastern states and those that lie between them. It would mean a return to
a kind of political autonomy in which, hopefully, the Western democratic
achievements will remain unscathed.

Inauguration of
Fugro's new office in
Macaé, Brasil

VIEW IN THE FUTURE
AND THE RIGHT
TO ENJOY YOUR WORK

—
—
—

Formulating a vision and a strategy entails thinking deeply about the future. Mostly this is a task for older members of staff. Their experience is valuable, but it can have a downside. Their frame of reference is the past decades. Thinking from the viewpoint of history can get in the way of developing a vision for the future. It is hard to say goodbye to familiar methods and tools.

Today's young global citizens of the borderless generation have seen a lot of the world before they start on a serious career. They want short-term variety, ample learning opportunities, fewer years in the field and rapid advancement. They are not generally interested in the expat lifestyle. An international company seeking new staff has to bear this in mind.
A twenty year old uses the social media to get dozens of answers to a question within minutes. It is their older superiors who feel uneasy about security on Facebook. More and more people are almost constantly active on the social networks, and that is where they find their information and their contacts.
Sometimes the abundance of alternatives makes younger people uncertain, however. Am I getting all I can out of life? they wonder. How can I be sure my choice or decision is the best possible? What opportunities am I missing? We can distinguish between maximisers and optimisers in this respect. Maximisers spend an eternity searching and comparing –

for example when buying new shoes. They are seldom happy with their purchases because of the nagging uncertainty that they might have found something even better if they had continued searching. Optimisers are prepared to pay a slightly higher price. They are unwilling to continue seeking because they have better uses for their time. The optimiser's approach is more laid back but not necessarily better.

Work and private life

The working environment increasingly overlaps private life for younger people, mainly because of the abundance of communication channels. A twenty year old sees nothing strange about spending an hour on *Facebook* while at work, and spending an hour of free time on a Fugro project in which they are involved.

Young people claim an entitlement to pleasure. They reason that work is a part of life and life must be fun, so work must be fun. Their grandfather worked to earn his daily bread, while their *Baby-boom* father did what his boss told him and didn't stop to wonder whether his work was fun. A twenty year old *Generation X* member is more inclined to throw in the towel if they are no longer enjoying their work and seek their fortune elsewhere. They are ambitious but also require feedback and guidance; they want to hear whether they are doing their work well. They combine work with leisure and family life, and intensely dislike being told to take it a bit easier. The entitlement to pleasure does not necessarily make life easier.

2027

FUGRO TECHNOLOGY

RICHARD WILLIAMS
FUGRO CHANCE,
USA

Fugro will be the leaders in precise subsea positioning. As the inventors of *Starfix* satellite positioning services, Fugro companies have turned their attention to precise positioning underwater, and for Arctic operations, under-ice. GPS radio signals stop at the waterline. Precise positioning integrating data from a number of sensors will enable highly accurate measurements to made at the seabed in any location in the world. Knowing where everything is precisely located in the undersea world also enables Fugro to quickly respond to inspection, repair and maintenance of these subsea facilities.

Geotechnical tests,
Leidschendam laboratory,
The Netherlands

Working visit of HRH
Prince Willem-Alexander
to Leidschendam
headoffice

WORKING TOGETHER
IN MULTIDISCIPLINARY
PROJECTS

'Fugro is a fascinating conglomerate which offers a phenomenal range of services. The only way to understand this company properly is to work for it. It has been a contract-based service provider since way back, but it is moving in the direction of risk-bearing partnerships. A good example of this are our recent activities in Mexico. They have so much oil there that the Mexicans have had the luxury of turning open the tap on an oilfield (extracting the first 15% of the reservoir needs little in the way of modern engineering) and, once it stopped producing, moving on to the next field. Pumping up the remainder of the resource required expert help. Fugro's grasp of all aspects of exploration and production allows us to become a credible, co-responsible partner here. In doing so, Fugro is taking a bold, ambitious step.

The geoscience business, the geology and the basis of reservoir engineering – in short, exploration – holds few secrets for us. But in the production universe as a whole – the optimisation of processes, well drilling, instrumentation and logging – we are less experienced. This makes it natural to work with a partner who performs these tasks, while we concentrate on improving the geoscience models.

'We might arguably consider taking over smaller companies who specialize in these downstream activities, but a more obvious step for us is to partner with a drilling company, as this is a highly capital-intensive, complicated specialism. Not only is the technology hugely expensive, but the mass of safety measures is a significant burden. You have to be really sure of what you are undertaking before you begin, because a small error can have disastrous consequences.'

Safety

'The safety requirements differ from one country to another. There are international bodies that issue recommendations but the legislation is the work of individual governments. The *Deepwater Horizon* drilling-rig

When the freshly graduated physics engineer **Eric de Graaff** took a job with Shell, he soon realized that additional geological knowledge would come in useful. He took a bachelor's degree in Earth Sciences and spent 28 years in a succession of varied assignments both in the Netherlands and abroad. Later in his career, after working as the head of exploration research in Rijswijk and then as the worldwide head of Shell's Geophysics department, he felt it was time for a move. Fugro fascinated him and he was welcome. He joined to help us with technology development and with the integration of operating companies.

disaster highlighted the differences in laws between the Gulf of Mexico and the North Sea. You can't get away with a single emergency shutdown valve in the North Sea: you need at least two here. This is politics: US President George Bush had a policy of minimizing state involvement, so the government pulled out of the supervising bodies. Forget about trying something like that in Norway, for example, where the government keeps a close watch on safety standards. The mentality is different there and the Norwegians aim to manage their oil reserves so as to assure their great-grandchildren of a steady income too. The Americans are more inclined to leave future generations to sort out their own problems.'

Higher targets boost collaboration

'Each of Fugro's operating companies is responsible for its own financial result. They are a bit like *Asterix* and *Obelix*, proud, independent fighters who jostle to get the first blow at the Romans. Replace Romans with clients and see what happens. One of my tasks is to promote integration so that we can win multidisciplinary projects. More mutual cooperation would make Fugro even stronger than it already is. The present model with its independent operating companies has proved very effective in the past, but we may be missing opportunities as long as they keep acting individually. 'Fugro can do just about everything for its clients. We have an excellent matrix for multidisciplinary projects, but the responsibility each managing director takes for his own profit and loss account reduces his eagerness to cooperate. I try to explain the usefulness of a common focus in multidisciplinary projects. The main priority is good communication among all those involved, so that everyone knows what the activities their sister companies engage in and a joint proposal can be formulated. The company that does the largest part of the work takes the lead and we draw up agreements on how the profits will be shared.

'The level of ambition of senior management plays a part in this. In the past, the corporate sectors that achieved 6 to 8% profit were generally left alone. But now a managing director may have a target to achieve 20 to 25% growth, so he must look wider afield. Increasing efficiency is not enough in itself; he will have to collaborate and offer a wider range of services. So higher profit targets stimulate collaboration.'

Social responsibility

'In order to take this approach to the market, we need senior managers who are not only operationally excellent but who can also think strategically. They must serve the concerns of Fugro as a whole. The oil and gas industry is not the only sector where Fugro is active. Infrastructural and wind-energy projects offer some splendid opportunities for survey and monitoring. That can apply in Africa as much as in Japan. Fugro, with its fleet of aircraft for

1989

All-in solutions

—
—

Fugro Middle East grew and became increasingly active in Dubai, Abu Dhabi, Oman and Qatar. The sharp decrease in the volume of offshore and energy projects had less effect on the group than in the past, thanks to the spread of activities over a broader base. Fugro-McClelland now carried out infrastructure and environmental projects; in Hongkong it established another company able to detect defects to buildings using infrared thermography.

Meanwhile, the group's technicians were continually engaged in improving the existing equipment and developing entirely new measuring techniques. It was now possible to reproduce three-dimensional geological structures on the computer screen. In colour too! Fugro was given the order for a CPT system for soil investigation 100 metres below the seabed in waters 3,000 metres deep.

Fugro's concept began to change. Before, one operational company knew all about subject A and another was the specialist on subject B. Now the group focused on all-in solutions for problem areas. The range of products stayed the same but the means of presenting them had changed. The assembled data became the property of the client, but the method and the equipment remained Fugro's property. That meant that the acquired expertise and know-how could then be deployed elsewhere.

mapping water resources, can also deploy its geophysical expertise in the humanitarian domain. In Africa, there is much to be done and to manage in this area.

'By taking a broader approach than a purely profit-driven one, we can make a social contribution by systematically combining technologies. It doesn't involve only the drilling technology for water wells, for example, but also sensible ways of managing them. There are countless other application areas where healthy business practices are consistent with accepting social responsibility.'

Diplomatic corps

'The Managers Meeting of May 2011 paid ample attention to cross-fertilization between the operating companies. This aroused enthusiastic reactions, although people rightly wondered what bearing it had on the responsibility for operating company profitability, where the objectives and financial results are what count. You can't expect managers to act solely out of idealism. I'm one of the few without a responsibility to make a profit so I'm part of that very small management overhead about which Gert-Jan Kramer once said, *Fugro's head office consists of two people – myself and the accountant who books all the operating company profits.* 'Many years back, the large oil multinationals held all the cards and national governments were glad if they could get 5%. Nowadays, the governments are the proprietors, take 98% or more of the profits and hire the multinational oil companies as subcontractors. I am studying how Fugro could work more effectively with the various state oil corporations. We know them well but they have usually been approached by individual Fugro operating companies; one would turn up to sell software, another to sell a survey. We must find a way to raise mutual communication to a higher level. That will take patience – it's not something you can bring about in one year. We must make sure that the same people always visit the clients and become familiar faces to them. If you aim to offer complete solutions instead of separate services, personal contacts play a part. They assure continuity. This calls for good PR people, not necessarily technical experts. Together they make up a kind of diplomatic corps. Fugro hasn't yet appointed suitable diplomats, but people have been identified in the collaboration matrix who are in principle eligible to take this responsibility.'

Seismic: long-term vision

'Fugro combines flair and boldness with a strong long-term vision, a blend which makes the company very attractive. Seismic is a good example. The division has taken a huge step forward by assembling a 3D seismic fleet of ten ships in a few years. You can't accuse Fugro of having a supermarket mentality, where the directors pore over the results every quarter and react in panic whenever there is a downturn – *time to reorganise, people must go.*

1989

>
This gave Fugro a qualitative head's start over its rivals, also onshore where there was a lot of competition and Fugro could stand out from the pack with efficient work rather than with equipment.
It was the same at sea: it was less the cone itself than being able to get it into the seabed in deep water. Fugro's operational skills justified the enormous daily costs of offshore operations. This was where reliability and experience were of great value.
Fugro carried out infrastructure work for the Danish bridge and tunnel project at the Store Baelt, the road connecting Denmark with Sweden.
—

And *the Wall* came down in Berlin, signalling the collapse of Communism and of the Soviet Union.

2027

TRANSITION FROM FOSSIL
TO RENEWABLE ENERGY

LUIZ ANTONIUTTI
FUGRO IN SITU GEOTECNICA,
BRAZIL

The energy matrix in Brazil has already an interesting balance. Despite this, the fossil will decrease in relative importance. The biomass will increase its importance (sugarcane and others), and the eolic farms might be a good bet, including some in nearshore. The nuclear alternative could become acceptable if the technology (avoiding risks) and the political approach allows it.

'A short-term outlook won't get us far in the geoscience business. Fugro didn't panic when there was a dip in the seismic acquisition market in 2009/2010. On the contrary, the Board predicted that all would turn out well. *We have a modern fleet and a healthy market. Let's sit this out.* The remarkable thing about the present recession is that demand hasn't fallen but supply has risen. Long-term agreements with subcontractors are fine until someone wants to taste the sugar and falls for the temptation of the spot market. In seismic, the efficiency of seismic acquisition is highly critical; if you have budgetted a project at 80% effective production, you can make huge losses if it turns out at 7%. On the other hand, if you manage to improve the performance to 85% you're doing great. Fugro operates with a long-term vision, but we are also sharp and businesslike. Fortunately, Fugro can cope with setbacks too, since there are always some parts of the company that are doing extremely well.'

Talent

'In the decentralised organisation, the operating companies are not in the habit of taking note of their sister companies. A central overview of all the high flyers in the Group and a systematic selection programme will be of benefit to them and to Fugro. High flyers must be identified and trained to put them on a fast track to higher functions. We not only need operational people, but also strategic thinkers who get the chance to look across the fence. The workforce may be seen as a pool of capable people whose performance you measure and improve in a systematic, consistent way. My task is to give advice, called for or not, but I can't tell people what to do. My success depends on the cooperation of my colleagues. One individual may hear me out and think *thanks, but no thanks* while another goes along with me. The few people who work in Corporate HR have a hard job: in Fugro, as elsewhere, someone who says *I'm from head office. I'm here to help* cannot always rely on a warm reception.'

Openness

'I'm in favour of having a corporate entry point for job candidates. New staff usually seek a particular opening because they know someone who works there. They don't realise how much more Fugro has to offer, and they might find a better fit somewhere else in the organisation. Fugro's breadth makes it unique. It's a technological company which has a small managerial overhead and is capable of taking quick decisions. The door to the boardroom is always open. There's money and there's flair. I know of no other company like Fugro.
'The frank businesslike attitude Fugro takes towards potential takeover candidates is fascinating. It's honest, pragmatic, and business focussed. I have been involved in acquisition talks several times. Sometimes I felt disappointed when it didn't go ahead; after all, only three takeover attempts

1990

Ships of our own

—
—

The newly installed FCI executive team (CEO Kramer, COO Koch and CFO Perrin) bought a jack-up platform and two ships for research purposes in the Gulf of Mexico and in East Asia. They took over Oretech Holding and bought back the Netherlands Hydrographic Services which they had recently sold; the two companies were combined as Fugro Survey. Bramlette McClelland swapped chairmanship of the Board of Management for a place on the Supervisory Board. The number of staff grew to 1275, but the professional quality was cause for concern. Fugro invested in quality control and training programmes.

—

And Microsoft's Bill Gates launched *Windows*, the software company's PC operating system.

in ten actually succeed. But Fugro is careful not to overpay for a company. Some takeover candidates present themselves more based on promises for the future than on actual performance and will promise you the world. Fugro's interest in a takeover isn't normally motivated by a gap in our portfolio but by the question of whether the company fits well into Fugro and the acquisition will enhance synergy.

'If we are to meet our growth forecasts, the Group will have to be managed differently from before, within a structure that promotes cooperation while preserving the performance of the individual operating companies. Some people take a rather conservative view and argue against changing those operating companies that are doing well. That will be hard to do. We have to find the overall optimum.'

▸
Seismic crew deploying streamers

◂
Geotechnical vessel Fugro Bucentaur in Rotterdam, The Netherlands

2027

TRANSITION FROM FOSSIL TO RENEWABLE ENERGY

TOM HAMILTON
FUGRO GEOSERVICES, USA

By 2027, the world will still be using fossil fuels as a primary energy source. Renewables will make up less than 20% of the world's requirement. However, at least in the US, oil and coal will have been replaced in many areas by the plentiful US resource, natural gas. Virtually all fleet vehicles in the US will be natural gas driven along with 20% to 25% of personal vehicles. All new electrical power plants will be gas-fired. In addition, the US will be an emerging exporter of natural gas. Worldwide, the most economical energy source will continue to be the local fuel of choice.

ADAPTING TO AFRICA

'Working out of the Survey Division in the Netherlands, we support the development of oil and gas fields both in the North Sea and in deep water offshore West African. Offshore Survey has been active in Africa for many years in geophysical inspections, seafloor mapping, installation support and positioning of vessels and drilling platforms. Fugro has been operating in Nigeria, for example, for over thirty years. Our geotech, subsea services and other business lines are also attracting ever greater interest from this part of the world. It calls for a coordinated approach, because the local situations are changing rapidly.'

Protecting interests

'The times have past that Western companies could sail into the African waters, do *their thing* and vanish again. The Africans are protective of their interests and insist that foreign firms invest locally and build their business by employing local people, materials and equipment, just as the Norwegians used to. Fugro is happy to follow these principles; the continent must be able to develop itself. Fortunately, the indigenisation hasn't reached the same level in Africa as in Brazil, where for instance foreign vessels importation are rarely accepted. Though in Nigeria and Angola, for example, international companies are forced to work with local partners. The use of local people and equipment is nowadays stipulated in the contractual terms. For years they are trying to reach this situation, but the lack of expertise forced them to rely on the foreign companies who consistently ignored the local wishes and requirements. The authorities now impose strict laws that contractually determine which companies are allowed to perform the work and under what conditions. A company that wants to work in Africa will have to commit long-term to the region by bringing in its own equipment and train local people. In Nigeria, Fugro is currently merging two operating companies in the field of survey, geotechnics and environmental to increase the Nigerianisation and to comply with the stipulated shareholding structure. Something similar is happening in Angola: we are setting up a joint venture

After graduating as a geodetic engineer followed by a year of travel and mountaineering, **Mark Heine** joined Fugro as a surveyor in 2000. During his probation period he wondered if he could ever keep it up; the work was not at all what he had hoped for. Matters started improving when he was asked to undertake an interesting project in Southern Africa. Together with a colleague, he spent a year surveying 22 airports for new flight approach routes. He was subsequently promoted to data manager, then operations manager and then director. Recently he was appointed as Regional Manager Europe and Africa for Offshore Survey. From his office in Leidschendam, he supervises various Fugro operating companies that are active in these regions. Developing Fugro in Western Africa has kept him busy in the last few years.

with a local party to end up with a majority of Angolan company ownership. Obviously, Fugro tries to retain some management control but also accepts that the world is changing fast. Anyone ignoring these developments will be out of business soon. Trying to push through a deal by cutting corners, won't work anymore: the Africans are in control now!'

Different scale

'Both Nigeria and Angola are now engaged in these indigenization processes, each in their own way. Some Westerners erroneously think of Africa as a single country, which is a common mistake. Angola, for instance, used to be Portuguese, while Nigeria was British – and this tells us a lot about the different national characters.

'Fugro is well aware that Western companies will have to delegate their activities to local firms. In Angola, we are gradually withdrawing our expats from the management echelons. We are currently building a single office for different Fugro divisions, and we are immediately introducing a different organisation structure. Traditionally, Fugro operating companies are specialised in a single discipline. However, the organisations we are building in developing countries consist of a cooperation of multiple divisions, headed by a single manager who reports to the respective regional managers. For some people in Fugro this is regarded as groundbreaking, but in fact it is the only way to operate fruitfully in these countries. Local regulations require us to have all kinds of affairs in order and it is obviously more efficient to deal with this for all three business lines at once. I expect we will be seeing more of these structures developing in other parts of the world, and very likely even on a larger scale.'

Booming Angola

'You could wonder are the Africans really trying to accumulate knowledge and do something with it? Consider a young Angolan man, fresh from University, likely studied abroad – we probably won't be able to hold onto him. His motivation to work is different from ours. He is building up his own base in his country's growing economy and sees a job as a springboard to the next step. He is one of his country's trend-setters. In many cases his family has enough money to diminish the urgency of keeping a job to survive and they can give its younger members a chance to study.

'Angola has proper primary schools and university education , but there is no secondary or higher vocational education. Fugro is very willing to fill the gap by taking people in hand ourselves. We have to carefully select who we take on, how we train them and retain them. In countries like this with a rapidly growing economy, we encounter bizarre situations and sometimes have to accept things that would never pass muster in the Netherlands. Employing African managers with Western European education level and mentality can easily bemore expensive than flying in expats. On top of

1991

Data collection and positioning

—
—

Fugro's successful expansion policy brought the group a spectacular increase in turnover, from € 104 to € 160 million, particularly on the strength of acquisitions in Australia, Singapore, Hongkong, Saudi Arabia, America, France and England. Meetings held to exchange information were to encourage the different subsidiaries to work together. The most important takeover of 1991 was of John E. Chance & Associates in Lafayette, Louisiana. This reputable company was especially active in precision measurements and offshore positioning. Its founder, John Chance, was getting on in years and wanted to keep his company from falling apart. GPS, the Global Positioning System, had arrived on the scene and was forcing many companies who preferred the more traditional positioning systems to sell up. Fugro on the other hand saw a lot of potential added value in positioning if one were to have a system that calculated and applied corrections, giving a greater accuracy. Fugro was generally focusing on new know-how and skills, on a balanced distribution of activities to reduce the group's vulnerability and on ways of drawing up integrated advisory reports. Clients were showing an increasing interest in across-the-board advice from a single office. The four core activities – Offshore Geotechnical Services, Survey Services, Onshore Geotechnical Services and Environmental Services – were pretty well equal in terms of turnover, as were the three

that we will struggle keeping these people, the demand for qualified staff is extremely high. In fact there are no alternatives; a company that chooses to operate in this region has to take these steps and accept the situation for what it is. It simply requires a significant investments in the development of the people.

'Africa is developing rapidly and it has become a serious market for Fugro´s business. Political stability remain a concern. Angola is reasonably stable, partly because the power is still in the hands of the small elite group of individuals who were once responsible for liberating the country. You can't get much done without their support. Few people realise that Angola now has the fastest growing economy in the world – even faster than China – and that Luanda has already been the world's most expensive city for some years. About six million people live in and around the capital, coupled with an equal population in the rest of the country. Everyone has crowded into the cities because of the civil war. Lobito, Benguela and other cities are similarly growing fast. The traffic problems are immense but the government has been investing in construction projects and currently in tourism too. It's partly due to China that things are moving fast in Angola.'

Minerals

'Africa is coming quickly to the fore. Other African countries, like Ghana, Tanzania and Mozambique are also progressing rapidly, but it will be a long time before they can manage without the Western support. Many African countries are rich in minerals and onshore work, like mining activities will become increasingly important. Fugro will be there too, establishing companies with local partners, helping to build them up and stabilise them. There are commercial opportunities to be pursued, but above all we should overlook our Corporate Social Responsibility dealing with Africa.'

1991

>
geographical regions.
The increase in scale had forced the management to make preparations for an initial public offering on the stock market to continue to guarantee sound financial debt-equity ratios and room for financing further growth. The group's equity capital had more than doubled in a year to € 36 million and the number of employees was now over 2,000, a 60% increase on the previous year. A trust office foundation was established as protection against potential undesirable takeovers.
The long-term economic recession in the US had made things difficult for the American operational companies. McKinsey & Co. was commissioned to assess whether Fugro's organisational structure in the US gave cause for restructuring.
Fugro was up to its eyes in work on the offshore construction of Hongkong's new airport, Chek Lap Kok.
—

And thanks to television the entire world was witness to *Operation Desert Storm*, the start of the Gulf War in Kuwait.

INVESTING
WITH VISION AND FAITH

'Is Fugro a conservative company? Not where our acquisition strategy is concerned, that's for sure. Financially it is. The financial policy of a listed company has to be conservative, irrespective of that company having a central or decentralised structure. Managing directors are responsible for their operating companies and for such aspects as their debtors paying on time. Not only because of potential deferred interest, but also to limit risks; the chances of debtors running into arrears are growing given the financial and economic situation in the US and Europe. In addition, Fugro wants to collect its funds as soon as possible to use for investment and growth. The current financial uncertainty caused us to tighten our terms of payment and introduce additional checks. We receive overviews from all our operating companies every two weeks, listing the ten longest outstanding receivables and stating the reasons for delays in payment and the subsequent actions taken by the operating company. We insist on rapid settlement of any dispute. Some clients invariably try to postpone or wriggle out of paying. As soon as our technical staff has completed a job they want to start on the next one. But a project isn't finished until the bill has been paid. So yes, with respect to such financial aspects, we are conservative.'

Clustering is lucrative

'Clients want a one-stop shop and sound, compatible data. A large project in Bonny Island (Nigeria) was worked on by eight Fugro companies simultaneously, and the construction of a pipeline from North Africa to Italy also involved various Fugro disciplines working together – both are proof of how successful joining forces can be. Our range of services is so broad that nobody can possibly know everything. Cooperating with each other is one of our *Golden Rules*. Obviously, an American operating company won't ship all its hardware to the Middle East for a single job but instead will subcontract the work to a regional affiliate. For the record, no compensation or finder fees are paid in such cases, which benefits both our revenue and

André Jonkman is one of the few Fugro top managers who doesn't hold a technical degree. After graduating in finance, he worked at a large auditors' firm before joining Fugro in 1988. He is not infected by the technology virus, but as the Fugro CFO whose areas include investor relations, he must possess some affinity with technology and innovation. André travels as much as the technical staff members and enjoys being told about Fugro's operational activities, as *it's good to see what we make our money with*. He describes himself as a cashier with a penchant for technology.

*Sailingteam skûtsjesilen
sportsday, Managers
Meeting, The Netherlands*

Newfoundland,
Canada

Fugro employees in
the Polar Challenge,
North Pole

the results of the entire Fugro Group. At corporate level, we obviously take it into account when an operating company farms out many jobs and as a consequence has lower results itself. We promote cooperation by fostering contacts between our managing directors, for instance at the annual Managers' Meeting. These personal encounters break down barriers. And we try to achieve cross-pollination by rotating managers.'

Investing with a vision

'As a member of the Board of Management, I am jointly responsible for strategy. A regular discussion topic in Seismic Services is how the seismic fleet should be composed. A clever mix of owned and chartered vessels enables us to adjust to market fluctuations. Admittedly, we are sometimes just a little late in adjusting the mix, but generally we do well. We are currently focusing on multi-client surveys, compiling *3D library sets* – data which we can sell to various players – these data sets are amongst others in Australia, the US, the Dutch continental shelf and Norway. This way we have built up a strong position in seismic expertise.

'Putting together a programme such as this is expensive, but Fugro's financial position is sufficiently healthy to continue investing elsewhere as well. We can afford to base our choices on our view of market trends and similar substantive arguments rather than on the available bank balance. Right now, Seismic Services are not performing so well, but through the cycle we have generated good returns. Major capital investments are not made just for a year. Eighteen months ago, we decided to build two deep-water geotechnical vessels, realising how the market would develop and keeping our large market share in mind. Our strategy is not just for tomorrow, but also for the day after and beyond.

'Fugro's business is for 75% in the oil and gas industry. On a global scale, the average production decline in existing fields is some 6-8% per year. However, in the Mexican *Cantarel* field, one of the largest in the world, the decline is much higher, at about 14% per year. The world's population is growing; upcoming areas such as China and India need more energy. Tata Motors is building huge numbers of *Nanos* – soon everybody in rural India will be able to drive one of these cars. These factors stimulate the quest for oil. The days of easy oil - just poke a hole in the Texan soil - are over; oil companies are moving into ever deeper waters and so they need our services. That's why losing out on a contract or even cancellation of an entire project doesn't worry us. In 2011, a fairly large project in India was cancelled, and consequently our results for the first half year were somewhat disappointing. But we could explain why. The work didn't disappear; we eventually did land the contract a year later.'

1992

Flotation and slump

—
—

The most remarkable occurrences this year were the first listing of Fugro-McClelland share certificates on the Amsterdam Stock Market and the painful slump several months later. The recently purchased John E. Chance was hit hard when the oil companies suddenly ceased activity after the price of gas hit a historic low. The Gulf of Mexico turned into a Dead Sea. Fugro-McClelland had paid € 70 million for Chance, which for years had been making profits of € 10 million and in 1992, literally nothing. The financial world suspected Fugro of misleading the market. The Amsterdam exchange council launched an investigation, had intensive discussions with Fugro and its banker Pierson and concluded that neither the company nor the bank could be reproached. Kramer kept his head throughout and concentrated on the long-term; he trusted Chance and signed a cheque for a million euros for a new satellite transponder that the survey company needed.

A board of directors was set up to promote cooperation between the operational companies. Of the many external companies who approached Fugro with the hope of being taken over, only a few met all of Fugro's takeover criteria. One was Keynes Inpark, to whom Fugro had once sold Fugro Geodesy and NHS (with the idea of buying it back when the economic tide had turned); this operational company was christened Fugro-Inpark. With the fall of the Berlin *Wall* Fugro's gaze was also on Eastern Europe. A branch office

>

Cashier with a penchant for technology

'The trend is for Fugro to move toward risk-bearing partnerships, but we remain conservative there as well. We debate the risks and, as a precondition, set benchmarks during the project, enabling us to stop when the risks grow too large. This also depends on our partners; we've known some of our partners from day one. A few years ago, risks of a few million dollars would have endangered much of our profits, but we can afford more now, thanks to our size. If there are a number of options, we weight them. If you don't want to take risks, you might as well leave your money in the bank. Investing in our clients' innovations enables Fugro to grow organically. I'm a cashier with a penchant for technology, an entrepreneur with a conservative approach. It's part of my responsibility to sometimes ask my fellow Board members: *is this what we really want?* It's also my duty to ensure that there are sufficient funds left to keep investing.'

New times, new standards

'I expect the banks to remain on their guard in the years to come. Fortunately, Fugro can also tap into other sources of funding thanks to its good reputation. In 2011 we were able to raise more than the equivalent of $ 900 million in USPPs (*US Private Placements*): loans from investment funds. These funds first assess a company's strength, before providing the money. During our road shows we visit European and American investors. We also annually hold some three hundred socalled *one-on-ones*. Ask any question you want: we know our company and the stock-market regulations and we are open and transparent.'

'I do expect a further tightening of regulations and legislation. When I was an auditor I would visit a client's accountant's office on Friday afternoon, so to speak, to discuss in a casual way a few things. I knew what was going on, there was openness, and personal contact was worth a lot. In the past, audit reports used to cover half a page. Unfortunately, that's now out of the question. The IFRS regulations (*International Financial Reporting Standards,* establishing the broad rules that annual reports should meet) have formalised a framework of procedures. Personal relationships have disappeared. It's all checklists these days that have to be ticked off. Auditors hedge everything formally and make sure they can't be held accountable. We've had to learn to live with it.'

Internal audit

'My six controllers travel all over the world to audit our operating companies. They don't differentiate between large or small, strong or weak operating companies. Risks are universal. The large companies have their own accounting departments, which could facilitate our job; but as the stakes are higher there, we give them as much attention as we do smaller or weaker companies, which could be slightly more error-prone. Each has its

2027

TRANSITION FROM FOSSIL
TO RENEWABLE ENERGY

PAT POWER
FUGRO GEOCONSULTING,
UK

Offshore wind will play an increasing part of the power generation mix in the future. Wave and tidal power will also play its part but I don't see this being as significant. Nuclear will also play a large part as there is a limit to how much renewable energy can contribute to total demand in the short to medium term. Solar energy will increase its contribution as technology advances and cost come down. But hydrocarbons will still provide a significant proportion of our energy needs. Unconventional sources such as shale gas will grow, new oil and gas provinces will be discovered and developed and enhanced recovery technologies will increase production from new reserves, extend the life of current fields and encourage the redevelopment of partially depleted reservoirs currently well past peak production.

pros and cons. We don't have *A* and *B* lists, but we do have a ranking. If we come across too many unacceptable aspects in an operating company, that company is placed under intensive care. This means that our people will keep visiting until the patient can return to the ward. The holding company issues an *in-control* statement in the form of consolidated annual financial statements. Then you can't say you didn't have time to check everything thoroughly.

'The advantage of our decentralised conservatism is that all the operating companies are relatively small. We receive their results every month and prepare the consolidated accounts. So we have complete monthly overviews of developments in the results. In case of changes in cash flow, movements of costs, debtor or creditor balances, work in progress etc., we can ask the appropriate questions immediately. We are continuously on the ball.

'Our controllers are regularly moved between divisions and regions, in order to prevent organisational blindness. They can all do everything everywhere. They do, however, have specific duties within the holding company; the one controller has more affinity with pensions, the other with taxes.'

A well kept secret

'Fugro has twice been awarded the *Financieele Dagblad's Henri Sijthof Prize* for the best annual report. It's gratifying to see that our reports are well received externally.

'We at Fugro are extremely good at a great many things, except at broadcasting to the world how good we are at all these things. Technical experts are so preoccupied with technology that they find it hard to tell the story behind it. Taking samples at a depth of 3,000 metres, drilling under extreme conditions – these would make spectacular success stories, but they are never compiled.'

1992

> was set up in Moscow, and joint ventures opened the way for Fugro to the Chinese and Japanese markets. Internationalisation and dissemination of know-how within the group were rooted in Fugro's conviction that multinational clients could then profit more from Fugro's global network.

—

And in Rio de Janeiro delegates from the United Nations agreed to work towards a better environment.

2027

FUGRO TECHNOLOGY

JOHN LAZARUS
**GEOSPATIAL SOLUTIONS,
AUSTRALIA**

Miniaturisation through the application of nanotechnology will have major impacts on the technology deployed. In addition replacing equipment operators with software systems will in place on a lot of technology.
In survey, aerial sensing and mapping will be in generally fully automated. To answer the question on major technology for Fugro is difficult. What is it now? In general far more autonomous equipment and semi intelligent robots will be used.

LEARNING MAKES LIFE MORE ENJOYABLE

Andy McNeill from Fugro Ltd in Aberdeen was asked to investigate the possibilities for group-wide training. He had already dealt with boosting leadership skills among senior staff. These posts are generally filled by high flyers in specific technological fields, for example when a surveyor is promoted to senior surveyor and then to party chief. But someone who is responsible for people, ships and equipment needs additional qualities. Andy investigated the possibilities for educating people – among other things in response to more stringent client requirements.
'I found a suitable firm to give courses. It clicked between us, and it was soon clear that we needed to train our people in other areas as well. The staff discussed these ideas around the coffee machine and a keen interest in courses and training became apparent. A pilot programme for management development started early in 2006, pitched at senior managers in the operating companies. It was a catch-up exercise; they would have taken the courses earlier had they existed.

'After a course, people tend to go back to work and quickly forget everything they have learned. I tried to counteract this by getting each of the five teams to present a realistic business proposal to the board of directors at the end of the course. This was a good way to assess the practical skills of the trainees, who might conceivably be involved in future acquisitions and would have to cooperate with other operational companies.

'These course participants had hardly ever met before, but working together on the proposals helped them build lasting contacts which would persist after the end of the course. This unexpectedly positive outcome was a factor in founding *the Fugro Academy*.'

Extended by popular demand

'Our experience with the training company was excellent. The lecturers stimulated and motivated the trainees. We repeated the Management Development programme twelve times in three years. People from Offshore Survey were able to swap ideas with their colleagues from Geotechnics

When oil and gas prices soared again in 2005 and the offshore survey market enjoyed a consequent boom, Fugro too experienced increased demand. Additional qualified employees were not to be had at a snap of the fingers, however. Many companies were fishing in the same pond, and improved internal career prospects for those with an existing job made them less inclined to seek opportunities elsewhere. At the same time, a declining student interest in engineering meant that less graduates were entering the market.

Fugro's larger operating companies were in a position to take on new employees and train them internally. The smaller units lacked the resources for this approach, making them unable to grow along with the rest. The Director of Offshore Survey, Köbi Rüegg, devised a clever plan.

and Geoscience. They proposed setting up something similar for the whole organisation. The Board responded positively to the ideas for a *Fugro Academy*. I was asked to set it up together with Martin Galavazi (Fugro Engineers), Ian Davis (currently Fugro Canada) and Emma Fenn (Fugro Robertson).

'Following the Management Development course, we were ready to extend the programme. We expanded our team, and began with a *Project Management programme* in 2009/2010. This was followed by a series of courses for the managers of the operating companies. They took part in a workshop where we told them what their subordinates had learned, and it emerged that they sometimes had difficulty understanding them. The managers wanted to know more about the courses for themselves, so we gave them a four-day summary of four courses which their subordinates had followed.'

Measuring benefits

'Formerly, when problems occurred on a ship, members of the support department would go on board to help, and they immediately functioned as trainers. But ships are costly and a satisfied client goes before all else, so training often took a back seat. They wanted to do it but there was rarely enough time. One of the achievements of *the Fugro Academy* is that in-house training is no longer the poor relation. We now work with dedicated, full-time trainers. Each of them has a specific range of subjects and gives the same courses worldwide. This consistent approach is beneficial to the quality of training. The training is internal, so the curriculum can be focused specifically on Fugro's processes and techniques. But what happens if a planned course clashes with an important project? In that case we alter the timetable. An external trainer would just send in an invoice for the missed course, but we are able to reschedule the course instead.

'The feedback we get from most courses is about the quality of the coffee and of the trainer. Those are not to be disregarded, but the long-term impact of the course is more interesting and, unfortunately, more uncertain. Measuring the benefits of training is difficult. The best evidence comes from employee satisfaction, especially from newcomers. Some training is indispensable, for example for someone who has just graduated and has to be acquainted with Fugro's in-house software.'

Personnel exchanges can be valuable for a variety of reasons. Fugro is in the process of standardising its technological systems worldwide, so it is not just useful but essential that everyone who uses them has had the same training. This relates to three areas:

a) standardised software and technology
b) standardisation of processes
c) standard training.

1993

Back on course

—
—

There were now 70 operational companies and 160 Fugro offices whose 2,800 employees generated a turnover of € 220 million this year. Fugro presented its mission statement. By now there were five divisions: Onshore Geotechnics, Offshore Geotechnics, Environmental Services, Onshore Survey and Offshore Survey. Fugro had become considerably less vulnerable to regional or national economic fluctuations. Profits rose by 40% to a record of over € 12 million, due in part to Fugro's geographical spread.
In Hongkong Fugro carried out in record time a major geotechnical investigation for Chek Lap Kok, the new airport to be sited offshore.
In Asia the market was improving, which compensated for the mediocre results in Europe and the US.

—

And Toni Morrison was the first African-American authoress to receive the Nobel Prize for Literature.

'This process is under way and our clients notice the improvement too. They notice the standardisation and comment favourably. Our worldwide training programme helps Fugro stand out from its competitors.'

E-learning

'The first courses were classroom-based. An experiment with e-learning had promising results but there was no budget for the investment required. The solution was a mix of classroom-based training and e-learning.
'One of the problems with organising our courses is that most of the potential trainees are hard to reach. They work offshore and are away from base half the time, and when they are on leave they want to be really free. Spouses and children, too, are not too pleased when the breadwinner disappears for yet another few days to attend a training course. This means we have to bring the training to these colleagues instead of vice-versa. When on board, they have free time between shifts and there are also periods when the ship is non-operational. E-learning has taken off in a big way in the last five years.
'The trainers, too, prefer not to be continually on the move. I predict that some day all technical training will take place through e-learning. The language is sometimes a problem. Fugro's corporate language is officially English, but hundreds of our Brazilian staff speak Portuguese only. *The Fugro Academy* is having its courses translated. E-learning packages are currently available in English, Dutch, French, German, Italian, Spanish, Portuguese and Chinese (both Cantonese and Mandarin).'

Course evaluation

How do you check if someone has learned and understood the subject matter? And how do you fairly assess their performance? 'Written tests are definitely unsuitable because of the language problems. Trainers have their own pet topics but written tests have to be standardised. Moreover, trainees are inclined to see the test as a kind of exam which they must pass at all costs. Seeing an evaluation test this way can have an undesirable effect. What would a score of 50% tell us about someone's knowledge and skills after an intensive week? In the early days of *the Fugro Academy,* by way of experiment, I had the trainees do the same tests at the beginning and at the end of the course. Some scored 40% in the final assessment after doing no better than 10% in the initial test. They had improved considerably, but if it had been a conventional exam they would have failed miserably. I am sceptical about the value of exams in general. I want to teach people, and above all I want to encourage them to keep learning. It's something that will stand them in good stead for the rest of their career.
'You learn most from errors and difficulties. When I used to work offshore, everything went pretty well, thank goodness. The client and my boss were both satisfied, and I was relieved to know it. But I had a nagging feeling

1994

The breakthrough of Offshore Survey
–

McClelland was removed from the group's name, as Fugro with its wide range of activities was much better known internationally. The one exception was the US, where the name remained Fugro-McClelland. Fugro kept on growing, largely due to still more takeovers, particularly in market segments beyond the uncertain energy sector, although even this gave Fugro two new acquisitions, Geoteam AS (Norway) and Wimpol Ltd. (UK and Singapore). An indirect reason for this takeover policy was the low price of oil. The oil companies had fewer research contracts to award and were obliged to buy at lower prices from the oil fields they were already exploiting. However, it was essential to keep on investing in technological advances and only the financially strong partners could make the necessary budget available. The weaker companies were faced with the choice of muddling on through or merging with the likes of Fugro, who partly as a result cornered a gigantic share of the market. Fugro's size had itself become a winning factor.
The onshore divisions grew too, if at a more modest scale, particularly in Hongkong and the US; in Europe things weren't looking too good.
Fugro started using the *Seascout,* a light version of the CPT equipment used for testing the seabed that could now be deployed on smaller ships.

>

that I had learned nothing new, that I hadn't developed in some way. It takes a lot of time, especially in the case of software courses, but a group of participants can only be together for a short time and the build-up has to be balanced. Differences in capacity between individual participants can be a hindrance, because a slow learner holds back a quick one. This is one of the major advantages of e-learning. Everyone can work at their own pace and repeat things as often as they like. Everyone needs the chance to practise. Currently we use recapitulations of the preceding day and quizzes which are matched to the competence of the trainees. We ask the trainees to do a task individually; the trainer watches how they perform and offers explanations. We discuss the results with everyone personally. We advise them about aspects they may need to practise in their operational team, and what skills they could develop further in practice. Most people have a good idea of what they are capable of.'

Internal networks

'Young people are nearly always eager to learn, but it differs from one region to another. It's partly a question of culture. Westerners appear less keen to learn or to excel than Asians do. I find that odd. The older trainees were enthusiastic because they hadn't had an opportunity to take a company course before. The best engineer isn't necessarily the best leader, just as a top-scoring footballer doesn't necessarily make a good team captain.

'Some of the enthusiasm of the trainees is due to meeting colleagues who they might otherwise never have met face to face. Colleagues learn from one another – not just about the course content, but also about other countries, other aspects of the business and other topics that aren't part of the course curriculum. One merit of classroom-based training is that it promotes bonding and networking. Project managers who have been on a course together are more likely to phone each other when they have problems that their own boss or team colleagues can't help them with. Personal contacts improve to the benefit of the Group as a whole.

'Following the Management Development and the technical courses, we intend to concentrate on coaching and developing individual skills such as presentation techniques. We are also considering language training, Health & Safety and IT as well as a course on *Cultural Awareness*. The last could be relevant now that personnel exchanges occur between countries and even continents. It's hard to say what concrete benefits it will have; how much is socially acceptable behaviour worth? While Fugro still works with local management, this seems less urgent than an English course for Brazilians.' No one has ever left Fugro through disappointment with the training, but good training does attract new talent. 'When I used to work in HR, the candidate was expected to sell himself to the employer. That the reverse is now true is a reflection of the shortage of manpower. Young candidates may have the choice of half a dozen jobs, and they see nothing odd about

2027

CONSEQUENCES
OF CLIMATE CHANGE

SANTANU MOITRA
FUGRO GEOTECH,
INDIA

The global climate change is expected to have a major impact on the Indian subcontinent, which as a region comprises India, Pakistan, Sri Lanka, Bangladesh, Nepal & Bhutan (and potentially Myanmar). The geomorphology of the subcontinent is constituted by the rugged high mountain ranges of the Himalayas in the north followed towards south by Indo-Gangetic fertile alluvial plains, followed further south by the peninsular shield areas ending in the island of Sri Lanka. India thus has a long coast line of approximately 4,500 km and a total population of more than 1.3 billion. The climate change, that is currently quite rapid, is expected to have the following impacts, like:

- Sea level rise – leading to coastal erosion, submergence of low lands, reduction of landmass.
- Melting of glaciers in the Himalayas – leading to reduction of their size, floods, reduction in flow of perennial rivers.
- As a consequence of erosion of the land surface and flooding, water management will be a major activity where Fugro will have to involve itself in a big way.
- Shortage of urban space will lead to vertical growth in residential, industrial and infrastructural sector resulting in need for stronger and deeper foundations where Fugro's expertise in providing specialized geotechnical and material testing services will be called for.

On the whole, climate change will have a major positive impact on the workings of Fugro in this region by 2027.

it. It's logical that opportunities for career development play a part in their calculation. In the first five years we held 900 courses and trained six thousand people for a total of thirty thousand course-days! The existence of *the Fugro Academy* is a reason to come to work for the Group.'

Internet connection needed?

The Fugro Academy is a recent development and still has a long way to go. It was crucial to develop an online system for e-learning so that courses could be followed offshore and the test results could be uploaded. 'But as long as there are places in the world with no satellite connectivity, online e-learning can't be relied on. We are now developing mobile training, which will provide workplace training regardless of where the trainee is located. Simple software on a *USB memory stick* makes it unnecessary to have an internet connection during e-learning.

'Subsea simulation software is another area gaining our attention. Our simulators are designed for ROV training, but they are also useful for offshore situations, geotechnics and onshore. Younger people are usually familiar with simulations through computer games like *Second Life*. In our case the *games* are fun to play but have a serious training purpose.

'Fugro has traditionally been strong in technology, but has been late to adopt it for in-house training. Many of our people are computer scientists and are familiar with using 3D animations. You can practice perfectly well with a 3D model of a GPS receiver instead of a real one, and this even has the advantage of possibilities for remote interaction. E-learning and simulation are the future for technological subjects. Advanced though the new methods may be, however, we won't abandon classic course training. The personal interaction and discussion are too valuable to lose.

'We ourselves have learned a lot at *the Fugro Academy,* among other things about human behaviour. It's clear to me that I have to sell *the Academy* internally, just as Fugro promotes itself to the external clients. Our clients see Fugro in terms of the services the Group delivers, but they are generally unacquainted with the broader picture. The same applies to *the Fugro Academy:* we provide training, but far from every one has a complete picture of the possibilities. I have to promote *the Fugro Academy* by showing what we can achieve. Unfortunately we are a long way from having an injectable training serum as in The Matrix movie that will turn people into instant experts.'

1994

> Offshore Survey stole the show when it doubled its turnover compared with 1993; Offshore and Onshore Survey together accounted for 50% of Fugro's total turnover. In 1990 this had only been 3%.
The Starfix satellite positioning system was completed, with a network of 70 fully equipped reference stations and the necessary lines of communication over the entire world.

—

And Nelson Mandela was chosen as President in South Africa's first multiracial elections.

2027 NEW GEOGRAPHIC AREAS

MAARTEN VAN DER HARST
FUGRO MIDDLE EAST, UAE

East Africa will be the next booming region for the coming decades. Africa is going through a major change in leadership. The changes in the management of the water resources will redeploy the development gravity centres of Africa. The economy of East Africa will concentrate infrastructure investments.

23

RUDOLF
D A S '012

RAISING THE DYKES IN 2030

Humans, the conscious inhabitants of the Earth, only recently became aware that their actions and in particular their CO_2 emissions may be affecting the Earth's climate. (Physical geographer and climate relativist Salomon Kroonenberg seriously doubts this claim– see page 76)

The fact that sea level rises is no longer questionable. A higher sea level could have serious consequences for densely populated, low-lying (and subsiding!) coastal nations, especially if combined with sustained periods of very strong wind. At spring tides, the sea level may rise above the sea dykes that protect the land.

Rudolf Das' drawing shows how a sea dyke (for instance in the Dutch province of Zeeland) could be raised in an ingenious way by incorporating vertical floating elements inside the core of the dyke bodies. This exceptional idea, the storm shield of Dutch engineering firm Oranjewoud, was nominated for the *Vernuftelingprijs [Innovation Award]* in 2009. It failed to win because of lack of construction specifications, but the chairman of the jury (and futurologist) Rudolf Das realised that it could indeed be implemented. He devised this *Green Machine*, which can rapidly construct a shield along straight dyke sections; bends in the dykes would still need to be raised in the conventional manner.

This drawing shows four stages in the reconstruction of a dyke. By using prefabricated elements made of lightweight, glued aerated concrete blocks, the machine could operate very fast.

Ⓐ — Original dyke
Ⓑ — Temporarily lowered and strengthened dyke
Ⓒ — Situation at normal high water level
Ⓓ — Situation at extremely high water level; dyke at maximum height.

LEGEND

1 Original dyke
2 Excavated, strengthened track for the *Green Machine*
3 Strengthening of the excavated trench
4 Freezing the soil while excavating the trench; coating with bentonite
5 Finished trench walls
6 Asphalt coating
7 Temporary props in the trench
8 Vertical floaters with horizontally hingeing lids
9 Water inlet, closed
10 The *Green Machine* partly fills in the excavated trench with soil
11 Floating elements at maximum height; stillage supported by hingeing elements
12 Manually operated post for additional support on the landward side of the dyke
13 Water inlet, open
14 The machine is moving away from the spectator. The machine excavates the soil; places track supports, freezes the trench soil in front of the excavator and pours bentonite along the trench walls
15 Placing pre-assembled floaters in the trench
16 Conveyor bands transport the excavated soil to the back of the machine, to fill the trench
17 Water inlet at extremely high water
18 Delivery of prefab elements
19 Moving sand with smaller machines
20 Concrete blocks for additional dyke reinforcement

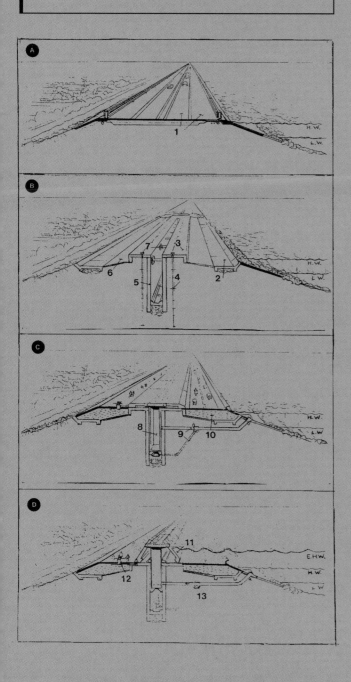

IV

ENERGY

GEOPOLITICAL ENERGY ISSUES

—
—
—

Lucia van Geuns read geology at Leiden University. After a career of 22 years in the exploration and production of conventional oil and gas with Royal Dutch Shell, she joined the *Clingendael International Energy Programme* (CIEP) in 2003. One of her research themes is the transition from fossil to sustainable sources of energy.

The Clingendael International Energy Programme (CIEP) is affiliated with the Netherlands Institute for International Relations Clingendael. Around the turn of this century the need was felt for an independent forum to study international energy issues, in order to provide better information to the general public, politicians, policy makers and the media. CIEP is funded by more than twenty public and private parties, such as ministries and energy companies that value a level-headed coverage of international energy issues. CIEP research focuses on three themes, on which it publishes reports and organises public seminars:

Energy policy in the European Union (EU)
This research theme provides a forum for discussion groups to brainstorm on the future fuel mix in the EU countries and on the role of natural gas.

International economic and geopolitical aspects of the oil and gas markets
The OECD countries, OPEC and the emerging markets in the BRICS countries are the key players in this theme. Russian oil and gas are important in the traditional bilateral relationships in Europe.

Energy and sustainable development
This theme is related to the first two themes. Discussions on sustainable development are held in the context of the changing global balance of power and focus on transition towards and governance structures of decarbonised energy markets.

'What will, for instance, be the significance of Germany abandoning nuclear power? Will Germany change over to natural gas or will it make an accelerated transition to renewable energy? How will they pay for it? What

about infrastructure and collaboration with neighbouring countries in the context of the liberalisation of the internal European energy market?
'Fuel mix is an important issue in CIEP. In the Netherlands, most energy is generated from fossil fuels: gas, oil and coal. Biomass, solar and wind energy account for only minor percentages. Their shares will undoubtedly increase over the next 25 years, but for the time being, fossil fuels predominate. Europe is covered by a patchwork of different fuel mixes. In France, nuclear energy is paramount, whereas Germany and Poland largely depend on coal. However, all the European countries should try to meet the EU 20/20/20 energy policy targets for 2020: a 20% reduction in greenhouse-gas emissions compared to 1990, 20% higher energy efficiency, and 20% of all energy to be generated from sustainable resources. Europe has decreed a target percentage for CO_2 reduction in each member state: it is 14% for the Netherlands. I wonder whether we can meet this target, how the other member states will manage, and what the repercussions will be for those who don't.
'These types of discussions are part of our research programme and we reflect on these issues. Our reports are freely available: everybody can download them digitally. Everybody is welcome at our conferences and we try to allow everybody to speak. We also communicate via the internet and through conventional channels. We are regularly approached by the media, usually about the oil price. I spent some time at the well site when I worked for Shell, so I know what drilling for oil and gas involves. In this political think tank, I am one of the few people with this type of background. Our experts in mathematics, physics and economics all have their own perspectives on energy issues. This multidisciplinary structure enables CIEP to lift the debate on the macro-economic and geopolitical aspects of the energy market to a higher level.'

Fuel mix and trends

'Every four years, we establish a new research plan; the third one will be launched in 2013. We are supported by a number of institutions with a fixed amount of funding for that period, and this enables the running of our organisation. These institutions support us in other ways as well – they actively contribute to our knowledge base. Without their intellectual participation in various CIEP brainstorm groups on oil, gas and the fuel mix, we would not achieve much. The composition of each group is different, in many cases the group members are employed in strategic departments, which themselves also benefit from the discussions. The power of this approach is that others are allowed an inside look into one's own organisation. We basically adhere to the *Chatham House Rules*. This principle stipulates that those present can freely use the information obtained, but are not allowed to reveal the source of their information.

1995

All hands on deck

—

The many takeovers and the geographical spread left Fugro less sensitive to the cyclic movements in the energy sector. Under Kramer's leadership turnover had risen from € 35 million to € 300 million, while the net result grew from a € 3 million loss to a profit of well over € 7 million. Yet the expected consolidation (and breathing space) was unforthcoming. Worldwide stagnation sent oil prices plummeting again. Consequently, there was no call for Fugro's expensive systems for positioning *(Starfix)*, CPTs *(ROST, Remote Optical Screening Tool)*, digital map-making *(FLI-MAP* and *Truck-Map)*, testing the seabed *(Seascout)* and drill hole measurements *(Wison XP)*. There was little work for Fugro's highly qualified (and highly paid) specialists. Turnover fell and profits were halved. So much for consolidation: it was a matter of all hands on deck.
The environmental market was saturated and was beginning to show flaws. There were forced redundancies; the Norwegian Fugro Geoteam had bought the world's most expensive ROV (Remotely Operating Vehicle) after being promised extensive orders but these failed to materialise. Investors lost faith and Fugro's shares fell. Kramer's inexperience on the stock market taught him a painful but useful lesson; you should bring the bad news with a smile and lay emphasis on the rosy future following the hard knocks – that in itself should send the prices up. Kramer himself had

>

'The CIEP Fuel Mix Group is a European affair. Participants come from ministries and power companies, but also from, for instance, the Port of Rotterdam, which wants to keep abreast of current trends and developments. All sorts of relevant issues come up. Should Rotterdam focus its strategy on trans-shipment of coal, oil, liquefied natural gas and/or biomass? How will opening up the Arctic region proceed – will Rotterdam soon have to compete with Murmansk? How will Brazil's bio-fuel (bio-ethanol) exports to Europe develop? Will Rotterdam remain a refuelling port for the maritime sector, or should it focus more on refined petroleum products for the hinterland's transport sector?

'The CIEP Gas Group addresses many relevant topics. Is shale gas a typical American phenomenon or will it also be successful in Europe? How will the European LNG market evolve? These discussions act as sounding boards for our studies, which are eventually reported through our website (www.clingendael.nl/ciep). We have no secrets and do not take sides. We want to provide balanced information to everybody, without any political bias.'

Scenarios

'CIEP researchers read a lot, surf the internet and visit conferences. Thanks to our good reputation we meet interesting energy scientists with whom we debate and discuss oil and gas issues as well as topics related to the energy transition. We are also involved in *Polinares*, a major EU research project, in which we address, together with other European think tanks, the question of whether the scarcity of energy and minerals resources may, in 25 years' time, create conflicts or rather result in rapprochement, because collaboration is improving. Predicting the future is difficult; it can only really be done by building scenarios and story lines. The diverse views regularly give rise to heated debates. Will a free global market prevail, in which companies will invest and the market decides the outcome, or will we move more towards the Chinese model, with a free market within the framework of long-term outlines defined in the State's *Five-Year Plans?*

'These different models can be plotted on a co-ordinate system, with one axis representing pure market thinking versus a free market with restraints. The other axis represents collaboration in a multinational framework versus bilateral agreements. China takes part in this multinational context, but takes a back seat. In the West we tend to address these issues far more actively. Institutions such as the World Bank and the IMF were more or less invented by the OECD countries. Will China adapt, or will the above institutions change so as to better match China's ways? Once a co-ordinate system has been defined this way, what world-views would be conceivable within the four quadrants? What events could affect the world in the next 25 years? What will be the role of the financial markets, the importance

1995

> invested a great deal of money and faith in the company. He remained on course while the financial world was white-hot, with a real threat of Fugro being taken over and his job hanging in the balance. Externally Fugro was on its knees, but internally it continued to develop, as did the investment programme. The negative publicity had a positive effect on the staff. Altogether, 1995 was not the most cheerful of years but Fugro would survive this dip as long as the product and service quality remained up to standard. A follow-up order for testing construction materials for the new Hongkong airport provided some relief.

—

And in Japan a serious earthquake in the Kobe region claimed 6,300 lives and left 350,000 homeless.

▶
Coastline survey,
Skikda, Algeria

Lunskoye-A platform,
Sakhalin, Russia

and price of oil, the risk of global conflicts (about energy), such as now occasionally occur on regional scales? CIEP makes no predictions, but surveys what may happen.

'The diversity of CIEP researchers' approaches is fascinating and helpful. One specialises in China, the other in global politics, the next is an expert on minerals, and the fourth is familiar with the gas market. I am currently examining China's energy diplomacy, and their state oil companies' strategies. China's lack of openness makes it difficult, but the amount of information is increasing. A CIEP expert recently reported on the huge progress made in China in, in particular, renewable energy technology and innovation. China is trying to learn from other countries and applies the know-how gained super-rapidly and on a large scale, whether it concerns solar or wind energy, or nuclear energy.

'Security of energy supply is extremely important for all major energy-consuming countries. China is still largely dependant on polluting, unhealthy coal for its electricity supply. They are actively pursuing the much cleaner natural gas, but, for the time being, still need to import both gas and oil. Generating renewable energy is a good way to become less dependant on oil and gas imports. China is now trying to produce gas itself from unconventional reservoirs, for instance by investing in coalbed-methane projects in Australia. The Chinese literally imitate technology by taking part in joint ventures and applying the new techniques in China. That is their operating strategy: clever energy diplomacy.

'The Chinese have been working bilaterally for quite some time. They go about this in a clever way, and on their terms. They have also used this strategy in the oil business in the past decade, through joint ventures with international and state oil companies, mostly at high political levels.'

Long-term perspective

'If you are talking about oil, you actually mean transport and petrochemistry. A range of primary forms of energy may be used to generate electricity: gas, coal, sustainable, nuclear and hydropower, but none of these can, for the time being, replace oil on a large scale. The petrochemical industry uses some 30% of the crude oil; and the other 70% are consumed by road, sea and air transport. So we still depend very much on oil and that's why the oil price is so important. In 25 years' time, electric cars will be commonplace, especially private cars in urban areas. But there is no solution for long-distance freight transport as yet. China recognises the weak link in the electric cars' energy supply: the battery – it needs to be charged every 70 kilometres. China is now becoming market leader in battery innovation and the Chinese look beyond the Western political time window. Even though their strategic long-term plans focus on replacing oil, they will still depend on it for some time, so they are also looking for an answer to the question

1996

Broadening the range of services
—

Business began to rapidly improve for Fugro, with 54% of its turnover coming from the sea and coastal waters. On land, infrastructure works brought a substantial increase in activity. Offshore Survey and Onshore Survey were to continue life as two distinct divisions. Fugro pushed on with the takeovers but at the same time grew as an autonomous entity. It now had two additional ships at its disposal, giving it a fleet of seventeen, seven of which were owned by Fugro.

New techniques opened new markets for investigation in very deep water and drilling in weak soil for constructing tunnels. The increasing interest in receiving equipment for positioning benefitted the new Fugro division in this field, with the *Starfix* and *OmniSTAR* satellite positioning systems achieving virtually worldwide cover.

Fugro began geophysical investigations off the West African coast.

—

And at 542 metres, the *Petronas Towers* in Kuala Lumpur were now the world's tallest buildings.

of where their oil should come from. For the time being, they will just need more oil. They will conclude more bilateral deals in Africa, Brazil and the Middle East, but also with countries such as Iran and Sudan. Their motives are purely economic, and they will soon be the second-largest oil consumer in the world, second only to the US.'

Bread and oil

'It is important for China's economy to keep growing as this will suppress any internal unrest. The government is dampening the overheated economy through its subsidy and tax policies. As a result, the general public hardly notices the rising oil prices. This costs the government a lot of money, but the population would become rebellious if they could no longer drive their cars or ride their mopeds. Bread and oil, instead of bread and circuses. This creates a distorted market picture. Europe levies high taxes, consumers in the US pay only slightly more than the net oil price, but there too, people dig in their heels when the oil price exceeds $120 a barrel. The 300 million US citizens make up some 4% of the world's population, but they consume 25% of the world's total oil production of 89 million barrels a day! A completely unbalanced relationship, but, after all, the US *invented* oil and built its economy around it. And the rest of the world imitated the trick.

'The Chinese government cares about two things. In the first place: ensuring continued economic growth, because if it falters, there will be discontent and unrest. In the second place: preserving the country's coherence, preventing it from breaking up. I don't think China is looking for expansion, but whether this will still be the case in another fifty years' time … They are proud of the fact that they have never been colonised. In that respect, they are now becoming world-wise, whereas they only used to look inward. They are now part of the global village. They have to get used to being part of the UN, the WTO and the IPPC. But they also play that role cleverly. To the IPPC they say: "We are a developing country, so don't blame us for our high CO_2 emissions. We are still in the industrial phase: you are past that in the West; you have a service economy. We have to act this way, if we want to develop. Admittedly, we have surpassed the US as the largest CO_2 emitter, but it is you who caused this mess over the past 150 years, not us. The climate issue should not prevent our economic growth. However, we would like to make a contribution too; just give us the technology for burning coal in a cleaner way." "Come off it," is the reaction of the Western companies, "Our technology is the result of our high investments in R&D. Who's going to pay for that? It is covered by patents and we are not prepared to give these away for free, not to other developing countries either so that they can start off by producing clean energy straight away in the most modern way."

'That's where our views clash and that's why the Copenhagen climate-change summit failed. Charity begins at home. Until 2008, the sky was the limit, but since the economic and financial crisis no government can

2027

CONSEQUENCES
OF CLIMATE CHANGE

CS HO
FUGRO HONGKONG

75% of the area of Hongkong is occupied by hills and the rainfall intensity is high. A large proportion of the surface run-off of rain falling on the hillside is carried by streams into drains that discharge into the sea. With the rise of sea level, the capacity of the existing drains will be reduced leading to flooding of the coastal area. The Hongkong government is reviewing the drainage master plans and Fugro Hongkong is actively pursuing the works.
Hongkong is affected by typhoon every year. The biggest electricity power supply company of Hongkong is concerned that with the climate change the wind speed will increase. They have commissioned Fugro Hongkong to study and upgrade the foundation and the stability of slopes surrounding their cable pylons. The works will last for many years for Fugro Hongkong.

afford this any more. In China, growth is still the motto, and the US wonder if they can remain the world's supreme power. Economically, they still are, but China is catching up fast, will come alongside and will probably surpass the US. What then? How will Europe anticipate and react to such major shifts in politics and the economy?'

Easy and tight oil

'The oil reserves of traditional Western oil companies are much smaller than those of the national oil companies, such as Saudi Aramco and the National Iranian Oil Company. They account for the bulk of production. The position of the Brazilian state oil company Petrobras is growing fast.

'The Western oil companies only have access to *easy* oil via joint ventures with national oil companies. Since the oil crisis of the seventies and eighties, international oil companies have been exploring for new reserves. Exploration licences are only readily awarded in a very limited number of regions. Oil production in the Arctic region or in deep water is technically and/or climatologically difficult. The good news about the Arctic region is that, in addition to Russia, it is mainly controlled by OECD countries: Canada, US, Norway and Denmark. There is a lot of exploration going on and also some drilling. However, people are concerned about pollution, especially after the 2010 disaster in the Gulf of Mexico. The principal onshore resources are located on the Russian Yamal Peninsula and there are offshore resources in the Barents Sea. Once Norway and Russia resolved their border dispute, they agreed on an exploration joint venture. Drilling is currently ongoing around Greenland and Shell is hoping to drill offshore Alaska in 2012. I think oil production will increase considerably in some Arctic areas, but not everywhere.

'The Gulf of Mexico is still important; exploration drilling has resumed since the *Macondo* blowout. Service companies such as Fugro are very active in that area. Operations in the North Sea and Norwegian Sea are still important – there, efforts are aimed at trying to squeeze just a little more oil out of the reservoirs. That oil should be produced while the infrastructure is still there. Once the platforms and pipelines have been dismantled in a few years' time, producing any remaining oil will no longer be economically viable.

'Angola, Nigeria and the Bight of Benin are rich in easy oil, but here the Western companies have to compete with the Chinese, Koreans, Japanese and Indians; everybody wants a slice of the cake. Smaller independent oil companies have found oil north of Mozambique, south of Tanzania; these companies will probably be taken over by their bigger brothers, just like in the US, where all the small cowboy companies that started with shale gas were swallowed up. The rules are much stricter now. Whereas small companies may occasionally make a gaffe, the large oil companies cannot afford any mishaps. US regulations have been tightened significantly since the Gulf of Mexico spill.'

1997

The year of Hongkong
—
—

The British transferred sovereignty of their colony Hongkong back to China on the expiry of the agreed 99-year lease. Hongkong was by now one of the world's foremost economic powers. Its airport was the world's largest building project and its container port was the world's busiest. Fugro had been working on the infrastructure round about the airport since 1982 and in time had entered into joint ventures with Chinese organisations and opened offices in Shanghai and Beijing. Since the handover, building activity had only increased. Some 800 employees were on the Fugro payroll in Hongkong; it was natural for the Chinese to turn to the Dutch when it came to reclaiming land and building dykes and dams. Fugro's CPT techniques were deployed offshore to locate the vast quantities of sand needed to provide new land.

Fugro spent 2% of the group turnover on R&D. Advances in technology enabled Fugro to operate offshore at ever greater depths and oil companies could search deeper for their reserves.

The High Speed Radar was a new invention for determining the quality of roads. In the past this had to be done at a walking pace; now vehicles could travel at 80 kilometres per hour while measuring the composition of the road and the underlying soil to a depth of four metres.

Disappointing returns and heavy competition caused Fugro to sell the environmental companies in America and the UK, but at the

>

STAFF RECRUITMENT
AND THEIR MOBILITY

STEVE DUFFIELD
FUGRO SURVEY,
AUSTRALIA

While staff will always be recruited based on technical skills and intelligence, their mobility across and up within the Fugro organisation will depend on their ability to participate successfully in teams, be able to generate new ideas and communicate them convincingly. Teams will be multi-cultural and most likely virtual.

Drive-Map survey, in coalmine, scanning sand and browncoal near Erkelenz, Germany

Export of expertise

'The Dutch expertise in gas-production technology is a valuable export product. Joint ventures between companies such as Fugro and Heerema can help the Russians produce the Yamal gas. The Dutch government's policy, as shown in the latest energy report, aims at a sound balance between fossil and renewable fuel. We are putting our cards on gas, the cleanest form of fossil energy. That will help reduce CO_2 emissions. But we are also investing in infrastructure and in sustainable products. As Günther Öttinger, EU Commissioner for Energy in Brussels, says: renovation of the electricity and gas transport infrastructure is the most important energy issue in Europe. The EU needs to invest hundreds of billions of euros. Who's going to pay for that? The authorities point the way, but in our market system, private enterprise will have to put up the capital and will eventually want to reap the profits.'

Political pipelines

'The sun only shines in the daytime and when the wind doesn't blow there is no wind energy. To solve this predicament, a base-load power-generation capacity is needed, for instance from gas or nuclear power plants. The liberalised European market has to be ready for this – in particular its infrastructure. The different systems are, however, not very well integrated. This applies at a local level, but also on regional and even European scales. It is a delicate matter that transcends national interests and about which EU countries should come to agreements. German Chancellor Merkel's decision to abandon nuclear energy *(Ausstieg aus der Atomkraft)* shook Europe's foundations. What will this mean for the neighbouring countries? And what type of energy will replace nuclear power? More gas imports from Russia? Or would they opt politically and economically for the *Nabucco* pipeline which Europe and the US want to build from the Caspian Sea, through Turkey and the Balkan countries? And if this pipeline were ever to be completed, would it be fully filled once Gazprom has laid its huge *South Stream* gas pipeline in the Black Sea? Europe would like to diversify European gas imports. Europe could also import more liquefied natural gas (LNG) from Algeria and further afield, but all the older Russian pipelines run from east to west, from the former Soviet states Azerbaijan and Turkmenistan to Moscow and from Russia to Europe. The former Soviet states only want to build the *Nabucco* pipeline through the *Southern Corridor* if Europe helps pay for it. This slows down the dialogue. Russian Gazprom is, in the meantime, proceeding with its pipeline through the Black Sea. If they cannot fill it themselves, they will buy gas in Turkmenistan and Azerbaijan. Europe prefers the *Nabucco* pipeline, but until it's there... The Russians also want to sell gas. That's partly old Soviet politics; Russia wants to retain control of its former republics of Azerbaijan, Georgia and Turkmenistan. These states need investors in order to become independent

1997

> same time it added to the group companies active in onshore positioning.

—

And in the Netherlands, the *Delta Works* were completed after 44 years when the flood barrier in the New Waterway was taken into use.

2027

TRANSITION FROM FOSSIL TO RENEWABLE ENERGY

ERIC DE GRAAFF
FUGRO SEISMIC SERVICES, THE NETHERLANDS

Fossil energy will continue to be the main source of energy in 2027; there are sufficient reserves and resources left, although extraction will continue to become more challenging and therefore more costly. In absolute terms, renewable energy will grow at moderate pace, with wind and solar continuing to be the main contributors. Wind energy though has significant limitations: unpredictable supply, aesthetic considerations especially in urbanized areas (like most of the Netherlands!), and a low *energy density*. Solar energy however will benefit from a spectacular drop in cost of solar panels, and we will see a rapid and innovative growth in application areas.

from Russia. Turkey is a key player, as the pipeline will cross its territory. However, Turkey is developing fast and may eventually prefer to use the gas for itself, and then it would never arrive in Greece! The Central Asian views and motives are interesting.

'China is watching closely and says: "If they can't make up their minds, we will build a pipeline and transport the gas eastward!" The same is already happening with an oil pipeline in Kazakhstan. It was constructed very rapidly; the Chinese are capable of an enormous pace, thanks to their national political system and the strategically controlled market.

'If Europe doesn't find an answer soon, it will lose the battle. As a result of our cumbersome decision-making process and the emerging nationalist trends in some EU countries, a decision, when it is finally taken, is usually only a pale imitation of the original idea, and will not achieve much. The EU's challenge is to ensure that Europe doesn't become a backwater.'

▲
LNG vessel in the Middle East

2027

TRANSITION FROM FOSSIL TO RENEWABLE ENERGY

RICHARD WILLIAMS
FUGRO CHANCE,
USA

Fossil fuels will remain the primary energy source in the world as additional resources are discovered and new technologies are enabling recovery of far more of these resources than was possible just a few years ago. Over the next fifteen years, there will be a move from oil towards natural gas where there are huge reserves around the world. The challenge will be to bring these reserves to market. Gas to liquids technology, compressed natural gas and the start of a move towards hydrogen based fuel alternatives will come about before 2027.

ACCURATE MEASURING
IS KNOWING FOR SURE

–
–
–

Some corridors are very congested, and to prevent damage to someone else's pipelines or cables, great care has to be taken when dropping anchors, laying pipelines and assembling installations on the seabed. An underwater robot – Remotely Operated Vehicle or ROV - has been developed especially for this kind of precision work down to great depths. An ROV is connected by an umbilical to its mother ship at the surface, and is controlled by operators in the control room on board this ship.

Aris Lubbes, technical manager at Fugro's Offshore Survey Division: 'It is impressive precision work requiring sophisticated positioning systems. An ROV can operate down to water depths of some three kilometres and take measurements that are accurate down to the centimetre, depending on the application. Such accurate positioning requires state-of-the-art systems. Software helps calibrate the mostly acoustic measuring tools and corrects for errors, caused for instance by the fact that the speed of sound in water varies with pressure and temperature.'

Mounting spool pieces

Special ships are used to lay pipelines. The usually twelve-metre-long pipe segments are welded together on board by the crew and one end of the pipe is slowly lowered into the sea from the stern of the boat to very close to the wellhead. Aris: 'Mounting the completed pipeline directly onto the wellhead is virtually impossible. The final link and perfect connection usually requires a spool piece that has to be tailor-made to ensure a perfect fit. Accurate in-situ metrology is needed to make this spool piece and the measuring process may take a full day. The seabed is never completely level, and a pipeline usually makes an angle with the wellhead, both horizontally and vertically. An ROV is launched from its mother ship to survey the exact locations of the well and the pipeline's end. The ROV places a gyrocompass on the pipeline and a number of acoustic transponders on the seabed; these transponders emit sound waves that are used to measure the distances between objects. All the measurements have to be perfect, so very

With the increase in telecommunication and offshore production of oil and gas, the number of cables and pipelines on the seabed has been growing fast. Cables for telecommunication and for electricity transport from offshore wind farms to shore; pipelines to pump oil or gas from the offshore wells to shore. All these cables and pipes are located in specific corridors. This network has been mapped accurately, in order for the owners and installation companies to take the existing infrastructure into consideration during maintenance or extension work.

Installation of pinpiles, Caspian Sea

Survey vessel Fugro Discovery

sophisticated equipment is needed. On the basis of these measurements, the dimensions and shape of the spool piece needed to make the connection can be determined. The actual spool piece is made at an onshore fabrication yard: it is usually an intricately shaped piece of pipe, with special mounting flanges on either side. These should seal hermetically, as a minimal deviation would cause them to leak and therefore render them useless. A workboat subsequently transports the spool piece to sea, to just above the location where it is needed to complete the connection of the pipeline with the wellhead, and lowers it slowly. This may take hours: lowering an object hundreds, sometimes thousands of metres down to the seabed with a slow winch is no speedy process. When the spool piece has arrived at the bottom, an ROV descends to fasten it. If it doesn't fit, the entire process has to be repeated, at huge expense. To measure accurately is to know for sure.'

Positioning

'Accurate measurements critically depend on very accurate positioning. The exact locations for the beacons on the seabed for collecting data are determined from the workboat, using acoustic equipment. The boat is the starting point and if you don't know its exact position, the locations of the acoustic beacons on the seabed can't be determined accurately either. Modern, refined onshore positioning systems can achieve an accuracy of five centimetres; at sea – under average conditions – we can achieve 10 centimetres.

'The spectacular breakthroughs in positioning have been made; we are now focusing on further improving their accuracy by successively eliminating the causes of inaccuracies. Even trivial things, such as a satellite being in the shade, make a difference. A Fugro R&D team led by two internationally renowned geodesists, Kees de Jong and Dariusz Lapucha, is continuously working on enhancing the system. Since Delft University of Technology's Faculty of Geodesy closed down – Dutch prospective students apparently don't find geodesy sexy enough – more staff members from other countries have joined our laboratory; recently we welcomed a number of very well qualified graduates from Warsaw University. Dariusz was the driving force behind much of this technology; he's working for Fugro in the US and is an icon in the discipline. Positioning is a daily routine in offshore surveys – it's not only essential for ROVs operating in the deep sea, but for all our operations, whether we are measuring jetties in the sea from a simple small boat close to shore or installing a huge offshore drilling platform: accurate positioning is necessary, always and everywhere. Hundreds of projects are ongoing simultaneously, all the time, all over the world.'

2027

CONSEQUENCES
OF CLIMATE CHANGE

PAUL WINSPEAR
FUGRO GEOTEAM,
NORWAY

The consequences for marine seismic acquisition are minor. Sea level rise will affect coastal areas and may open up our operating zones by transforming areas which are presently less than 10 metres depth and therefore inaccessible to towed streamer, to over 10 metres depth and therefore within the reach of our vessels, but this effect will be subtle in terms of the number of new operating areas it may transform. On a related note, should climate change be accompanied by more extreme weather conditions, noting that hurricanes and tropical cyclones form over large bodies of warm water, this will affect the safety of our vessels and could provide more frequent interruptions to the surveys, which can only be conducted in sea states of typically 3 metres or less.

Time is money

'Refining and enhancement of surface positioning systems increase accuracy but we are also working on other measuring methods that are expected to save time. This will enable us to deploy our expensive vessels as efficiently as possible. An offshore operation involving a workboat and an ROV easily costs in excess of € 80,000 per day and some of our clients' large vessels can cost ten times that amount.

'Our R&D staff is currently developing inertial navigation systems (INS). An accelerometer can determine variations in motion, and by adding up all the accelerations you can calculate the speed. The sum of all the speeds yields the displacement. The systems we now employ were originally developed for defence and aviation purposes. They contain the equivalent of a gyrocompass to determine the direction of movement relative to the magnetic North, as well as three accelerometers, one for each axis. Together, these tools measure a vehicle's speed and the direction in which it is moving. 'The process of adding up and rounding off creates inaccuracies that are commonly referred to as drift: the data gradually drift away from the actual value. However, there are ways to compensate for this drift, for instance by a speedometer or a slightly less accurate positioning system. Usually a doppler log (an acoustic speedometer) is mounted underneath an INS, which greatly improves the accuracy. This combination together with just two transponders can replace a ten-transponder array and achieve the same accuracy in a much shorter time. Installing ten transponders takes approximately twenty-four hours, because, once they are in place, their positions still have to be surveyed to know their exact locations. The first INS trials have been successful, the system works well. It's a promising new tool.'

Aquarium effect and other challenges

'One of the challenges is that such an INS tool has to be mounted on the flanges of a docking station, in order to determine the actual positions of the flanges. This is a complex and time-consuming manoeuvre. One tenth of a degree can make a critical difference. We are now testing a visual positioning system. We want to shoot images of a flange from different angles with a video camera; by superimposing these images, distances and angles can be determined. CAD software is subsequently used to produce a model of the flange. There are methods to overlay the model of the flange exactly over the video image. It will only fit one way – scale serving as a measure for the distance and obliqueness as a measure for the angle. By repeating this process many times, and invariably ending up in the same

1998

The development continues
–
–

After the enormous projects in Asia were completed, the market there decreased by 40%, but Fugro's results continued to develop positively. Its strength lay increasingly in the offer of combined activities and better solutions for long-term infrastructure projects on land and nearshore. Divisions joined forces. When oil prices plummeted, there were mass redundancies in the Gulf of Mexico area, but those at Fugro gathered up their belongings and left for San Francisco to carry out soil investigations for the foundations for a new bridge. The combination of synergy and scale was paying off in terms of both technological innovation and the integration of data flows. Fugro was the preferred supplier for an increasing number of clients. Fugro Middle East lacked its own means of mapping offshore water depths from the air but it could act as general contractor by bringing in its specialised colleagues.

Fugro retained an interest in small, specialised companies whose know-how and expertise meant an addition to Fugro's package of services. In 1998 most of the newly acquired companies were active in Offshore Survey or Onshore Geotechnics. Everything was geared to reducing the independence of the energy market.

The flow of orders in South America and the Caribbean justified opening offices in Trinidad

>

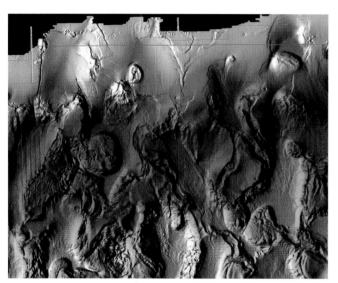

>

and Venezuela; France was another to gain a branch of Fugro. Takeovers gave Fugro a foothold in Western Canada and Kazakhstan. By then, *OmniSTAR* was a market leader worldwide with its accurate positioning apparatus and did well in the mining, fishing and land surveying sectors as well as in agriculture.

Vast reserves of gas were discovered in the Caspian Sea. Gazprom commissioned Fugro to carry out geotechnical research in the Black Sea for the pipeline from the south of Russia to the north of Turkey.

Largely thanks to its combined expertise, Fugro was able to perform investigations to water depths of 3,000 metres.

The remaining environmental activities were absorbed by the Onshore Geotechnics Division.

—

And *The Voice* (Frank Sinatra) died aged 82 in Los Angeles.

spot, it is possible to calculate where the flange was in relation to the camera, whose exact position was already known.

'In deep water, there's no natural light so there the system has to operate under extreme conditions. Standard underwater cameras suffice, as long as these are properly calibrated, and the lenses' deformations are known in order to incorporate them in the final measurements. We are, for example, studying image distortion caused by the refractive index of water: the aquarium effect. Water turbidity also presents a challenge, but as salt and fresh water produce the same optical effect, it is possible to calibrate the camera in an onshore tank before taking it offshore.

'As long as our clients require centimetres, these methods suffice. In future, we may want to measure with a millimetre accuracy, but to do so we first have to overcome a great many obstacles.'

1999

Scale of operations

—

—

The persistently low oil prices forced oil companies to a reassessment and even a few mergers. Everywhere the investment level was low. Fugro's great scale meant that it could move its people and resources around internally. It bought up four companies in Canada, Australia and South Africa. These carried out airborne geophysical surveys for mining companies and government agencies and now continued life as Fugro Airborne Survey.

The system for burying cables and pipelines in the seabed had been further refined to accommodate a water depth of 1000 metres. In England they now had measuring equipment able to detect metal objects such as unexploded bombs to a depth of 30 metres underground.

The Starfix.Plus positioning system was the first GPS to compensate for ionospheric disturbances, thereby increasing the accuracy of global positioning systems.

Continuing growth of the group necessitated enlarging the office in Leidschendam.

—

And in Europe the *European Monetary Union* came into effect.

▸
*Testing airborne
equipment*

▸
*Seabed profile of the
Gulf of Mexico*

◂
*Survey at mudflats,
The Netherlands*

RENEWABLES

—
—
—

T he International Energy Agency (IEA) and major oil companies and governments all agree: demand for energy will increase greatly in the coming decades. The inhabitants of the BRIC and other developing countries would also like to ride scooters and drive cars and live in air-conditioned houses. Oil companies formulate their own scenarios, but these are based on the same information and most scenarios therefore paint a similar general picture: most energy is used in power generation, transport, industry and households. Oil, coal, gas, nuclear power and renewables are currently the main sources of energy, in that order. Gas consumption is increasing rapidly and will move to second place in the next few years.

'CO_2 emissions are rising alarmingly, coal being particularly disastrous. It is unbelievable and irresponsible that Europe is allowing new coal power plants to be built and at the same time claims that it will meet its 2020 emission targets. Forget it,' says Paul. 'Organisations such as Greenpeace come up with other scenarios, and they claim that these are technically and economically feasible. The Greenpeace reports are professional, sound and responsible and are amazingly convincing, just as well-founded as the IEA reports, and Greenpeace's view is corroborated by the EU websites' renewable-energy figures. So, there are two utterly conflicting opinions. I think the truth lies somewhere in between, but, from a renewables point of view, the IEA scenarios are probably too conservative.'

Cost comparison

'Exxon, surely a very conservative oil company, expects a major price rise if CO_2 has to be stored underground. Their study assumes electricity generation from fossil fuels, with a modest tax imposed on CO_2 emissions. Tax measures will not only stimulate emission-reducing measures, but also raise the cost of electricity generation from conventional fuels, bringing it on a par with that of wind and nuclear power. A slightly higher but still reasonable tax on CO_2 emissions would be enough to make the new sources

Contrary to general consensus, energy from renewable sources, says **Paul van Riel,** is not marginal business; in fact it is beginning to approach that of fossil fuels, also in terms of economic standards. It is virtually impossible to increase the yield of traditional coal- and gas-fired power plants; whereas the relatively young wind-power business is making giant leaps forward, e.g. by developing new wind-turbine designs. Solar power development is also booming; the new type of solar collectors in Southern Europe already makes solar power generation cost-effective in remote places. Other forms of renewable energy are waiting for a break through.

of energy cheaper than conventional sources. Availability also comes into it. Wind power can meet the current global demand for energy two hundred times over, and solar power more than two thousand times over. Green energy offers plenty of prospects. Wind power and solar power are the most likely candidates; the possibilities of other natural resources are more limited. In my opinion, one of these – geothermal energy – has been largely ignored. Geothermal energy is expensive and we don't know enough about it; moreover the risk of earthquakes soon throws a spanner in the works. Geothermal energy is used in only a few places in the world. The trick is to access the heat and exploit it in an economic manner; the same applies to solar power. Nuclear power's cost-effectiveness has been proven, but this form of energy will only break through once the safety issues have been resolved.'

Exponential increase in wind power

'The breakthrough of renewables is mainly prevented by technological issues. *Moore's Law* undoubtedly applies: Gordon Moore predicted in 1965 that the number of transistors placed on a chip with the same surface area would double approximately every 18 months. This trend has now continued for almost half a century. A similar law, in all likelihood, also applies to the productivity of solar panels; solar power will most probably be cost-effective in large parts of the world by the time of Fugro's 65th anniversary. Incidentally, Fugro is not involved in small-scale solar-energy projects. This is more likely in major projects, for instance in projects involving a set of mirrors liquefying salt in a facility that resembles a water tower. The huge amount of heat generated by this process is used in a steam turbine to generate electricity. Constructing the foundations of such a facility is our job, but it isn't spectacular.

'The growth of wind power is bringing about an exponential increase in generation capacity. The European Union (EU) has taken the lead and is investing large sums. By 2010, the EU had a total installed wind capacity of 84 GW, which is effectively 50 GW. This means that some fifty conventional power plants were replaced by wind-power plants. Wind farms are increasingly offshore projects. Every year, several new wind farms are built in the North Sea, each with a capacity of several hundreds of MW. The average capacity of a turbine is 3 MW; so 200 wind turbines are needed to generate 600 MW. There are now also 5 MW turbines and the first batch of 7.5 MW turbines is on the way. The trend is for ever larger wind turbines – these are relatively cheap to maintain – but like trees there is a limit to their height. These structures can be hundreds of metres tall and the optimum has still to be determined.

'Few people realise that more capacity has been built in the EU during the past five years for generating renewable energy than for conventional energy. In 2020 the wind market will be three times as large as in 2010.

2000

Everything and everybody is working

—

—

Fugro had the wind in its sails, with 30% higher turnover and 13% higher net return. Apart from offshore seismic exploration, all sectors were functioning well. With a price increase of 85% Fugro was up in the top five best performing companies on the Amsterdam stock exchange. Fugro issued a subordinated, convertible loan of € 100 million; the group was now in an excellent position financially. Fugro's *Starfix* and *OmniSTAR* positioning systems were a success. Supported worldwide by ninety base stations, *OmniSTAR* improved the position accuracy of the GPS from 15 metres to a few centimetres. It enabled greater efficiency in management in the agricultural sector; not a single square metre was missed, or treated twice.
Fugro received an order for the first phase of a seabed survey for a worldwide glass fibre cable network. Young technicians followed an extensive training and education programme to acquire knowledge of other disciplines.
Fugro, Boeing and Oceaneering joined forces in the development of AUVs (Autonomous Underwater Vehicles).
Thanks to *Extranet*, Fugro and its clients could exchange project data online.

—

And after a controversial recount it wasn't Al Gore but George W. Bush who became the 43rd President of the United States.

The underlying annual growth in capacity to be installed shows how fast this form of energy is developing. Offshore wind farms produce a better return than onshore ones. The wind blows harder and more steadily at sea. Foundation costs of an offshore wind farm are three times as high as for an onshore one. These mega structures require sound foundations as the mast and blades are subjected to enormous forces. Every wind turbine requires a thorough soil investigation.'

Intelligent grids

'It isn't common knowledge, but the wind always blows on the North Sea. There may not be a breath of wind in one spot, but 50 kilometres further on it is blowing. Operators intend to connect all the wind farms in the North Sea by installing an *intelligent grid,* a network of thick cables on the seabed that ensures that in the network power is generated all the time. Moreover, onshore gas power stations – the only type of power station that can easily be turned on or off – can be plugged into the network in order to compensate for peaks and lows. Prior to the construction of such a network, much soil investigation is required, in connection with the effects of currents, waves, storms and other kinds of hazards. Inspections, maintenance and repairs also mean more work for Fugro. We have been doing these jobs for the oil and gas industry for years. Some things are slightly different in the wind industry, but no new capabilities are needed. Our expertise can be supplied *off the shelf* and there clearly is a growth market, because we *must* reduce CO_2 emissions.

'Worldwide investments in the oil and gas industry amounted to some $ 600 billion in 2010, in wind $ 70 billion and this will increase rapidly. Wind power is big business, especially offshore and the trend can't be stopped. Government subsidies still obscure the overall picture somewhat, but it is not unreasonable to expect that people will have to pay for emitting CO_2 – and in that case wind power is cost-effective. The Dutch government also spends huge sums on raising the level of the dikes – which is necessary because of the rise in sea level, and that again may partly be caused by the consequences of CO_2 emissions.'

Legal aspects

Two groups are currently active in wind power on the North Sea: electricity companies and commercial operators. Developers of wind farms form consortia, apply for licences for building offshore wind farms and sell the electricity to power companies. 'When the issue was raised of whether electricity was being delivered onshore or offshore, Germany took the lead in formulating statutory regulations. The Germans rapidly pushed the legislation through parliament; they now have an offshore off-take obligation. Many wind farms are being built in the UK, Denmark, Belgium and the Netherlands. France is building the first wind farms in the Atlantic

◄
*Installation of windmills
from Fugro Seacore jack-up
platform in the North Sea*

2001

Together across borders
–
–

The Fugro group was now as solid as a rock. Its greatest challenge was finding good people and holding onto them. Fugro scoured universities in search of smart youngsters but these would rather work for hip dotcom companies than in the oil industry. The best outcome was to continue investing in cutting-edge technology – smart solutions meant less staff doing more work.
Fugro began an internal exchange programme to further career development. There was no day care centre in the basement or fitness club on the top floor. People didn't work at Fugro for the money, although they were paid well; what counted most was the sense of family and the noses-to-the-grindstone mentality.
The annual Managers Meeting was of tremendous value. It was where people could air their grievances and get to know each other. It was more team building than holding meetings about policy or job distribution.
All the subsidiaries had their own historical backgrounds, but the typical Dutch ambience

>

Ocean. There are few firm projects in the Mediterranean, maybe because there is not enough wind there.

'Europe is the global leader in wind power, but wind farms are also springing up elsewhere. *The Great Plains* in the US is ideal for generating wind power – the wind is always blowing there. Fugro, as a member of an American wind-power consortium, is involved in firm plans for offshore wind farms off the US East Coast and in *the Great Lakes*. There are already many onshore wind farms in China, and the first offshore one is under construction. Fugro is involved in studies into offshore wind farms off Hongkong.

'In Fugro's *Cross Divisional Marketing Group* an expert on wind power is keeping a close eye on developments. Because most projects are initiated in Europe, we have a wind power group coordinating the activities of our British, Dutch, French and German operational companies, in order to anticipate all the planned projects and be ready to submit tenders. Fugro sometimes has up to four vessels working on the North Sea simultaneously for different wind farms; a Seacore jack-up platform is currently working full time on near-shore jobs. For that matter, Seacore is also closely involved in the construction of experimental tidal and wave-action power plants in Scotland. The development of power generation from waves and tides lags behind that of wind power, but is an attractive proposition as the masse of flowing water can easily drive a heavy turbine. Such a plant will be subjected

2001

>
welded them into an engaging business culture.

Fugro stood out from the pack through its advanced technology and creative people, and any company wishing to vie with Fugro could expect to incur huge capital costs.

The principle still held that the operational companies did their own financial administration instead of centralising this at Leidschendam. All company directors had control over their own staff and managed their own company's affairs. They enjoyed the complete faith of the Fugro top, as long as they reported on their movements now and again and on any difficulties that should arise. It was not the most efficient form of organisation in all situations but the gratifying sense of autonomy that everyone felt was ample compensation. Fugro's experience and financial resources meant that it could stimulate and support small companies and help them across hurdles. When Fugro took over Robertson Research International and Jason Information Systems (world market leader in quantitative investigation into oil and gas supplies) it initiated its third core activity, that of Geoscience, in which Fugro embedded other operational companies with relevant activities.

—

And in New York Al Qaida's suicide hijackers reduced the *Twin Towers* to rubble on September 11th.

to huge forces, and this requires thorough soil investigations and anchoring. Fugro is keeping a close eye on these developments, in case the technology breaks through.'

Hydropower and underground storage

'Concerning the use of hydroelectric plants, Fugro is becoming increasingly involved by monitoring the condition of the great many dams that were built all over the world in the first half of the 20th century. In the US, concrete dams were built during the *Great Depression* as job-creation projects. Many of these dams are located in earthquake-prone areas. They are about seventy years old by now and the service life of concrete is not infinite. Are the dams still structurally sound? Have they become weaker over a period of sixty to seventy years? European countries that use hydroelectric power, such as France and Switzerland, also realise that monitoring is necessary. What can be done if a dam is found to be structurally unsound? A range of geotechnical problems crops up and this results in a growing number of requests for advice. One of our teams is currently working in the Himalayas at a height of 3,000 metres; hydroelectric power never really got off the ground in that region, even though it is the easiest, cheapest and greenest method of power generation.

'Underground storage of energy is also an interesting topic. Areas with sufficiently large groundwater resources can be used for cooling in summer and for heating in winter. Soil investigations are also needed for this application. Is the soil sufficiently porous? Are the water flows sufficiently large? This requires very specialist studies, but the activities are still low key, as is the technology for possible underground CO_2 sequestration. Underground CO_2 sequestration on land meets with opposition, but there are plenty of potential storage locations offshore. Much research is still needed though.

'Fugro is at the forefront and is closely watching the technological developments for all these alternatives of energy. We may take part in research and development and will participate actively once they really get off the ground.'

2002

The third leg

The acquired companies Jason Information Services and Robertson Research joined forces with Fugro's seismic activities and Airborne Survey as the third division alongside Geotechnics and Survey: Geoscience. The new division held out good prospects for synergy and was expected to generate approximately a quarter of the total group turnover, as well as further increase the operational cash flow and profit margin.

The *Fugro Explorer* was taken into use; this state-of-the-art drill ship was unique in being able to conduct geotechnical soil sampling and testing at water depths of up to 3,000 metres. With *Starfix-HP* Fugro introduced a GPS with an accuracy of less than a decimetre.

Yet again, flexibility and a spread of activities proved to be a benefit and a necessity. As the market for research into subsea cable routeing had collapsed, staff and equipment could successfully be deployed in the improving oil and gas market.

Fugro landed the largest ever airborne geophysical survey contract for the collection of 1.8 million linear kilometres of magnetic data in Saudi Arabia.

The Euronext electronic stock exchange entered Fugro in the Amsterdam Midkap stock index.

Fears of a decline in investments in the oil and gas industry as a result of 9/11 proved unfounded; investments for 2002 were expected to be 10% higher than what they had been in 2001.

And *Down-to-Earth and Up-to-Date*, a book chronicling Fugro's history, was published to celebrate the company's first forty years.

EFFICIENCY
IS KEY FOR PROFITS

After graduating in Civil Engineering, **Harry Kolk** joined Fugro in 1974 and – as he says himself – stayed on by sheer chance. At the time of Fugro's fiftieth anniversary he has made it to director of Fugro Engineers, the largest operating company in the Offshore Geotechnics Division.

'Fugro has traditionally been market leader in soil investigations and everybody in the oil and gas industry knows the company. However, other clients and competitors are involved in the wind-energy market – many companies that are familiar with onshore operations trust that they will be able to apply the same know-how and expertise offshore for building wind farms in shallow water. Offshore operations hold no secrets for Fugro, but the wind-energy market is new and requires a new approach. Site investigations prior to the construction of oil and gas platforms only require a few – very detailed – geotechnical boreholes at a single location. For wind farms, however, a detailed foundation analysis is required for every single wind turbine, so a wind farm comprising 150 wind turbines, for instance, requires 150 boreholes and associated analyses. For this much higher production, operational efficiency determines competitiveness and profitability. Onshore, time is also money, but offshore, time is an even more important factor: offshore time costs a lot of money. At sea, weather conditions play an even more important role; surveys can only take place in so-called weather windows: limited periods of relatively favourable weather. Therefore, Fugro focuses on optimising production.'

New areas

'In recent years, the oil and gas industry is becoming increasingly interested in surveys in areas with less favourable soil conditions. Soft soils, steep and unstable slopes, volcanic activity and vulnerability to earthquakes (or combinations of these conditions) are geohazards that need to be assessed. These types of geological challenges are, for instance, present in the southern part of the Caspian Sea, with its huge fossil fuel resources. Production of oil and gas resources is moving to ever more difficult locations, such as the deep waters offshore West Africa and the Arctic Region, and exploration for alternative sources of energy is becoming more profitable.

'Producing the Canadian tar sands, for instance, offers onshore perspectives for Fugro while interesting offshore developments are foreseen in bringing gas hydrates into production: these huge volumes of gas contained in marine shelf sediments may become an interesting source of energy. As profitable exploitation of conventional oil and gas resources is becoming increasingly difficult, and economic incentives therefore stronger, extraction of gas hydrates may become booming business. However, the technology is not sufficiently developed as yet. The key question is: how can we safely tap this gas? It is contained in ice, deep in the frozen ocean floor. Bringing the ice up to the surface will reduce the pressure and make it disassociate into the gas phase, resulting in a huge increase in volume, and risk of explosions. So it will have to be converted in situ in a safe manner. Japan is seriously looking into the technical possibilities and Fugro is involved in studies in Korea and other places. These countries lack indigenous conventional oil and gas resources and therefore have every reason to be interested in developing this technology.'

Project management

'The world and the manner in which Fugro operates have become more complex in a short time. Competition is increasing and both technological and organisational issues demand more attention. Fugro puts a lot of effort into effectively organising human resources, recruitment, training, health and safety. The focus is additionally on more efficient project management and better cooperation between our operating companies to minimise risks by better communication and correct, timely information.

'A project management leadership team focuses on improving project management in Fugro N.V. A small mistake made by somebody offshore may mean losing a full day ship's time and therefore loss of profit, as the costs tick on. The objective for 2012 is to utilise everybody's competences optimally in a modified organisation and have people doing the jobs for which they are most suited. The same applies to new recruits, whether coming straight from school or university or from another employer. Their knowledge should be up to par in the shortest possible time in order to perform Fugro Engineers' specific operations properly. That is why Fugro devotes much time and money on training and education, both in classroom courses and e-learning, through *the Fugro Academy*.

'A key element of our new way of working is the commercial department, which was traditionally doing marketing, business development, tendering, making quotes etc. If they were successful in winning a contract, they were also made responsible for the project supervision, financial reporting and full evaluation. Anyone who can take care of that entire package is a true all-rounder. In the new set-up, a group focuses on business development and tendering, in other words especially on clients and external contacts. Project

2003

In search of new fields
—
—

By now the oil and gas industry was providing two-thirds of Fugro's turnover to the tune of € 822 million. This reflected Fugro's efforts to develop further as a supplier in this sector. The strategy was boosted considerably when Fugro acquired Thales GeoSolutions, their biggest acquisition yet. (Its 1700 employees in 30 branches turned over € 240 million annually.) This takeover strengthened Fugro's position in the province of offshore survey but also added new activities to its roster, such as the deployment of Remotely Operated Vehicles (ROVs) and deepwater diving operations in Brazil.

With existing oil and gas fields declining, investments put on hold and the worldwide need for energy growing, investment budgets of the oil and gas companies rose dramatically for both onshore and offshore operations. Exploration and development in deep water were concentrated in the Gulf of Mexico, West Africa and Brazil. Fugro focused on two segments and two cash flows within the oil and gas sector, namely optimising existing fields and exploring and developing new ones. Fugro remained active in these areas in the Middle East, the Caspian Sea, Mexico, Asia and Australia. It was worthwhile investing in more detailed knowledge so as to keep up production in existing fields for as long as possible.

The Autonomous Underwater Vehicle (AUV)

>

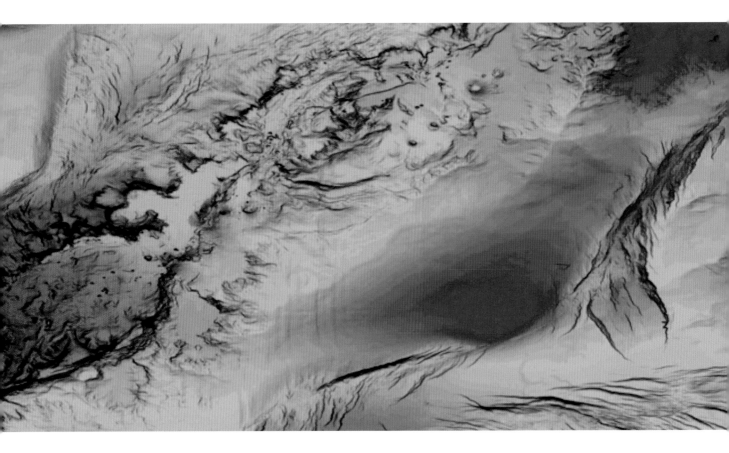

▲

Survey result of an AUV

◄

Deployment of Fugro Pressure Corer for gashydrate sampling

supervision requires a different type of person, one who can make a process run smoothly and efficiently and look after the financial supervision, in other words someone with a more coordinating focus.'

Different organisation

'One of the main challenges is: how do we make a group of local operating companies into a single, efficient, internationally operating organisation? Optimal deployment of people and equipment will result in increased efficiency. An operating company that wants to do everything itself, while sister companies have surplus and/or better qualified staff, is missing opportunities. Fugro is developing towards a single virtual office; every person should feel part of a single, global organisation. Managers were traditionally educated in having their own operating company or department perform optimally and maximising profits, while considering the entire group's profit optimisation and other interests as secondary. Easily said, but it will be a while before this change has been achieved. It all boils down to a different mindset: whoever believes that he can always do better than his colleagues in another branch office, should change his attitude.

'On paper the organisation is already in place: Fugro is one club, but gains are still to be made in operational activities. The objective is not inspired by a lack of work, but by the need to utilise the group's capacities more efficiently. In general, our employees should feel part of a greater whole, like world citizens. Fugro has, over the years, definitely not suffered from a lack of confidence, but now this is no excuse not to look also at what is going on elsewhere in the world. Globalisation is a major theme in the organisation. Fugro Engineers' extra task is to set up better services for developing and supplying onshore and offshore geotechnical equipment. We should look at what types of hardware and software other operating companies have invented and developed. All our companies should make better use of each other's technology. Engineers are intrinsically creative – they want to be inventors. Management is trying to make them look first at what already exists, in order to make better use of Fugro's own technological achievements. As far as that's concerned, much can still be gained internally, but we should also watch what our competitors are doing. Our rock-solid market position made some clients encourage our competitors into developing new technology. We will have to be prepared in some cases to abandon our own technology and adopt someone else's. But we have to be very alert, especially now, and react immediately when a competitor approaches one of our clients with his own technology. We have to watch out, improve our own technology and beat the competition. We cannot afford, these days, to lean back and simply trust in the rock-solid name we built.'

2003

> was brought into use for geophysical surveys to water depths of over 3,000 metres.

—

And the sale of electric cars got under way, with Toyota selling 834,700 examples of its hybrid *Prius* in Europe alone.

2027

STAFF RECRUITMENT AND THEIR MOBILITY

JOHN LAZARUS
GEOSPATIAL SOLUTIONS, AUSTRALIA

I do not believe this will change significantly from today's scenario. Whilst recruitment methods (social media use, web, *iPod* broadcasts) may change the final judgement on candidate suitability will still come done to a personal evaluation. Mobility within Fugro will always be related to organisational issues and personal motivation.

THE BILLION-DOLLAR DEAL
FOR OFFSHORE RESOURCES

—
—
—

The need for clarity about which country could successfully claim ownership of the natural resources that may be present in a certain offshore area, increased in parallel with the oil and gas companies' interest in exploitable resources – not only in coastal waters, but also in deeper water further offshore.

What belongs to whom?

Exploitation rights can be worth a lot of money, so it is crucial for a coastal state to know exactly where its own territory ends and that of its neighbour begins. Some coastal states assert that their territory doesn't end at the limit of the EEZ but extends to the edge of the continental shelf and in some cases even right to the foot of the continental slope. The shelf edge usually corresponds with a sudden steep drop in the sea floor. The shelf surrounds all the continents and is 50 miles wide on average, but in Europe it may extend as far as a thousand miles. The shelf off the east coast of North and South America and around Africa is also wide; it is, however, very narrow off the west coast of North and South America. Property disputes such as *What is ours?* and *Where does our neighbour's territory start?* therefore have both legal and geological aspects.

The International Seabed Authority used to be the authority for matters concerning the sea floor beyond the 200-mile zone. This will change as the states involved stake claims beyond this zone, corroborated by scientific research. The high seas used to be international waters: free for all nations to use, but belonging to none of them. There was no international legislation covering economic activities on the high seas, so there was no jurisprudence. In days gone by, the *might-is-right* principle applied on the oceans; whoever had the best war fleet ruled the waves.

So it was high time to organise more comprehensive exploration and exploitation rights for the sea-floor resources and the United Nations was deemed the most appropriate authority. And so the *UN Commission on the Limits of the Continental Shelf* (UNCLOS) was established. From 1989,

Until a decade ago, disputes on territorial waters between neighbouring countries were limited to fishing grounds and alleged navigational errors by ships. Today, the boundaries of the national territories are defined by the traditional 12-mile limit *(Territorial Sea),* the 24-mile limit *(Contiguous Zone)* and the *Exclusive Economic Zone* (EEZ) – the latter extends a maximum of 200 nautical miles from the coast. The importance of these zones and in particular of the exact boundaries between the zones of neighbouring countries increased dramatically as development of onshore oil and gas decreased as a result of overproduction. Once oil and gas fields had been discovered offshore, the attention and facilities of the large oil companies gradually shifted from the land to the relatively shallow waters off the coast.

it focused on this new role and published *the Law of the Sea*. Article 76 of this Law is by far the most important; this article covers the underwater extensions of all the continents, i.e. the continental shelf extensions, and the exploration and exploitation rights that coastal states can claim for these shelves. The new legislation is applicable to 155 coastal states of the 192 countries that signed the UN treaty. Eighty-four of these 155 coastal states have the opportunity to formally submit an *Extended Continental Shelf* (ECS) Submission (in accordance with UNCLOS, Article 76) beyond 200 nautical miles.

Coastal baseline is key

The increase in global demand for energy led to a rise in fuel prices, making it economically attractive to produce fossil fuels from places that had previously been inaccessible. Assumed or proven resources at great water depths prompted the development of improved technologies; and the resulting new, improved tools and materials could be used at greater depths. Moreover, scientific developments and engineering advances enabled the exploration for and production of resources in deeper water.

Oil and gas companies as well as mining companies are prepared to pay huge sums to the rightful national governments for licences to explore for offshore natural resources and, once discovered, for permission to produce these. Maritime boundaries are delineated at particular distances from the so-called coastal baselines – originally mean low-water marks (in the form of *Normal Baselines* where gentle, regular coastlines are seen to occur) and/or as *Straight Baselines,* an additional and more modern approach where jagged (deeply indented irregular Coastlines are simplified through long straight segments), identified long ago with obsolete surveying methods. In the present conditions, however, one mile more or less may make the difference between success and wealth on the one hand, and empty pockets on the other. Many coastal states therefore have much at stake and request new surveys of their coastal baselines with new modern surveying methods.

Writing software *and* surveying

Geoscientist Robert van de Poll knows everything about *the Law of the Sea*. In 1999, he was working for Caris, a Canadian company that develops and sells software to make land and maritime maps, including GIS *(Geographic Information Systems)*. This company was invited by the UN to develop specialised software for integrating the legal, technical and scientific aspects of *the Law of the Sea*. Rob became the manager of this new project. He switched to Fugro in 2006 in order to assist coastal states more directly in (i) their claims to extend their maritime boundaries in accordance with Article 76 and (ii) provide technical assistance in every aspect of *Law of the Sea* related to *Maritime Limits & Boundary* dispute applications.

2004

Prize

—

—

The Annual Report for 2004 was awarded the *Henri Sijthoff Prize,* presented annually by leading Dutch financial newspaper *Het Financieele Dagblad* for the best financial reporting on 2004. That year was a year of transition; strategically the company had never been better placed. The integration of Thales GeoSolutions in 2003 cost a great deal of time, attention and energy. Consequently, Fugro made no further acquisitions in 2004 so as to let the organisation 'settle'.

Fugro laid great emphasis on security aspects related to the use of ICT infrastructure and the internet. The data traffic over Fugro's networks was protected against hackers using the latest encryption technology *(Virtual Private Network)*. ICT audits were carried out so as to signal and solve potential problems.

Fugro's investments for 2004 went in part towards a better system for acoustic positioning, also in deep water; improving drilling systems on board ship, which meant a greater ability to operate in bad weather; and optimising airborne surveys through the use of Unmanned Airborne Vehicles (UAVs). Operated by remote control, these pilotless planes *(drones)* were equipped with a range of sensors.

—

And while Europeans were enjoying breakfast on Christmas Day, the west coast of Sumatra was struck by a natural disaster that would go on to affect large parts of Asia. The word *tsunami* was a household word across the world for weeks on end.

Rob: 'The software that Caris developed for the UN is largely based on geology and geodesy, with a pinch of hydrographics and geophysics thrown in. It underlies the identification and documentation of boundaries and territorial claims made by countries within the framework of *the Law of the Sea*. At Fugro I was given the opportunity to develop the software further and combine advice on *the Law of the Sea* surveying. We can also help countries by performing surveys and interpreting the data. Fugro operates globally in ever deeper waters. We understand and recognise the importance of *the Law of the Sea*. My experience, international connections and know-how come in handy, as I was not only instrumental in building the software but also, for many years, maintained good relationships with UN experts all over the world. As a result, the full range of experience and topographic information has been combined in a single global database, comprising all the maritime treaties, measurements, survey results and boundary disputes of all the coastal states in the world. The database is consolidated in a Caris geographic information system, which provides geodetically correct spatial calculations, and integrates and visualises topographical, hydrographical, geological and geophysical data. The accompanying imagery makes this database comprehensive, complete and up-to-date.'

Scientific research

'Before a country can submit its claim to the *UN Commission on the Limits of the Continental Shelf* to extend its maritime limits (and thus the acquire the rights to exploit that area) officially and once and for all, that country should first ratify the UN *Law of the Sea* treaty. Prior to that, our database makes it possible to assess the likelihood of the application to the UN being successful. If there is a chance of an extension, the country should prove the validity of its claim with scientific underpinning.

'Despite the importance of *the Law of the Sea* not all the coastal states have ratified the treaty. On the contrary, almost 60% of the 520 maritime boundaries between coastal states have not yet been delineated and are unresolved or under discussion, making local boundary disputes difficult to resolve. This includes the *new* countries on the Caspian Sea. Originally, the Caspian Sea was split 50/50 between Iran and the Soviet Union. When some of the coastal states became independent after the break-up of the Soviet Union, Iran had to deal with three new neighbours that all claimed part of the oil-rich inland sea. Russia had already signed the UN *Law of the Sea* treaty and the three new countries agreed, but Iran wouldn't sign, with potential political consequences. Incidentally, such unresolved border disputes also exist in Western Europe. Up to now, for instance, no agreement has been reached between the Netherlands and Germany on the boundary of their 12-mile zones. However, the recent construction of a German wind farm close to the coast of Schiermonnikoog prompted talks between the two countries.'

2027

TRANSITION FROM FOSSIL TO RENEWABLE ENERGY

JOOST GEISE
FUGRO ENGINEERS,
THE NETHERLANDS

By 2027 about 25% of the energy required in North West Europe will be provided by renewable sources such as wind, solar, hydro, tidal etc. The majority of this will come from offshore wind which will see a significant increase in installed capacity during the years 2015-2025 and probably beyond with an anticipated contribution of 35% by 2030 of renewable energy. Future years will also see tidal, wave and current energy taking a leap forward as appropriate technical solutions will be developed that can deal with the conditions at the sites.
A *North Sea Power grid* will be developed such that the balance in power generation can be addressed as wind loads are likely to vary over the North Sea and the energy companies need to avoid having to call upon gas fired power stations to compensate for periods when wind energy output may be low.

▶

*World Map of
Law of the Sea*

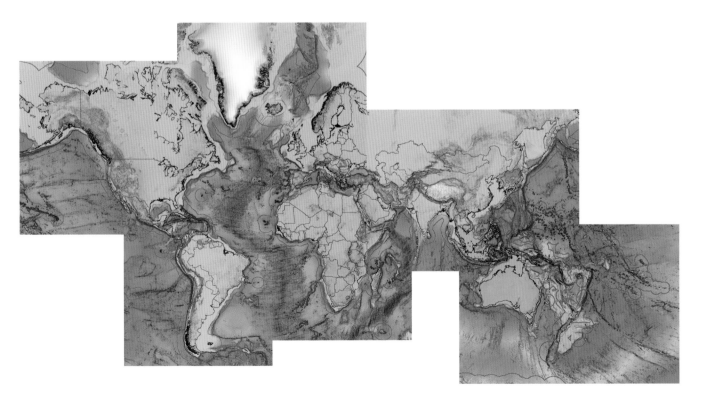

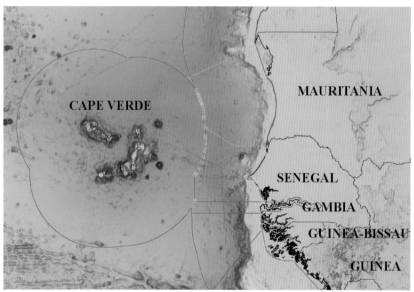

CAPE VERDE

MAURITANIA

SENEGAL

GAMBIA

GUINEA-BISSAU

GUINEA

Diamonds and other mineral resources

'Most disputes and conflicts are about oil and gas, but occasionally other mineral resources are at stake. A good example is the case of who owns the property rights of the placer diamonds in the Orange River estuary in South-West Africa. This river forms the border between South Africa and Namibia. So it is crucial to know how and where exactly the border between the two states is located. According to Namibia the border runs through the centre of the river, but South Africa considers the northern Namibian riverbank its national border, and as a consequence claims the entire river as South-African territory. In such a case, a difference of a few hundred metres may decide which country can claim ownership of diamond riches that lies in the heaviest concentrations at the mouth of the delta as it flows into the Sea.

'Potential disputes don't just involve boundaries on the continental shelf. Volcanic activity has resulted in concentrations of gold, platinum and other precious metals in the deep oceans. States in the vicinity are interested in these metals, while the pharmaceutical industry takes a great interest in the anaerobic organisms that live on sulphur compounds. The chances of discovering mineral resources when the maritime boundaries are extended, and the consequent economic boost, encourage states to join the UN *Law of the Sea* treaty. After a country has ratified the treaty, it has ten years to analyse the area, gather data, see whether it can lay a claim in accordance with Article 76 of UNCLOS, and, if so, submit that claim. (There are no deadlines for analysis of or research within the EEZ, therefore the present day 60% of the worlds *Maritime Boundary* disputes will not be resolved within this ten year deadline.) A country has to submit its analysis to the *UN Commission on the Limits of the Continental Shelf* (CLCS). This commission consists of 21 experts; the UN has divided the world into seven regions and appointed three scientific experts for each region.'

At the time, Rob trained many of these CLCS scientific experts in the use of the Caris software. He says the experts are first-rate scientists who can competently judge dubious claims.

Oil in Africa

Conflicts may readily arise if exploration for new oil fields is carried out before a country has secured its maritime boundaries with its neighbours with state-of-the-art methods in accordance with *the Law of the Sea*. Rob: 'If success and riches are at stake, boundaries that were historically determined by a gentlemen's agreement and a handshake are rarely sufficient, as became evident a few years ago in West-Africa. One of the major oil companies had done exploration work on the continental shelf in 1970s, and had concluded that no oil or gas was present, so it had left again. But a few smaller oil companies didn't give up so soon and continued exploring. At the time, I advised the government of the coastal nation involved to arrive at a

2005

Kramer takes his leave

—

With a substantial increase in investments by the oil and gas industry, the year 2005 saw Fugro reach record highs in terms of turnover and net result. In the preceding decade, the company's structure, composition and market positions had led to a well-balanced portfolio of activities. This enabled a continuously high capacity utilisation. Fugro deployed its ROVs and integrated systems for acoustic and inertial navigation to map the damage done by *Hurricane Katrina* to pipelines and oil rigs in the Gulf of Mexico. With its equipment, people and experience Fugro was able to provide the necessary services as a single package. The increasing call for seismic services justified investments in this sector. When Fugro missed the boat in its bid for the Norwegian company Exploration Resources, it took the decision to build its own fleet for seismic survey. With these ultramodern ships (partly to replace a number of chartered vessels) the management sought to triple the turnover from seismic activities between 2005 and 2008. This would elevate Fugro-Geoteam to one of the world's leading seismic services. In November, Gert-Jan Kramer stepped down as President and Chief Executive Officer. He had managed Fugro for 23 years and brought it to great heights. He was succeeded by Klaas Wester, who had joined Fugro in 1981.

—

And China's unstoppable economic growth resulted in new energy-political relationships; more and more products in Western shops were *Made in China*.

2027

COMMUNICATION METHODS

PAUL HARWIG
FUGRO HORIZONS,
USA

Wireless technologies will not experience *dead zones*. People will wear glasses that have direct 3D video conferencing in them, replacing email and the associated miscommunications associated with typing. Personal communications will occur with this virtual face to face communications and video environment.

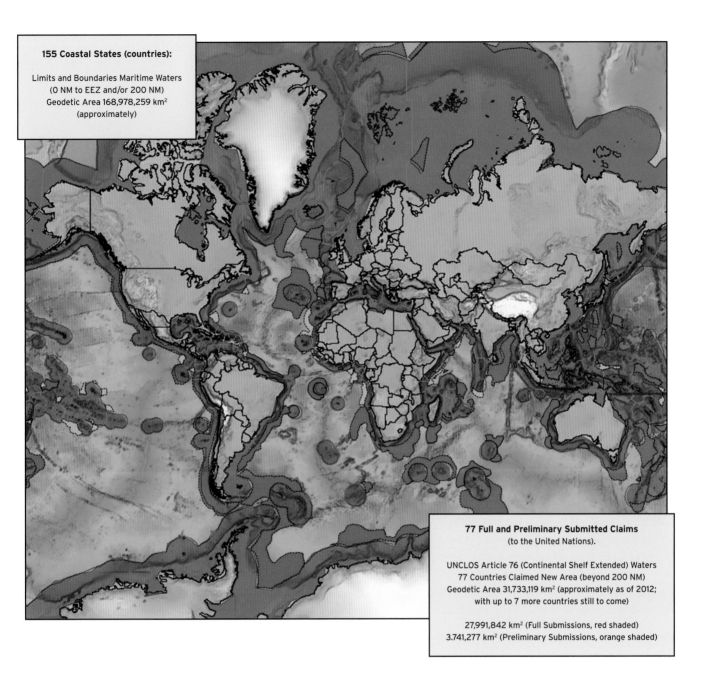

155 Coastal States (countries):

Limits and Boundaries Maritime Waters
(0 NM to EEZ and/or 200 NM)
Geodetic Area 168,978,259 km^2
(approximately)

77 Full and Preliminary Submitted Claims
(to the United Nations).

UNCLOS Article 76 (Continental Shelf Extended) Waters
77 Countries Claimed New Area (beyond 200 NM)
Geodetic Area 31,733,119 km^2 (approximately as of 2012;
with up to 7 more countries still to come)

27,991,842 km^2 (Full Submissions, red shaded)
3.741,277 km^2 (Preliminary Submissions, orange shaded)

◤
*Geotechnical investigation
vessel Mariner, Australia*

▲
*Overview of locations
with boundary issues*

2027

ORGANISATIONAL DEVELOPMENT

GLYNN RHINEHART
JOHN CHANCE LAND SURVEYS,
USA

We will continue to multiple
decentralised offices around the
world but such will not be known as
separate opcos wihtin Fugro. They will
all been known as just *Fugro*.

formal agreement with its neighbouring countries about the borders within the EEZ and to ratify the UN treaty, just in case oil might still be discovered. Even though I pointed out to the government officials that it would be long before any oil or gas could actually be produced from such deep water, they only focused on the procedures of the continental shelf extensions (UNCLOS Article 76) that are subject to the ten-year deadline. They didn't heed my argument that oil companies were active in ever deeper waters off their coast, where they had no formal agreements with their neighbours. They saw no cause for concern – their friendly relationships with their neighbours would keep trouble at bay. However, when in mid 2007 one of the oil companies discovered easily producible oil valued at some five billion dollars sixty kilometres offshore, close to the boundary that had never been exactly established, the fat was in the fire. Within a very short time, the discovery made the country one of the main oil producing countries in Africa. The neighbouring country saw what happened and submitted an appeal to the UN in accordance with Article 76 of *the Law of the Sea* and also started reviewing the validity of the old gentleman's agreements from the past, to confirm that part of the oilfield was located within its territory and that it was therefore entitled to part of the proceeds.'

Maps and talking

Rob has access to all the data held by Fugro concerning sea-floor mapping, pipelines, cables, coastline mapping, coastal development etc, and also to the information held by the UN and many government authorities. 'This literally involves thousands of documents and maps. In fact, it is about geographic coordinates and accurate mapping. All these details enable us to pinpoint potential points of contention in survey areas. This can be explained more easily by talking on the basis of maps than by just talking. Most material is 3D. We are continually expanding our database, because data change every week. If two countries decide to solve their thirty-year-old dispute today, we are always informed of the critical coordinates through my contacts at the UN or the US Foreign Office. Data become outdated fairly rapidly, so we produce monthly updates. We therefore possess the most up-to-date knowledge, which enables Fugro to serve government authorities and other industry stakeholders.'

A Dutch Canadian

If valuable natural resources are involved, governments can be extremely secretive and very selective in whom they will trust. 'I have the advantage of being a Canadian with a Dutch name, who is working for a Dutch company with a good reputation all over the world. This gets us into every ministry. A government representative frequently begins by asking: "We're taking an active interest in the offshore industry, but know nothing about the Law of the Sea. Please tell us the ins and outs." Using all the known

2027

EFFECTS OF
GEOPOLITICAL DEVELOPMENTS

JOHN TEN HOOPE
FUGRO MIDDLE EAST,
UAE

The *Arabic Spring* that started in 2010 will have a positive effect on the relation between the Arabic countries and the West. The Arabic nations will become more liberal and more open. The large sport events such as the *Fifa World Cup* will further close the gaps between East and West. The *Arabic Spring* will eventually overthrow the regime in Iran. The new regime will be less radical and restore the relationship with its neighbouring countries and the West and releasing the tension in the Gulf Region.
The *Somali Pirates* have completely changed their strategies as well. Rather than high jacking vessels they have shifted their interest into the much more lucrative tourist industry. In 2027, many holiday resorts have emerged along the beautiful Somali coast and the pirates run theme parks like *Pirates of the Gulf of Eden* or *Captain Crook*. They also run real life adventure trips in small boats and play high jacking of a seagoing vessel under the leadership of an experienced pirate veteran.

data about the area involved, we then prepare a presentation for all the stakeholders, in other words *Law of the Sea from A to Z*. We inform them about their boundaries, neighbouring countries, coastline, geology, about the oil industry and about what they could expect to get from it. It's basic to begin with, a sort of *Reader's Digest* version at senior government level. The technical intricacies come when the senior executives in ministries and companies understand what it's all about and pass it on to their technical staff. On the basis of our figures, they can apply for a relevant budget for exploration, seismic surveying and geophysics to gather the information required by the UN. Similar Fugro applications can be undertaken when specifically addressing *Maritime Boundary* issues as well. Fugro subsequently supplies a report up to several hundred pages, fully in accordance with UN regulations and conditions. Fugro also offers introductory courses on the *Law of the Sea* software and clues on how to use this software when preparing a claim with the UN.'

Paranoid application

When a country asks Rob for advice, he will consider all the pros and cons. 'The investigations and the procedure cost money. But if you aren't prepared to make the investment, you risk missing out on the wealth. I come across paranoid situations. Every country watches its neighbouring countries very attentively. "Rob, we saw you dealing with our neighbour last year, what were you doing there?" The actual information is of course confidential, but I can truthfully answer that the neighbours are very seriously looking into the *Law of the Sea*. This will increase their interest. "If our neighbour is looking into it, shouldn't we be doing the same? What if they were to hit the jackpot and some of the riches lay within our territory?" I'm frequently asked questions like these.'

By 2011, 77 countries (under UNCLOS Article 76) had submitted claims outside the EEZs totalling more than 32 million square kilometres. Add to that a further 3 million square kilometres up to seven other countries with deadlines after 2009.

If you don't sign, you don't play

During the past 25 years, oil companies have found easily accessible and producible onshore oil and gas resources. In the 1970s, the companies switched their focus to shallow offshore waters. Governments awarded licences in *safe* waters: areas that would not become bones of contention with neighbouring countries. Later, when technological advances enabled exploration in deeper waters, the states started to award licences there too, for the so-called *offshore blocks*.

In the last ten or so years, all the *safe* waters have been given out. States smell profits, expect ever higher returns from oil and gas discoveries and have to resort to licences in *unsafe* waters: the areas that had originally been

2006

The Fugro Academy

—
—

Fugro's workforce of close to 10,000 strong saw revenue rise this year to more than € 1.4 billion. Another reason for this, besides the favourable market conditions, was that Fugro was able to carry out increasingly complex projects involving a combination of Fugro's activities and services.

The acquisition of Seacore (UK) gave Fugro access to large and technically advanced jack-up platforms for geotechnical investigation relating to infrastructure works such as landing stages, bridges and offshore wind farms. Spectacular projects included relocating the 100-year-old *Shanghai Concert Hall* 80 metres from its original site, searching for gas hydrates for the Chinese government, a soil survey in the Caspian Sea for new production facilities, a 3D seismic survey near India and data gathering with an ROV for construction work in Brazilian waters.

The year 2006 also saw the acquisition of Rovtech in Aberdeen. This substantial addition to Fugro ushered in one of the most striking developments of the coming years and would reinforce enormously Fugro's market position in the use of Remotely Operated Vehicles (ROVs). Besides combining with Fugro Survey's existing activities in pipeline inspection, Fugro Rovtech concentrated on deploying underwater robots from a survey mother ship for video inspection of pipelines to a water

>

avoided because they might have been a cause for dispute. As said, some 60% of all the 520 maritime boundaries in the world are contentious. As a result, the number of disputes between neighbouring states about their boundaries increases.

Some experts claim that 25% of the world's undiscovered oil resources are located underneath the Arctic ice cap. This region is not a country, like Antarctica, but is classified as open sea. Norway, Denmark, Russia, Canada and the US have interests in the area, on the basis of their EEZs. Not all these countries have signed the treaty; some are considering joint ventures to keep down the high costs of investigations.

Generally speaking: as long as a boundary has not been established definitively, the current location of the border is only an approximation. The countries involved then have to hold high-level bilateral talks and sign a treaty. The original aim of *the Law of the Sea* was to regulate the exploitation of the deep sea beyond the EEZ, but governments now also feel compelled to settle territorial disputes within the EEZ, where by no means all the boundaries have been defined.

Rob: 'Take the North American continent, which includes all the Caribbean states. This continent consists of 22 countries with 122 maritime boundaries within the EEZ. There are no agreements as yet for 78 of these boundaries. So 64% of all the boundaries off North America and in the Caribbean are uncertain. These situations first require legal agreements. Countries know where they stand thanks to the UN mechanism. *The Law of the Sea* is a good incentive to speed up the decision-making process and put affairs in order. Ten years ago, no one had heard of *the Law of the Sea,* but now nations are beginning to realise that they are obstructing their country's development and depriving their inhabitants of wealth if they don't take part.'

2006

depth of three kilometres.
In 2006 the Fugro Academy opened its doors. This component of the company developed and offered worldwide training schemes for Fugro employees as support for company-wide enterprises. There were local and regional courses on a range of subjects such as leadership, project management and management in general but also specialised technical programmes for Fugro's professionals. Fugro wanted to use the same systems and follow the same processes wherever possible to be able to establish global standards of competence, train staff in accordance with the same international criteria and deploy them worldwide.

And Al Gore's film *An Inconvenient Truth* had the emotions running high in the discourse on climate change that it unleashed.

Seismic vessel
Geo Barents

Helicopter platform
on board of seismic
vessel Geo Celtic

THE FUGRO FACTOR

—
—
—

'My freedom is amazing; one would expect more interference. Obviously, we must produce reports periodically, meet HR standards and adhere to Fugro's business principles *(The Golden Rules)*, but these are by no means unreasonable or illogical. If an operating company has trouble adapting, it's the operating company's fault rather than the Group's rules.'

Is it time for a new, different structure, with almost 14,000 employees worldwide? 'Fugro's decentralised structure is its cornerstone and is partly responsible for its success. However, stricter EU regulations on human rights, personnel management, export policies and legal aspects of materials transport will create challenges in the next few decades. These regulations will affect Fugro's autonomy, but are expected to induce growth rather than decline.'

Patient parent

Paul cannot comment on whether Fugro should – or would wish to – downsize by divesting business lines. 'I hope not, as Geoteam could be one of the casualties. The seismic industry is cyclic and the downs seem to last longer than the ups. Oil and gas companies are still our main clients, but we are affected by the flood of new vessels on the market. So if there were to be a candidate for divestment, seismic services might be one of the first in line ... I keep telling this to my staff – not to scare them, but to make it clear how happy we should be with this solid, patient parent company. Our rapid growth and the building of four ships within a very short period, with all the seismic equipment on board, have cost hundreds of millions. These huge investments show that Fugro intends to remain a player in seismic services. Geoteam is an outsider in the group of seismic players. We are relatively small, but have always managed to keep up with the major competitors. Our staff is extremely committed to making a profit as soon as possible. Geoteam's ten vessels are almost continuously fully booked: a major achievement in the present market. We are doing our utmost to prevent

After graduating in Geophysics and being on a payroll for eighteen years, **Paul Winspear** had been working as an independent consultant for two years when he was asked to join Fugro's Geoteam in 2007. He was quite settled in his one-man business, so he found it difficult to decide, but he seized his chance and is now one of the Group's youngest managers. Geoteam's five hundred employees generate over 15% of the Group's revenue.

any vessel lying idle in port. It would be easy to *buy* work by dropping our prices; we are trying to strike a balance between a filled portfolio and upholding our prices. Staff quality will make the difference; after all, anybody can buy the necessary hardware off the shelf.'

The right people

'Our short-term objective is to be as efficient and productive as possible, in order to at least break even, no matter how poor the market. If we manage to do so, we could achieve great successes as soon as the market recovers. To achieve this, we need the right vessels, equipment, processes and prices, but above all, the right people. But to be honest: we can't compare ourselves yet with the industry's giants who can afford their own R&D departments, with dozens of researchers. Our four R&D people also need to help with collecting data. I see this as a dilemma: if we wish to make Geoteam grow and be the best in quality assurance and technology, we will have to invest in the best people, even if we can't really afford to in these lean times. We will have to reduce costs and try to put the right people in the right places. This is possible, but we should focus more on improved mobility within Fugro, create opportunities for exchange, and identify smart win-win scenarios. We could set an example by increasing mobility at management level for a start, and show it pays off. We have to stimulate and motivate, stress the positive aspects. To make such a scheme work, it may be necessary to adapt the group's structure.'

Young rising stars and éminences grises

'Geoteam will continue to have trouble gaining new people as long as some competitors pay better salaries. In job interviews, I always stress *the Fugro Factor* and most applicants are attracted by that. In this flat organisation, everybody can express their opinion without fear of repercussions. There is freedom for initiative and growth – a valuable combination. Most companies, including the American ones, publish quarterly figures, but Fugro looks much further ahead. *The Fugro Factor* may compensate the slightly lower salary in comparison with other employers, but if our salaries are more than just a little lower than those of our competitors, people won't join us.

'In addition to young rising stars, we also need wise grey eminences on our staff. We try to strike the right balance and introduce more dynamism in the company. People who only look at their salaries, without any interest in the company as a whole, will not make progress. People who perform well have prospects of promotion. Last year I took on somebody who is now vice-president of the Western hemisphere in our branch; he rightfully regarded the opportunities within this large, solid company with easy access to the top level, as a form of income.'

2007

Seismic vessels and Geospatial Services

—

Investments by the oil and gas industry increased this year by almost 19%. Three quarters of Fugro's annual revenue (well over € 1.8 billion) came from this sector. Fugro's turnover increased by 26%, largely through autonomous growth.

Fugro acquired EarthData (US), a market leader in cutting-edge technologies in the fields of aerial mapping, geographical data, radar images and 3D images taken with the *GeoSAR* camera system. This data in combination with other Fugro systems supported new applications related to climate change, alternative energy and monitoring oceans.

Fugro joined the search for the whereabouts of Odysseus' island of Ithaca, using its technological know-how to contribute to the advancement of international culture.

Three seismic vessels – *Geo Barents, Seisquest* and *Geo Celtic* – were added to the fleet together with a further four ships for other offshore activities. This brought the Fugro fleet up to 50 vessels, 28 of them self-owned. By now Fugro had in addition 105 ROVs, 4 AUVs, 400 kilometres of seismic streamers, 25 jack-up platforms, 65 CPT trucks, 215 drilling rigs, 50 aircraft and 105 satellite position system reference stations. The existing onshore survey and positioning activities were

>

Staff recruitment will more and more
take place by having close contacts
with universities and research
facilities around the world. The drive
will be to acquire top of the line,
well paid junior staff for initially
field positions that can provide a
premium service while being able
to sell neighbouring services to the
clients they deal with. Our future HR
strategies will be more and more *up
or out* while maintaining structured
staff rotation through the group.
Career development will be a focus
of attention.

Deploying seismic streamers

Streamer inspection on board Geo Atlantic

2027

SIZE AND COMPOSITION
OF WORKFORCE

BIGHNA N NAYAK
FUGRO SURVEY,
INDIA

Our business will continue to expand
and likely have workforce of 600-700
by 2027. Workforce will mainly
comprise of engineers specialising
in construction support activity
regionally and will also support
operating units where workforce is
more expensive or not willing to work
offshore.

Seismics is fascinating

Surveying the earth's subsurface by sound waves is pure high tech. People who work on a state-of-the-art seismic vessel are lucky: fantastic equipment; many facilities for comfort, recreation and physical exercise; proper safety programmes; management-system training. 'I sometimes contemplate returning to offshore duties again myself! Seismic surveying is an attractive business, a fascinating mixture of science, logistics, people and equipment. A working seismic vessel is spectacular, even if only for its specialised hydrodynamics. It is a fascinating business for young people looking for a thrill, and few ever consider leaving seismics.

'The seismic industry has been the target of environmental pressure groups for a long time, partly because it is part of the oil and gas industry and partly because of its operations. The impact of acoustic energy on marine life worries people most. Various studies have, however, shown that fish suffer no ill effects from an acoustic shock. An underwater explosion has a sharp peak, and some claim that this could harm mammals such as whales and dolphins; acoustic signals might interfere with the communication between them during migration. But I didn't observe any visible effects when I was working offshore Australia, with whales only two kilometres away. They could swim off, but didn't. When we start working such an area, we use the so-called soft-start method: we first create a small explosion. This makes mammals leave the zone. When we are fully operational and shoot the full array, dolphins sometimes even approach our ship: the seismic boom doesn't seem to worry them. But we have to admit that we are in their habitat. It's a delicate matter and we therefore pay much attention to technological innovation. Instead of a sudden pulse, we could generate a *sweep* covering various frequencies, but that technology has not been sufficiently developed. We feel jointly responsible, but refer the environmental pressure groups to our clients.'

Customer focus

'Our ambitions are realistic. Fugro Geoteam currently adopts a so-called fast-follower business strategy. The industry operates in ever deeper waters and is becoming increasingly complex. Things that were impossible a mere twenty years ago are now feasible; things that were then prohibitively priced are now becoming economically viable. Clients request solutions to their problems. A potential opportunity for improvement is for us not to sell a solution before we understand the problem. Fugro is trying to change this mindset, from working on a project basis to working with a customer and solution focus. If we are closer to the client and understand their specific problem, Fugro can come up with solutions by integrated deployment of its various operating companies, supplying a wide range of expertise.

'The limited supply of oil and gas doesn't mean that technological innovation will come to a halt. On the contrary, technology is becoming increasingly important in oil and gas production; great technological feats are required to squeeze the last drops of oil out of a reservoir, for 4D monitoring, measuring changes in pressure, oil/water contacts, oil/gas contacts, 4D characterisation and passive monitoring.'

Health and safety

'My most important duty as a manager is to make sure that everybody gets home safe and sound. The teams that perform best in *Health, Safety and Environment* usually also perform best operationally. Planning, making risk analyses, thinking things through and making money tend to go together. Incidents demand a lot of time from management and may lead to higher insurance premiums and staff resignations. A good HSE performance makes for motivated employees and equals good business. An employer who ensures good HSE factors shows he cares for his employees. At the time, a crew may not appreciate the importance of a bus used for crew changes in a remote part of India being equipped with safety belts, but later they will realise: *I'm working for a good company.*

'The BBC is running a series of TV documentaries, *Horizons*, on the role of technology in solving society's most pressing problems in the next decade. The series included a programme on natural gas. They used footage of our vessels and came to our office in Oslo for interviews.

'For the time being, seismics will continue to play a role in the energy business. It will be quite a while before solar energy and other renewables will take over from conventional sources of energy. The world is craving for fossil fuels, so eventually these will run out, no matter how good and efficient our cars become. Our industry is merely playing for time.

'The economic recession caused a worldwide reduction in demand for energy and the current overcapacity in this line of business, but we are affected more strongly by factors such as environmental disasters, piracy and geopolitical conditions, such as the unrest in the Middle East and North Africa. We had a good chance of winning a bid for a survey off the coast of Tunisia, but it was cancelled. China's ambition to operate a seismic state fleet of its own will also affect this market. In this respect, I trust that our clients will be true to their words: "We value a high HSE standard and will keep paying for good quality". That will ensure Fugro can make the most of its opportunities.'

2007

> combined as Geospatial Services, together with the acquired companies EarthData and MAPS Geosystems (VAE).
Fugro signed contracts for, among other things, the inspection of levees in New Orleans and California, a project to support work on a nuclear power plant in Normandy, site investigations for the widening of the Panama Canal, a study to select the best route for a gas pipeline from Algeria to Italy and 3D seismic surveys in Norway, Mexico, India and the Middle East.

—

And new media such as *Facebook, Twitter* and the Dutch *Hyves* gave a modern thrust to the social game. If their parents had something like five friends, youngsters passed the 500-mark with ease and added the verb *to unfriend* to their vocabulary.

2027

STAFF RECRUITMENT
AND THEIR MOBILITY

ED SAADE
FUGRO EARTH DATA,
USA

Social media will be the driver, although it is likely to be much different than the versions we utilise today. We will be recruiting for Fugro not just for the local operating company. All offices will be organised to look for Fugro recruits for employment worldwide. Partnership for growth will be the filter/conduit to allow this to begin happening now.

DELTAS ARE HOT SPOTS

O il forms from organic debris, such as plant remains, which is transported by rivers and laid down on the sea floor in front of the river mouths. Over time, this organic debris is buried by thick sequences of sediments. The high pressure and temperature caused by the heavy load of this thick pile of sediments eventually generate oil and gas. A quick look at a map shows that many rich oil fields are located in deltas at the mouths of large rivers such as the Mississippi, Niger, Rhine, Mekong, Yellow River, Euphrates and Tigris. So deltas are hot spots, and therefore large oil resources are also expected underneath the Arctic ice cap as many large rivers discharge into the Arctic Sea. General geological principles suggest that oil can be expected there, but its presence still has to be proven by further seismic surveys and drilling.

African oil

West Africa's oil wealth is largely found offshore, to the benefit of its coastal states. Quite apart from the political situation in Africa, exploration in deserts and jungles is difficult. Fugro's airborne group carries out exploratory investigations, for instance by measuring magnetic properties from a plane to determine where sedimentary basins are located. The presence of, for instance, uranium can also be measured from a plane. Oil may also be present in the East African *Great Lakes* region; this rift zone is an incipient tectonic plate boundary where new plates are gradually moving apart to eventually form new continents. The rift zone will gradually widen to become an ocean as is currently also happening in the Red Sea, which is the spreading centre between the African and Arabian plates. The geological properties of opposite shores of the Red Sea are very similar: these were originally parts of a single connected continent, as were Africa and South America.

Fugro scientists also know the speed at which the continents are drifting apart. For accurate positioning Fugro has reference stations all over the world, the exact locations of which are continuously measured. Satellites

2027

EFFECTS OF
GEOPOLITICAL DEVELOPMENTS

JOHN LAZARUS
GEOSPATIAL SOLUTIONS,
AUSTRALIA

The Peoples Republic of China (PRC) will be the most influential geopolitical force in the Asian region and the globe. Opportunities for Fugro will occur in the domestic PRC market over time as current restrictions become less and less.
However the biggest opportunities for Fugro will come from the major PRC national organisations investing in major resource projects outside of PRC. The focus for Fugro will be on the PRC organisations investing in the oil and gas and mining resource rich nations.
Benefits for all Fugro operating companies should be significant provided that it is managed well. However, a Fugro policy for dealing with PRC as a whole is required.

▲

*Delta of Rhine, Meuse
and Scheldt,
The Netherlands*

orbiting the Earth stay on course, but some reference stations may move
as much as 12 centimetres per year, due to the drifting of continents –
geologically a very fast rate. The new coordinates are entered into the
systems every three weeks. *Noblesse oblige:* if you pretend to be capable
of positioning with an accuracy of a decimetre, you have to be sure of your
base points.

Uncharted areas

There are few regions in the world – apart from the lands and sea floors
underneath the ice caps – whose surface has not been mapped. But
our knowledge of the interior of the Earth is still limited. Japan has a
programme in place to study the deeper parts of the plate boundaries: the
sources of the devastating earthquakes that regularly strike the country.
Fugro is studying earthquakes in California with its in-house developed
monitoring equipment. Seismic technology now makes it possible to *look*
some ten kilometres deep into the Earth. The distance to the Earth's inner
core is known, but there is still much to discover inside the Earth.

NOTHING VENTURED,
NOTHING GAINED

—
—
—

After graduating, **Marshall Pounds** didn't know what kind of job he wanted. So he kept on studying: History, Spanish, Civil Engineering, Geotechnics, … until he felt ready to start work. 'I had my first job interview with Scott Rainey, at Fugro-McClelland. He was looking for someone for a posting in Mexico.'

After graduating, Marshall Pounds didn't know what kind of job he wanted. So he kept on studying: History, Spanish, Civil Engineering, Geotechnics, … until he felt ready to start work. 'I had my first job interview with Scott Rainey, at Fugro-McClelland. He was looking for someone for a posting in Mexico.'

It was a relaxed interview, no tie, unshaven. 'We spoke the same uncouth language. A week later I was on my way to Mexico. After five years I left Fugro for a job in the construction industry. There, I learned how bureaucratic most companies are. I became frustrated by the slow pace and increasingly often hired Fugro for soil investigations etc. After a couple of years I had seen enough. That's when Scott happened to phone me and invited me for a beer. The timing could not have been better. That's how I rejoined Fugro and I am no helping to set up Drilling & Well Services. A new line of business for Fugro which recently had taken over TS Marine – a company that also carries out well intervention.'

A fascinating ship

In 2011, Marshall was ordered to form a team for the drilling vessel *Fugro Synergy*. 'A beautiful and fascinating ship. I found out that quite a few things still needed doing to it to make it the intended marketing sweet spot. I had assembled an operational team of people who knew about positioning, vessel management, ROV services, drilling services – with more experience than I have myself. The composition of this team shows Fugro's typical team feeling.

'Drilling platform culture differs greatly from that in geotechnics and geoscience. It makes for an exciting mix of disciplines. Fugro employs people with different backgrounds and education levels. Our drill crew devoted their hearts and souls to building the rig. To me that's more important than twenty years' experience. Building a completely new organisation without much experience is exciting, and then proving the concept to a world that may not be ready for it.'

Building competencies

'I would rather like to be a member of the vessel's crew myself, but I'm a manager now, stuck behind a desk. However, I plan to be on board during projects as well. After all, an expert crew will be needed as there will still be many things to learn. Clients also have to get used to a single company performing all the jobs at a well site. We are convinced that this set-up will be financially more attractive, partly because we are working with a fairly small vessel. Especially so when a client has several jobs in a single region; it is inefficient for a ship to travel to the other side of the world for a single job. Well intervention will become more important and standard packages will develop. We believe we can build up our market position and skills best by focusing on the following services to the global oil and gas industry:
   • drilling and installing casings;
   • installing so-called Christmas trees;
   • well maintenance and cleaning, and
   • well decommissioning and dismantling.

'We want to prove our concept with the *Fugro Synergy*. It's a daring business model; all the revenues will have to be generated by a single asset. There will be no income when the vessel is in port or under way. So we have to operate regionally and the vessel will have to travel fast from one site to the next.'

Trust

Fugro has invested in a versatile vessel. This approach agrees with Fugro's new modus operandi: more customer focus. 'That could be more profitable, but also requires technical and economic risk management. We invested much capital in a business that still has to get off the ground. But nothing ventured, nothing gained.

'*Fugro Synergy* is one of Fugro's most expensive vessels; it took many months to complete. It takes a lot of patience to see such an expensive ship lie idly in port while the equipment is installed on board. Luckily, Fugro has patience, but we are bursting with impatience to get cracking and make it a success. The pressure I'm now feeling is entirely self-imposed, because we are given trust – that's more important for a professional than salary or other aspects of the job. I've only been with Fugro for sixteen years and I'm already responsible for an asset that could affect the share price. I enjoy this responsibility but will only be really happy when the first order for a special well intervention job has been booked. We will go wherever a client needs us. There'll always be a *hot* region somewhere. You have to plan well ahead before leaving for such a region. In the next few years billions will be invested in deepwater off Brazil. It would be great if Fugro could get a slice of the cake. However, subsea developments in Australia also generate many drilling jobs and related services.'

2008

From exploration to decommission

—

HRH Prince Willem Alexander presented Fugro with the *King Willem I Prize*. This national business award is presented every two years to a company that excels in terms of courage, initiative, perseverance and innovation. A second award would follow: Fugro received for the second time the *Henri Sijthoff Prize* from *Het Financieele Dagblad* for the best financial reporting on 2007 in the *Mid- and Smallcap* category.

In 2008 Fugro continued to acquire companies from all over the world to obtain more state-of-the-art technology and increase its market share. The Geotechnical division consolidated its position with seven new companies specialising in earthquake hazard assessment, road and pavement management and water management.

Survey for its part acquired five companies whose activities included pipeline inspection and satellite mapping techniques. Even Geoscience acquired six companies, specialised in electromagnetic exploration, data storage, geochemical analyses, gravimetric surveying and the digital reconstruction of seismic data. These acquisitions and the favourable prospects brought in a further 2,150 employees; Fugro now had well over 13,600 workers on the payroll.

With its broad spectrum of closely related services, Fugro was increasingly involved with the entire life cycle of oil and gas fields: from searching for new fields to decommissioning

>

Track record and innovation

Fugro is successful in identifying niche markets and traditionally doesn't worry too much about what others are doing. 'We don't even win all the orders in our strongest business lines. The way we market ourselves is changing. Our competitors are also getting better. Fugro's safety requirements and modern, specialist equipment is not always unique. We're moving towards a situation where we can distinguish ourselves better by our performance, innovation and teamwork within the Group. That's something that can't be imitated by others. But the question remains: what is the incentive to cooperate, and how do you do it? When everybody is free to choose their partner? There are brilliant new developments in technology, software, management systems, presentation tools etc. But new technology by itself is not enough; it's teamwork that creates added value. A certain amount of internal competition keeps everybody on their toes and is necessary for success. You should do something that others can't. There is internal competition for the highest R&D budget. That forces us to innovate and that's fine.

'We are aware that competitors do some things just as well as we do. Worse still: we sometimes have to imitate others. It should be the other way around! Fugro has much more to offer, but we still sometimes feel that we should sell ourselves better. We feel threatened by some small companies, even though they are no smarter than we are, because they approach our customers with a strong motivation and a multidisciplinary team, cutting through our reputation and relationships.

'Fugro should no longer only speak with the clients' technocrats. We have plenty of in-house power and high-quality staff to talk straight to the decision-makers at an organisation's highest levels. Technocrats are becoming less important. We used to come in as a consultant and were judged for our technology, but every deal is based on an economic decision. Our track record is impressive, we can show the evidence. We're big enough to talk directly with decision-makers about large, multidisciplinary projects. By delivering these in an efficient manner, we can manage risks and add value. That will be the new course for the coming years. Cross-divisional marketing is a good first step.'

▸
*Crew on deck of the
Fugro Synergy*

◂
*Installation of the
drilling tower on board of
the Fugro Synergy*

2008

›
platforms once exploitation had been terminated.
In September Fugro was included in the AEX index, the list of the 25 most actively traded securities on the Amsterdam exchange.
Gas was a global growth market and liquefied natural gas (LNG) met some of the demand. High energy prices made the development of gas fields far from the user markets more attractive.
The world economy was rocked by the financial crisis, which had been escalating since August that year.

—

And the bankruptcy of Lehman Brothers signalled the start of the global financial crisis; the lack of trust meant that the *live today, pay tomorrow* approach had had its day.

2027

COMMUNICATION METHODS

IDAR HORSTAD C.S.
**FUGRO MULTI CLIENT
SERVICES, NORWAY**

3D video phones with contact lenses display, switch between brain view and conference view based on where in the brain the focus is. The vocal and hearing will be in the ear only and we therefore don't need speakers or head sets to communicate.

RUDOLF
D A S '012

WIND TURBINES ON THE NORTH SEA IN 2025

By 2025, almost all new wind turbines will be floating. That will make it possible to install wind turbines in deep water, where the winds are strongest.

The appeal of this new wind-turbine design is that four-bladed rotors yield more power for the same diameter as three-bladed ones, at considerably lower maintenance costs. Moreover, two blades can be easily removed by tilting the mast to the central platform, in case any of the blades needs to be repaired or requires maintenance, and the wind turbine remains operational even then with just two blades.

The drawing shows only the parts that are visible above the water surface of a group of turbines. They are connected under water (see detail), enabling them to be automatically aligned with the wind.

LEGEND

1 Four three-metre-diameter, sixty-metre-long steel pipes connected by a cruciform *hub*
2 *Hub* with electricity production cable to shore
3 Four tethers connected to rotating moorings
4 The submarine part is symmetrical to the current; it is trimmed with ballast water so that the four ends of the floating cross keep floating horizontally, five metres below the water surface
5 Generator and gearbox can be tilted towards the central platform for major repairs or maintenance
6 The four rotor blades can be individually removed from the central ring containing the blade gears

V

EARTH UNLIMITED

WHAT'S NEXT?

FOLLOW AND LEAD

—
—
—

'We have a choice: distinguish ourselves by our unique products and services, or become a price buster in a market for standard products. If we go about it the right way we can do both.'

Mark Heine, one of Fugro's younger managers, voices his thoughts on Fugro's course for the coming decades: 'Fugro should above all remain a technology company. Technology is developing exponentially and continuing innovation is crucial. We have to actively acquire new technology and use it to make our technical solutions more ingenious. If you want to remain a leader, you have to keep looking at yourself critically.'

Front runner or price buster

'As a front runner we can employ the latest technology, for which clients pay us well. But after a few years, it's no longer new. So we will have to consciously improve our efficiency and come up with another innovation. By doing this consistently and systematically we can stay ahead of our competitors. We must never relax. It isn't easy, but a company like Apple shows it's possible.

'But Fugro could tackle some things differently, to ensure the company remains sexy in this modern technological world, and to make sure we're not seen as a conservative, stuffy engineering company. The choice of sticking to the healthy Dutch solid image and in particular not to behave too fancily, is understandable and fine, but the effect is gradually wearing off. I'm afraid the new generation won't see our traditional brown colours as a sign of soundness and expertise but as old-fashioned. These aspects also matter if we want to be regarded as a technology front runner. If Fugro becomes just a price buster in a market for run-of-the-mill products, we might as well close down – we won't manage to survive with our original form of organisation.'

Sharing knowledge

'The Fugro Group is getting a more regional organisation structure. Making one manager responsible for our combined services in Africa or Europe is a good move. Operational activities have to be coordinated regionally – but technological developments require a central approach. All these aspects are important, but in the end it all boils down to people. As a knowledge organisation, Fugro could focus more on the new generation's specific characteristics and wishes, adapt its organisation accordingly and ask itself how best to share its knowledge. Even employees who have been working for Fugro for fifteen years still don't know everything that is going on in all the divisions – I keep hearing new things myself. Interesting maybe, but it also makes us miss opportunities. People who know all the activities and divisions are valuable to an organisation. This is why Fugro created the cross-division marketing group which brings together expertise from the various divisions. I think it's a good initiative. A structure with regional managers is a logical next step, which specifically focuses on cooperation between divisions. Fugro most certainly doesn't need to manage everything top-down and it won't be easy to strike the right balance between central and decentralised. Whatever the case, we have to keep thinking creatively and dare to look at ourselves critically.'

Wanted: creative thinkers

'Former Fugro colleagues are working for many of our competitors. They are just as good as we are, unless we introduce a number of game shifters and plot a strategic course to a target in ten years' time, which we'll doggedly follow. Let others go all out in the market now – in ten years' time they will be on the sidelines and we'll distinguish ourselves through our technological innovations. Fugro is capable of patiently steering business developments in the long term, providing some people with vision and ideas get together now to think about the future. *Carte blanche*. The members of this think tank don't necessarily have to be young, as long as they can think flexibly. How many Fugro employees read Shell's scenarios and know what the Shell Group thinks about the world in 2050? The information is there for the taking. Some experts claim we should stop with wind energy tomorrow because there is more future in geothermal energy. Currently, investments in geothermal energy are exceedingly limited, though strategically they are rock-solid. The government seems more interested in politics. There's no sense of urgency – after all, *we're doing just fine*. Fugro should avoid becoming this complacent. A large company can't change tack too radically. Consolidating is sensible, but I'm simply more future-oriented. We also have to make money tomorrow and the day after that. If you ask me, we need creative thinkers who can come up with ways to go about it.'

Investing in people

'*The Fugro Academy* supports us with training and offers a wide range of opportunities, but it should also reflect our long-term strategy. It's an excellent initiative, but we have to realise that *the Academy* not only trains our own employees but also the entire industry's. Our technological courses are top-notch but if participants quit soon afterwards, we must be doing something wrong. How do we make our new employees feel that they should stay with Fugro for thirty years? How do we hang on to them? Obviously, by investing in them and offering them flexibility. People want to get the feeling that their jobs suit their lifestyles. This requires a Human

2009

Regrouping
for further growth
–

Fugro's management did some reshuffling in the Survey and Geoscience divisions. The ROV operations (by now with a fleet of 125 ROVs) passed from Offshore Survey to the new business line, Subsea Services. All GPS activities, before then shared by Offshore Survey and Geospatial Services, were assembled in a single Positioning Group within Offshore Survey.
From now on, the Geoscience division would consist of Seismic Services, General Geophysical Services and Information Services. The Development & Production business line was split into Seismic Services (data acquisition and processing) and Information Services (data management, reservoir modelling and geological consultancy).
Airborne Survey continued life as General Geophysical Services. This business line specialised in exploration and research activities in the mining and now increasingly in the oil and gas industries.

>

Resources policy that takes employees' life stages into account, for instance by lightening their workload during the period they have young children. Such a policy is part of corporate social responsibility. That's the way to retain staff and save money, because you don't need to attract and train new people all the time. Training is fun and useful, but the more competent and dedicated people there are on the staff, the less training is needed.

'Let's keep our eyes fixed firmly on the future. Anyone who has money can build fine new ships – we don't stand out there. People and innovative products make the difference, and so you have to keep up to date with new technological developments. Follow Google, Apple, Facebook and other internet companies. Let's embed their technology in our activities and think further along these lines. What's the use of in-house development of brilliant new software which you intend to depreciate in fifteen years if nobody uses a desktop PC in five years' time? Will PCs still be needed at all by then? And if so, what will they look like? We should attract the smartest brains in the IT industry and hold on to them. They should be beating on Fugro's doors for work placement and to do their finals with us, and we should make them feel that we enjoy supervising them and maybe even want to offer them a job.'

Collaboration

'There are also external incentives. The oil and gas industry asks us specific questions. They want to know, for instance, how, in five years' time, we will carry out surveys and inspections under the Arctic ice. We don't have to do it on our own. To stay a front runner, Fugro should engage in joint

2009

> The Geotechnical division acquired a high end provider of static pile load testing services. Survey expanded with acquisitions in pipeline inspection, simulation and visualisation software, subsea engineering and airborne hydrographic services. The Geoscience division welcomed on board companies specialised in data management and storage as well as electromagnetic data management. The multipurpose vessel *Fugro Synergy* commenced service and Fugro introduced Smart Pipe and *Smart Surf,* two tools used for the design of pipelines in deep water. Exemplary of Fugro's involvement in large projects in new regions was the contract for investigations and consultancy work for the new *Izmit Bay Bridge* in Turkey.
The changes in market circumstances brought on by the worldwide financial crisis occasioned a slight drop in revenue, although all divisions continued to make a profit.
—
And Barack Obama was the first candidate to conduct a large part of his election campaign online, and with success; *Yes we can!* – the slogan of the first African American US president – was inspirational and gave the US and her allies new hope.

◄
Fugro's data processing centre, Mumbai, India

research projects with universities and research institutes, and organise these partnerships centrally. That requires a large financial commitment and accepting that it doesn't produce immediate returns. Competing at a high level costs money. You have to dare to tell shareholders: "Dividends will be lower this time, since we still want to be a leading company in ten years' time." By then, our competitors will perform work the way we are executing now, but that technology won't mean much to us anymore as it won't make us a front runner.

'Fundamental choices cost money. Where can we grow and expand? In my opinion, we should no longer acquire companies that are doing what Fugro itself is already doing, unless these companies operate in geographic regions that are new to us. For us, it is not about economies of scale or our market share. We should focus on identifying companies that have been through interesting technological developments and invented things that no one else has. If we manage to integrate that type of company in the bigger picture of Fugro, we can become even more competitive than we already are.'

Fugro is building the world

'Microsoft is still making $ 2 billion a year from its obsolete *Microsoft Office* software. A new product has probably been lying on the shelf for ages, but they don't dare changing anything for fear of killing their money-spinner. Shell, on the other hand, acquires companies that are involved in alternative energy, in order to keep a better handle on how soon Shell will leave the traditional oil and gas business and switch to new sources of energy. Microsoft and Shell thus acquire control over the pace of technological developments. Fugro can learn something from these companies, in order to still be a front runner in 2027. Follow what is happening, lead the way and collaborate. Nobody knows how the survey division will operate in 2027, but we can now put creative thinkers together to exchange ideas about it. We should now formulate a strategy based on the vision that Fugro will help determine how the world will look in 2027. If we want to live in a world we like, we should help build that world.'

2027

TRANSITION FROM FOSSIL TO RENEWABLE ENERGY

JOHN LAZARUS
GEOSPATIAL SOLUTIONS, AUSTRALIA

Fifteen years is a very short period in relation to geological and climate history. Therefore government policy and fossil fuel costs will have the greatest impact on the rate of transition to renewable energy. As fossil fuel prices go up renewable energy will become more competitive. In addition other fossil fuel sources (tar sands, coal seam gas, shale gas) that are currently uneconomic will be further developed.

Renewable energy sources that impact on the social environment (wind and possibly wave) will be subject to increasing public pressure to be sighted in *out of the way* locations. This will mean they will generally be sighted in locations where there is minimal social infrastructure.

Solar generated power is the most expensive to install and until there is a breakthrough in manufacturing technology it will remain dependant on government subsidies to be viable. Its advantage is that it can be connected to domestic grids very cheaply and generates power where its required.

Wave power has the greatest potential for growth but will require significant investment in the technology and needs suitable sites on the coast. It does have the advantage of being invisible.

In 2027 wind power will remain the dominant renewable energy source on a global basis.

THE CONTINENT OF THE FUTURE

—
—
—

In the early 80's with the fall of *the Iron Curtain,* democracy began to show its ability to engineer sustainable development in most states that had been bold enough to dismantle military rule.

The result of social changes

Today several African countries are breaking the wall of false development into meaningful, sustainable developments such as the indigenization of resource exploration and exploration in many West Africa states, which is the regional operation area of Fugro Nigeria Limited. More oil and gas has been discovered in Nigeria, in offshore areas, Equatorial Guinea, Ghana, Liberia, and the Ivory Coast and more recently in the Republic of Benin. Similarly with the assistance of the World Bank, several West African states have been able to develop a strong and reliable databank of solid minerals available in their countries using the most modern airborne radiometric and electromagnetic geophysical methods. In addition to resource inventory, most of these states have developed human capital and capacity in modern technology and now have access to information technology.

These discoveries and improvements have formed the foundation for the increasing standard of living and access to the benefits of modern technology and social changes in the West African states. These emerging social changes have resulted in strong demand for constant electricity from all forms of energy resource and, thus, have generated into a strong need for supporting infrastructure for the regional development of West African states.

One-door entrance into West-Africa

Fugro Nigeria is the focal point of Fugro Services in West Africa. Today Fugro Nigeria offers only five of the forty-eight and above business lines within Fugro world-wide, while services are rendered to clients in West Africa on a need basis only. Consequently, Fugro Nigeria through its consolidation of existing services has developed a five year plan that will

At the turn of the last century Africa began to experience the transition from a colonial geo-political system and economy to a partial political and socioeconomic Independence. The agitation of several African states for political independence turned out to be simply a struggle for self-rule and not economic emancipation. Thus several of these states continued to depend on their colonial masters for political advice, products, goods and services as well as, their input into strategies for industrial and technological development. However, following the spread of military rule in many of the African states, the need for economic and social development began, but most of these projects turned out to be mostly white elephant projects that added little value to the wellbeing of Africa. **Goodwill C. Ofunne,** managing director of Fugro Nigeria, expresses his thoughts about Africa's future.

2027

NEW GEOGRAPHIC AREAS

ROD PULLIN
**FUGRO AIRBORNE SURVEYS,
AUSTRALIA**

As we move towards 2027 I believe
the technologies offered by Fugro will
become well utilised within China.
This vast landmass has enormous
potential for the services offered by
Fugro and with its technology hungry
population is ideally placed to become
a major contributor to Fugro's future
activities.

change its focus from simply being an onshore geotechnical/offshore survey data collection company to a contemporary technology based geosciences/ engineering company offering solutions to client problems in West Africa and ultimately Africa. To do this, Fugro Nigeria has established an international office in Abuja, Nigeria to encourage a one-door entrance into West Africa and cross divisional marketing for other Fugro business lines. Consequently, our vision for Fugro Nigeria in 2027 is that of a company that will embrace several Fugro business lines, Fugro technologies and expertise; in addition, to offer a cross divisional and integrated solutions and technologies for the development of Africa and its numerous resources. We also foresee a multicultural Fugro personnel profile working in West Africa and stronger geopolitical democracy in West Africa with good security and a safety culture.

Closing the gap

In 2027, Fugro Nigeria foresees a strong *Economic Community of West African States* (ECOWAS) that will liberalize trade among West African states. Perhaps, there will also be a common currency in West Africa. The apparent gap in resources and infrastructure in West Africa may begin to close. Fugro Nigeria foresees that in 2027, there will be a great need for Fugro data collection and interpretation services in the area of geospatial, geotechnical engineering, construction material testing and environmental management. With the growing influence of clean gas and hydrocarbon, the slate in oil and gas production will change in West Africa. Crude oil will become the complimentary product to gas and this will require gas collection, transportation and storage infrastructure. In 2027 Fugro will

2010

Standing firm in troubled times

—

—

Signs of improving economic circumstances were reflected as the demand for energy begins to rise again, particularly in East Asia, but most markets were still feeling the squeeze, although even there positive changes were beginning to make themselves felt. Fugro's risks were well distributed but the group was not immune to these global developments. In the segments marked by overcapacity, such as offshore seismic and construction support activities, Fugro had to be satisfied with lower profit margins. The acquisitions were less in evidence than usual. Fugro placed orders for the construction of two ships for carrying out geotechnical work in deep water, and three survey vessels. One of these three, the *Fugro Searcher,* commenced service and with the delivery of the *Geo Caspian* and *Geo Coral* and the acquisition of the *Geo Celtic,* the expansion of Fugro's seismic fleet was completed.

In 2010 the oil and gas market was still the mainstay for the success of Fugro's offshore geotechnical operations. Developments in deep water were on the increase; in 2010 Fugro conducted deep water projects in all the major oil and gas locations. Competition in the wind farm sector increased too, but the greater volume of work leading to better utilisation largely compensated for the lower profit margins.

By now Fugro's seismic fleet consisted of nine 3D seismic vessels (four of which it owned),

 >

> one 2D seismic vessel and ten support ships. A *Partnership for Growth* programme was launched to add structure and consistency to the existing relationship between Fugro and its employees, particularly for the further development of their careers.

—

And towards the end of the year the *Arab Spring* burst into full flower in North Africa; thousands of those who had been oppressed for decades encouraged each other and themselves by mobile phone, closed ranks, sent pictures to the world at large and achieved what had hitherto been regarded as unachievable: dictatorial regimes shook and toppled like dominoes.

then be well positioned to help West Africa develop in this area. Other areas of growth will be in the mining sector, where the *Fugro Geoportal System* will be the main marketing instrument for geophysical mining data in West Africa. Similarly Fugro Water Services will find a strong role in water resource management, sustainable drinking water development in the arid areas of West Africa. In addition, the Dutch longtime experience in water and flood defense will assist many coastal West African states manage flooding that may result in sea rise and climate change. Therefore, we foresee Fugro Nigeria playing a greater role in water research and water resource development in West Africa.

Above all, we see an expanded Fugro presence in Nigeria, Equatorial Guinea, Ghana, Liberia and the Ivory Coast as well as, in the Niger Republic and indeed the entire West Africa. Africa is the continent of the future, and Fugro is well in position to be a front runner in the field of geosciences and data management in 2027.

2027

TRANSITION FROM FOSSIL TO RENEWABLE ENERGY

JOHN TEN HOOPE
FUGRO MIDDLE EAST, UAE

The political climate and will to make the required investments into renewable energy will be below par as a result of the economic crisis. The effects of the double dip of 2011/2012 will stretch to a couple of years beyond 2012 and will negatively effect the investment into research, new technologies and new projects. Fossil energy will get more expensive but will still be much cheaper and more reliable than the renewables.

▲
Niger Delta, Nigeria

HOW OLD WILL YOU BE IN 2027?

—
—
—

Casper ter Kuile, *Global Shaper* of the World Economic Forum, works and lives in London. He is Co-Founder of the UK Youth Climate Coalition. His invitation is the final chapter of *Earth Unlimited.*

It's often said we overestimate what we can achieve in a day and underestimate what we can do in a year. Needless to say, we can expect a lot to change over the next fifteen years.

Nelson Mandela once reflected on overcoming apartheid in South Africa, saying that, *it always seems impossible until it is done.* This is how young people around the world look at the challenge of sustainability – we understand the size of the task, and we know we are capable of achieving it.

In my role as a youth organiser, I look to the future with a twinned sense of fear and hope. Fear, because I have seen firsthand the impact of our warming climate – notably in the Arctic. As I travelled with a Russian crew to the top of the world a few years ago, they explained how their boat had never reached so far north, that the ice had never been so absent. Fear, also, because I understand that a melting Arctic makes oil and gas reserves there ever more tempting with dangerous consequences for local ecosystems, and more broadly, our stable climate.

Yet there is also great hope. Everywhere I turn I see people changing things for the better. Young people are welcoming in a new era of energy efficiency and renewable power. In India, youth are developing tools to manage solar power distribution through mobile technology. In low-income communities in the United States, young people are retrofitting homes for the elderly to save carbon and money. In Malawi, William Kamkwamba famously built a windmill to power his village energy needs using just bamboo poles and bicycle chains and is inspiring countless others to follow suit. Across the world, my entrepreneurial peers are empowering their neighbours through community-owned microgeneration.

Even the tech company that most defines my social life – Facebook – announced last year that it will move away from polluting coal power and

William Kamkwamba

2011

Records

—
—

Global economic recovery stagnated, but the oil price remained high: Brent oil fetched in excess of 100 dollars per barrel. The *Arab Spring* continued with the revolution and handover of power in Libya. In Japan, a tsunami flooded a nuclear power plant. This led to worldwide reconsideration of the use of nuclear energy; Germany decided to quit altogether and phase out all its nuclear plants. Governments in the US and Europe saw their budget deficits increase further and were forced to announce major cutbacks. The Euro's very survival was threatened by Greece's impending bankruptcy.

Amidst all these turbulent events, Fugro managed to achieve a growth in revenues to a record high of almost € 2.6 billion and the net result also reached a new high: € 288 million. In addition to organic growth, revenues also grew because of an active acquisition policy. Nine acquisitions were completed for a total purchase price of € 219 million, the most important of which were TSMarine (Australia), De Regt Marine Cables (Netherlands) and OBN (Ocean Bottom Nodes, Norway).

All three divisions achieved a positive result, although some activities including marine seismic surveys and support services for offshore installation jobs had a difficult time of it. In May, Frank Schreve stepped down as Chairman of the Supervisory Board after serving it for 23 years. Following the untimely death of his successor, Herman Scheffer, Schreve resumed his chairman's duties

>

run it's enormous computing capacity fully on clean, renewable energy. Large consumer product companies like Unilever are setting targets to decouple growth from environmental impact. Wherever I look, I find innovators and established-players searching for solutions and boldly leading their sectors towards a safer and cleaner energy future.

It is becoming clear to me that we are in a time of great transition – fundamental truths are looking less certain, tried and tested solutions seem only to bring us more complexity. This is the time to ask the big questions of ourselves, and of our work. We have the opportunity, today, to re-imagine how we want to live.

Within this great transformation, our energy system cries out for change.

IDAR HORSTAD C.S.
FUGRO MULTI CLIENT
SERVICES, NORWAY

We will have a geographical organisation with an ability to move our resources quickly from region to region based on client needs. Our project based organisation, covering all divisions and products will be very attractive and we will prioritize regions and markets with the highest return and low political risk.

Indeed, the shift from fossil fuels to renewables is already well under way. In 2011, for the first time, investments in clean energy plants were ahead of those in oil, coal and gas. The author William Gibson once remarked, *The future is already here – it just isn't equally distributed yet*. He may have been talking about jet packs and space exploration, but the idea applies to how we power our society just as beautifully.

This shift represents not only the hope that new models of powering our society are possible, but is also a clarion call to government, industry and others who can make a difference in building the foundation upon which people the world over will be safely able to work towards a better future.

Let inventors and engineers innovate their way to a solution, even if at first failure seems a constant stumbling block. We need the relentless conviction, creativity and social engagement of companies like Fugro in order to achieve that breakthrough success. From what I know about Fugro's story, there is no shying away when confronted with a difficult task.

This is not just about the transfer of technology, or the tranisition to a clean energy economy; it's about organisations showing leadership by helping to bring out the very best in people – so that everyone can contribute to the best of their ability. Let us keep dreaming beyond what we today think is impossible, and let us surprise each other with what we're capable of. We need each other's help and support if we're to reach this goal. I invite you to join me in the building of a world in which all of us can thrive.

Let the ingenuity and persistance of William Kamkwamba be an inspiration to us all. The simple windmill that he put together with pieces of left-over material stands in contrast to the high-tech apparatus with which Fugro's specialists work the world over. How beautiful it would be if, at Fugro's 65th birthday in 2027, we can say that we've overcome this gaping void. And if we can do it before then, that's fine too.

In 2027? I'll be 40 years young.

2011

>

late in the year at the Supervisory Board's request. Because of Klaas Wester's upcoming retirement, it was decided to appoint Arnold Steenbakker as Chairman of the Board of Management as of 1 January 2012.
To support further growth, the organisational structure of three divisions was to be strengthened, with decisions made on a more collective basis by the Board of Management. Business prospects were improving and preparations for the 50th anniversary celebrations with the theme *Earth Unlimited, 50 years Fugro – what's next?* were in full swing.
—

And Europe was doing its utmost to maintain its unity and collectively drive away the dark clouds that were casting a shadow, however temporary, over Greece and other generally sunny countries.

◀

Sand dunes in the Algerian desert

EARTH UNLIMITED

———

REGISTERS

OVERVIEW OF ACQUISITIONS
AFTER THE MERGER BETWEEN FUGRO AND MCCLELLAND IN 1987

COMPANY	YEAR	COUNTRY	ANNUAL REVENUE	EMPLOYEES
GEOTECHNICAL / INVESTMENTS				
McClelland Management Services, Inc. (50% and remaining 50% in 1991)	1987	USA	4	96
Oserco BV	1990	NL	1	1
MateriaLab Ltd.	1991	HK	5	223
Umwelt- und Wirtshaftsgeologie mbH (UWG)	1992	GER	4	125
Geotechical Instruments Hong Kong Ltd.	1992	HK	1	26
Ecolyse Nederland BV and Ecodemka BV	1992	NL	2	46
IEP Inc.	1992	USA	6	74
Staal, Gardner & Dunne Inc.	1992	USA	6	36
BSN Bodemsanering Nederland BV (50%)	1993	NL	5	21
Aegis Environmental Inc.	1994	USA	3	38
Hoogovens Technical Services Ecoplan BV and M & O BV	1994	NL	3	25
Studiebureau VFD N.V. (25% and remaining 1997/1998)	1994	BEL	4	31
Fugro Geologic BV	1995	NL	1	18
Ubac, G&P Leipzig, G&P Cottbus GMBH	1995	GER	1	24
Prodec Fugro Ltd. (50%)	1996	NIG	1	20
Alluvial Mining Ltd.	1996	UK	3	28
Instituut Geotechiek Nederland BV	1997	NL	6	70
Brent Rauhut Engineering Inc.	1997	USA	3	37
Terraform Ltd. (50%)	1998	HK	3	32
Sarg Enterprise S.A. and SEERS Foralo S.A.	1998	FRA	4	24
Gulf Coast Testing Laboratory, Inc.	1998	USA	1	20
Sicsol SA	1999	FRA	3	28
Sores SA	1999	FRA	7	82
Sol Essais SA	1999	FRA	2	13
Infrasol	1999	FRA	1	20
Foundation Engineering Ltd., Middle East branch	2000	UAE	4	140
Crystal Drilling NV	2000	BEL	1	10
Via NDT Inc.	2000	USA	2	15
Marsco Inc.	2001	USA	4	15
Surbsurface Consultants Inc.	2001	USA	5	32
Maxim Technologies Inc.	2001	USA	1	15
Harza Engineering Corp.	2002	USA	4	39
Part of Subsea 7 (Assets and business)	2002	NOR	20	2
Foundation Exploration Services Ltd.	2003	UK	15	111
Comprehensive Geotechnical Investigation (Zhejiang) Co. Ltd.	2005	CHN	1	62
Espana Geotechnical Consulting Inc.	2005	USA	2	20
ECOS Umwelt GmbH	2006	GER	1	8
Surrey Geotechnical Consultants Ltd.	2006	UK	1	3
Seacore Ltd.	2006	UK	35	160
Aperio Ltd.	2006	UK	3	35

(AMOUNTS x EUR 1 MLN.)

COMPANY	YEAR	COUNTRY	ANNUAL REVENUE	EMPLOYEES
LGU GmbH	2007	GER	1	12
GECO Umwelttechnik GmbH	2007	AUT	1	15
Sobesol SAS	2007	FRA	8	70
William Lettis & Associates, Inc.	2008	USA	10	75
HGN Hydrogeologie GmbH	2008	GER	8	120
Pavement Management Services Pty Ltd.	2008	AUS	4	40
Roadware Group Inc.	2008	CAN	9	130
In Situ Geotecnia Ltda.	2008	BRA	4	100
Risk Engineering, Inc.	2008	USA	2	5
GEO LLC	2008	USA	7	14
LoadTest group of companies	2009	USA	14	40
Statnamic Kft and Geo Pannon Kft	2010	HUN	3	18
ERT Scotland Ltd.	2010	UK	3	25
Bluestone Offshore Pte Ltd.	2011	SIN	14	40
Sial Geosciences Consulting and Engineering	2011	TUR	2	21
AOA Geophysics Inc.	2011	USA	2	14
Geo-log	2011	GER	2	20

GEOTECHNICAL / DIVESTMENTS

COMPANY	YEAR	COUNTRY	ANNUAL REVENUE	EMPLOYEES
Environmental activities	1997	UK/USA		
Fugro Milieu Laboratorium B.V.	1999	NL		
Stability Department VFD Fugro N.V.	2001	BEL		
Environmental activities	2002	NL		
Crystal Drilling N.V.	2003	BEL		
BSN Bodemsanering Nederland BV (50%)	2004	NL		
Geotechnical business of Fugro Japan Co. Ltd.	2007	JPN		
Fugro België NV	2007	BEL		
Geotechnical business in south of France	2011	FRA		

SURVEY / INVESTMENTS

COMPANY	YEAR	COUNTRY	ANNUAL REVENUE	EMPLOYEES
Oretech BV	1990	NL	8	37
John E. Chance & Associates, Inc.	1991	USA	29	400
Ocean Sciences International Pte Ltd.	1991	SIN	6	16
Associated Survey Int. Pty Ltd.	1991	AUS	8	93
Inpark BV	1992	NL	4	349
Surveying activities Marconi – UDI	1993	UK	12	101
Oceansismica S.p.A.	1994	ITA	1	12
K-C Geotechnical Associates Inc. (West coast division)	1994	USA	1	12
Fugro Geoteam AS	1994	NOR	27	200
Wimpol Ltd.	1994	UK/USA	25	200
Geodetic & Construction Surveys Ltd.	1994	SWI	15	140
Geos New Zealand	1994	NZL	-	2
Elbocon BV	1994	NL	1	4

COMPANY	YEAR	COUNTRY	ANNUAL REVENUE	EMPLOYEES
International Subsea Mapping SA	1995	FRA	7	32
Geos Ltd.	1995	NZL	6	51
Surveying and positioning activities Oceonics Group Plc	1997	UK	8	79
Oceaneering International Inc., Survey division	1997	USA	3	6
GeoMetius BV and Commetius BV	1997	NL	1	6
Paras Ltd.	1998	UK	2	11
Underwater Surveys Pty Ltd.	1998	SAF	2	10
Marine Weather Services Pte Ltd.	1998	SIN	1	6
Part of Van Mourik BV	1998	NL	-	2
Sesl Geomatics Ltd.	1998	CAN	5	85
Photec Air Surveys Pty Ltd.	1998	AUS	1	2
Clarke Land Surveys Inc.	2000	CAN	1	7
Geoid SA	2001	FRA	4	30
Exploration Mining Consultants Pty Ltd.	2001	AUS	1	10
Galileo Geophysical Inc.	2001	USA	1	3
Osiris BV	2001	NL	10	67
Nortech Geomatics	2002	Oman	2	35
Installocean Ltd.	2002	UK	1	6
Noble Denton Ltd.	2002	UK	1	5
Oceanor Holdings ASA	2003	NOR	9	56
Svitzer	2003	UK/DK	20	110
Thales GeoSolutions	2003	UK	210	1,686
BTW Hydrographic Ltd.	2005	NZL	2	9
Elcome Surveys Pvt. Ltd.	2005	IND	5	69
Fugro-OceansatPEG (62% in 2005, 38% in 2008)	2005	BRA	20	250
Rovtech Ltd.	2006	UK	35	120
OSAE Survey and Engineering Gesellshaft für Seevermessung m.b.H.	2006	GER	8	40
Improv Ltd.	2007	UK	9	30
Earthdata Inc.	2007	USA	40	340
MAPS Geosystems	2007	UAE/LBN	12	200
BKS Surveys Ltd.	2008	UK	6	100
SureSpek ISS Pty Ltd.	2008	AUS	3	16
VIB Weinhold	2009	GER	3	26
Tenix LADS	2009	AUS	13	60
General Robotics Limited	2009	UK	1	12
Submec Pty Ltd.	2009	AUS	1	10
Interra SA and Terralaser SA	2010	CHILI/ PERU	3	45
Riise Underwater Engineering AS	2010	NOR	35	25
TSmarine Group Holdings Pty Ltd.	2011	AUS	90	170
EMU Limited	2012	UK	20	150

SURVEY / DIVESTMENTS

COMPANY	YEAR	COUNTRY		
Equipment Department UDI	1999	UK		
ROV activities Thales GeoSolutions	2004	USA/ MEX/ CAN		
GeoMetius BV	2004	NL		
Diving activity Thales GeoSolutions	2005	MEX		

COMPANY	YEAR	COUNTRY	ANNUAL REVENUE	EMPLOYEES
GEOSCIENCE / INVESTMENTS				
Lafehr Chan Technologies Inc.	1998	USA/UK	10	75
World Geoscience Corporation Pty Ltd.	1999	AUS	16	200
Geoterrex-Dighem Ltd. and High Sense Geophysics Ltd.	1999	CAN	30	222
Seismic Australia Pty Ltd.	2000	AUS	2	7
Geodass (Pty) Ltd.	2000	RSA	6	40
Geologic Consulting Services BV	2001	NL	1	14
Robertson Research International Ltd.	2001	UK	46	500
Jason Information Systems BV	2001	NL	16	90
Sial Geosciences Inc.	2001	CAN	4	35
Spectra Exploration Geosciences Corp.	2001	CAN	2	6
Kevron Pty Ltd.	2001	AUS	9	70
Tesla 10 Pty Ltd.	2001	AUS	5	50
Airesearch Mapping Pty Ltd.	2001	AUS	5	60
Lacoste Romberg - Scintrex, Inc. (10%)	2001	CAN	3	25
Petcom Inc.	2003	USA	1	8
Volumetrix Ltd.	2003	UK	1	5
Seiscan Ltd.	2003	UK	1	6
C&M Storage Inc.	2004	USA	2	18
Beardall, Parry and Associates Ltd.	2005	UK	1	3
Trango Technologies Inc.	2006	CAN	1	14
ProFocus Systems AS	2007	NOR	1	3
Kestrel Data (Canada) Ltd (business and assets)	2007	CAN	4	65
4th Wave Imaging Corp.	2007	USA	1	4
Electro Magnetic Marine Exploration Technologies (60%)	2008	RUS	-	43
Nigel Press Associates Ltd.	2008	UK	3	30
NexTerra Geophysical Solutions Pvt. Ltd.	2008	IND	1	12
Phoenix Data Solutions Ltd.	2008	UK	3	6
GeoLab Nor AS	2008	NOR	2	15
Allied Seismic Ltd.	2008	CAN	3	22
Divestco Inc.	2009	CAN	2	12
Interaction AS	2009	NOR	1	8
De Regt Marine Cables BV	2011	NL	25	110
Kelman Technologies Inc (seismic processing business)	2011	CAN	8	40
Ocean Bottom Nodes activity of Seabird Exploration PLC	2011	NOR	70	25
GEOSCIENCE / DIVESTMENTS				
Laboratories in Wales (Fugro Robertson Ltd)	2005	UK		

RESULTS 1962-2011

	2011	2010	2009	2008	2007	2006
INCOME AND EXPENSES (€ x 1.000)						
Revenue	2.577.765	2.280.391	2.052.988	2.154.474	1.802.730	1.434.319
Third party costs	994.037	765.587	624.413	722.321	604.855	503.096
Net revenue own services (revenue less third party costs)	1.583.728	1.514.804	1.428.575	1.432.153	1.197.875	931.223
Results from operating activities (EBIT)	349.330	351.479	367.422	385.732	324.813	211.567
Cash flow	526.928	489.757	456.773	438.902	337.106	226.130
Net result	287.595	272.219	263.410	283.412	216.213	141.011
BALANCE SHEET (€ x 1.000)						
Property, plant and equipment	1.482.981	1.291.314	1.043.227	859.088	599.298	412.232
Investments	446.716	446.755	330.244	337.469	299.699	203.944
Depreciation of property, plant and equipment	220.984	201.493	173.593	140.429	107.684	78.169
Total assets	3.861.595	3.089.991	2.366.317	2.123.306	1.700.130	1.405.698
Loans and borrowings	1.215.173	590.862	441.339	395.384	449.957	341.997
Equity attributable to owners of the company	1.655.785	1.508.318	1.187.731	928.329	699.989	562.417
KEY RATIOS (in %)						
Results from operating activities (EBIT)/revenue	13,6	15,4	17,9	17,9	18,0	14,8
Profit/revenue	11,2	11,9	12,8	13,2	12,0	9,8
Profit/net revenue own services	18,2	18,0	18,4	19,8	18,0	15,1
Total equity/total assets	43,4	49,3	50,7	44,1	41,6	40,2
DATA PER SHARE (€ x 1,-)						
Equity attributable to owners of the company	20,34	18,79	15,08	12,12	9,94	8,08
Results from operating activities (EBIT)	4,41	4,49	4,82	5,29	4,67	3,08
Cash flow	6,65	6,25	5,99	6,01	4,84	3,29
Net result	3,63	3,47	3,46	3,88	3,11	2,05
Dividend paid in year under review	1,50	1,50	1,50	1,25	0,83	0,60
SHARE PRICE (€ x 1,-)						
Year-end share price	44,895	61,50	40,26	20,485	52,80	36,20
Highest share price	63,53	62,06	41,85	59,95	62,00	36,64
Lowest share price	34,47	37,095	19,085	19,32	34,91	27,13
NUMBER OF EMPLOYEES						
At year-end	13.876	13.463	13.482	13.627	11.472	9.837
SHARES IN ISSUE						
Of nominal € 0,05 at year-end	81.392.981	80.269.684	78.772.478	76.607.958	70.421.443	69.582.201
Of nominal € 0,20 at year-end						
Of nominal NLG 1 at year-end						
Of nominal NLG 10 at year-end						
Of nominal NLG 100 at year-end						

As a result of the share split (4:1) in 2005, the historical figures have been restated

2005	2004	2003	2002	2001	2000	1999	1998	1997	1996	1995
1.160.615	1.008.008	822.372	945.899	909.817	712.934	546.760	578.207	482.096	375.276	296.636
405.701	364.644	273.372	328.401	331.685	250.124	176.067	197.258	172.346	123.337	99.378
754.914	643.364	549.000	617.498	578.132	462.765	370.648	380.948	309.750	251.939	197.258
144.070	104.236	63.272	111.873	98.470	73.694	61.805	61.669	46.195	25.911	12.434
176.093	125.802	80.480	119.161	105.301	85.583	77.233	74.057	60.670	39.479	26.773
99.412	49.317	18.872	72.220	61.732	46.013	40.704	37.800	31.084	16.018	7.170
262.759	232.956	268.801	192.293	163.298	120.524	114.035	108.181	93.479	68.521	64.800
90.414	71.028	123.983	100.036	89.352	49.008	37.301	61.487	58.220	27.000	24.776
69.445	66.139	54.004	46.941	43.569	39.570	36.529	36.257	29.586	23.460	19.603
1.138.660	983.350	1.056.003	793.245	814.772	474.745	380.495	338.021	289.512	216.272	170.122
300.753	184.268	431.895	273.520	121.450	120.706	23.234	24.368	17.153	18.741	23.823
465.460	223.913	211.196	271.698	244.660	101.465	107.909	90.575	77.370	61.260	51.050
12,9	10,3	9,2	11,8	10,8	10,3	11,3	10,7	9,6	6,9	4,2
8,6	4,9	2,3	7,6	6,8	6,5	7,4	6,5	6,4	4,3	2,4
13,2	7,7	8,3	11,7	10,7	9,9	11,0	9,9	10,0	6,4	3,6
41,3	23,2	20,2	34,6	30,4	22,1	29,3	27,9	27,7	28,9	30,4
6,76	3,60	3,48	4,57	4,17	2,10	2,29	1,91	1,65	1,36	1,11
2,18	1,76	1,09	1,95	1,86	1,48	1,27	1,30	0,98	0,58	0,27
2,67	2,12	1,39	2,08	1,98	1,72	1,59	1,56	1,29	0,88	0,58
1,51	0,83	0,33	1,26	1,16	0,92	0,84	0,80	0,66	0,36	0,16
0,48	0,48	0,46	0,46	0,40	0,34	0,31	0,28	0,25	0,17	0,08
27,13	15,35	10,20	10,78	12,53	17,19	9,23	4,99	7,01	3,48	1,96
27,40	16,41	12,86	16,50	18,91	17,81	9,98	10,99	8,28	3,71	4,14
15,14	10,05	6,13	9,88	10,75	9,31	4,10	4,06	3,44	1,93	1,45
8.534	7.615	8.472	6.923	6.953	5.756	5.114	5.136	4.429	4.222	3.968
17.206.250	15.548.000	15.165.912	14.862.214	14.669.830	12.761.999	12.612.351				
							12.170.396	11.918.135	11.513.289	11.510.900

RESULTS 1962-2011

	1994	1993	1992	1991	1990	1989
INCOME AND EXPENSES (€ x 1.000)						
Revenue	300.130	221.490	178.926	140.808	107.637	80.591
Third party costs	100.104	65.344	52.412	41.249	42.338	27.091
Net revenue own services (revenue less third party costs)	200.026	156.146	126.514	99.559	65.299	53.501
Results from operating activities (EBIT)	21.146	18.015	13.568	15.746	7.941	6.625
Cash flow	33.625	26.728	20.465	19.467	10.165	8.077
Net result	13.931	12.388	8.849	11.526	5.491	4.629
BALANCE SHEET (€ x 1.000)						
Property, plant and equipment	65.254	55.497	48.055	48.237	21.010	15.202
Investments	39.434	25.639	14.294	36.212	10.664	4.765
Depreciation of property, plant and equipment	19.694	14.339	11.617	7.941	4.674	3.449
Total assets	176.702	141.579	121.522	104.143	55.996	45.287
Loans and borrowings	30.449	7.260	6.671	33.217	5.218	5.400
Equity attributable to owners of the company	58.402	62.168	56.586	35.803	15.973	13.432
KEY RATIOS (in %)						
Results from operating activities (EBIT)/revenue	7,0	8,1	7,6	11,2	7,4	8,2
Profit/revenue	4,6	5,6	4,9	8,2	5,1	5,7
Profit/net revenue own services	7,0	7,9	7,0	11,6	8,4	8,7
Total equity/total assets	33,8	44,7	47,0	34,7	30,0	31,3
DATA PER SHARE (€ x 1,-)						
Equity attributable to owners of the company	1,39	1,71	1,64	1,74	0,91	0,78
Results from operating activities (EBIT)	0,50	0,50	0,39	0,77	0,45	0,39
Cash flow	0,80	0,74	0,59	0,95	0,58	0,47
Net result	0,33	0,34	0,26	0,56	0,31	0,27
Dividend paid in year under review	0,17	0,17	0,15	0,17	0,11	0,09
SHARE PRICE (€ x 1,-)						
Year-end share price	3,88	4,17	2,94	-	-	-
Highest share price	4,75	4,46	4,48	-	-	-
Lowest share price	3,69	2,64	2,44	-	-	-
NUMBER OF EMPLOYEES						
At year-end	3.557	2.824	2.664	2.029	1.275	1.105
SHARES IN ISSUE						
Of nominal € 0,05 at year-end						
Of nominal € 0,20 at year-end						
Of nominal NLG 1 at year-end	11.509.900	9.092.400	9.086.400			
Of nominal NLG 10 at year-end				716.201	441.026	427.510
Of nominal NLG 100 at year-end						

1988	1987	1986	1985	1984	1983	1982	1981	1980	1979	1978
77.007	65.798	35.440	45.786	49.644	39.396	35.821	38.156	38.594	35.398	29.641
28.997	20.057	12.207	16.518	22.507	12.673	10.171	11.409	11.946	8.229	5.308
48.010	45.741	23.234	29.269	27.136	26.723	25.650	26.747	26.648	27.169	24.333
3.630	1.588	(2.950)	1.225	2.314	1.781	(537)	1.068	3.727	1.845	997
5.445	4.220	(45)	5.082	3.766	1.462	459	1.388	5.428	2.427	2.475
2.087	272	(2.995)	2.087	1.588	(477)	(1.704)	(1.078)	3.317	16	(48)
14.929	10.482	10.664	8.486	5.627	5.119	5.405	7.046	6.826	6.082	5.877
6.262	1.860	5.128	6.171	2.768	-	2.257	3.119	-	-	-
3.358	3.948	2.950	2.995	2.178	1.939	2.163	2.466	2.111	2.411	2.523
43.336	35.168	22.916	28.089	27.862	23.340	19.923	21.523	20.081	19.800	16.843
6.489	3.358	3.585	2.904	2.314	2.628	2.884	2.845	2.471	2.793	3.005
10.936	9.711	4.629	7.714	4.810	3.192	3.669	5.374	6.451	3.195	3.221
4,7	2,4	(8,3)	2,7	4,7	4,5	(1,5)	2,8	9,7	5,2	3,4
2,7	0,4	(8,4)	4,5	3,2	(1,2)	(4,8)	(2,8)	8,6	0,0	(0,2)
4,3	0,6	(12,9)	7,1	5,9	(1,8)	(6,6)	(4,0)	12,4	0,1	(0,2)
27,9	30,2	20,2	24,4	17,3	13,7	18,4	25,0	32,1	16,1	19,1
0,70	0,61	0,62	1,31	0,82						
0,02	0,10	(0,39)	0,21	0,39						
0,35	0,26	(0,01)	0,86	0,64						
0,13	0,02	(0,40)	0,36	0,27						
0,05	-	-	-	-						
-	-	-	-	-						
-	-	-	-	-						
-	-	-	-	-						
969	941	524	587	553	511	542	604	608	747	636
390.147	400.285	187.930								
			14.705	14.705	13.500	13.500	13.500	13.500	13.500	13.500

RESULTS 1962-2011

	1977	1976	1975	1974	1973
INCOME AND EXPENSES (€ x 1.000)					
Revenue	29.104	24.819	27.603	29.851	11.451
Third party costs	7.279	-	-	-	-
Net revenue own services (revenue less third party costs)	21.825	24.819	27.603	29.851	11.451
Results from operating activities (EBIT)	813	2.262	1.900	4.138	1.426
Cash flow	951	1.967	2.570	2.962	813
Net result	(1.011)	304	806	1.629	282
BALANCE SHEET (€ x 1.000)					
Property, plant and equipment	5.805	5.063	4.818	4.686	3.358
Investments	-	-	-	-	-
Depreciation of property, plant and equipment	1.963	1.663	1.764	1.333	530
Total assets	15.773	14.279	13.878	15.095	8.757
Loans and borrowings	2.134	2.167	2.489	2.516	2.267
Equity attributable to owners of the company	3.269	4.058	3.346	2.141	639
KEY RATIOS (in %)					
Results from operating activities (EBIT)/revenue	2,8	9,1	6,9	13,9	12,5
Profit/revenue	(3,5)	1,2	2,9	5,5	2,5
Profit/net revenue own services	(4,7)	1,2	2,9	5,5	2,5
Total equity/total assets	20,7	28,4	24,1	14,2	7,3
DATA PER SHARE (€ x 1,-)					
Equity attributable to owners of the company					
Results from operating activities (EBIT)					
Cash flow					
Net result					
Dividend paid in year under review					
SHARE PRICE (€ x 1,-)					
Year-end share price					
Highest share price					
Lowest share price					
NUMBER OF EMPLOYEES					
At year-end	626	644	641	635	401
SHARES IN ISSUE					
Of nominal € 0,05 at year-end					
Of nominal € 0,20 at year-end					
Of nominal NLG 1 at year-end					
Of nominal NLG 10 at year-end					
Of nominal NLG 100 at year-end	13.500	13.500	13.500	13.500	7.000

1972	1971	1970	1969	1968	1967	1966	1965	1964	1963/1962
4.879	3.787	2.966	1.857	1.124	1.124	919	349	488	449
-	-	-	-	-	-	-	-	-	-
4.879	3.787	2.966	1.857	1.124	1.124	919	349	488	449
581	480	428	420	250	177	126	65	59	5
591	418	346	251	90	183	133	88	29	3
200	95	113	121	90	69	50	16	29	3
1.862	1.757	1.417	738	457	337	146	84	103	122
-	-	365	425	-	276	123	-	-	-
391	323	233	130	-	114	83	71	-	-
3.740	3.448	3.024	1.784	1.121	750	543	358	251	366
1.463	1.656	1.407	-	-	-	-	-	-	-
440	526	541	278	228	180	83	76	72	68
11,9	12,7	14,4	22,6	22,2	15,8	13,7	18,6	12,1	1,1
4,1	2,5	3,8	6,5	8,0	6,1	5,4	4,7	5,9	0,6
4,1	2,5	3,8	6,5	8,0	6,1	5,4	4,7	5,9	0,6
11,8	15,3	17,9	15,6	20,4	24,0	15,2	21,3	28,5	18,6
210	203	199	143	83	60	46	37	25	14
3.000	3.000	3.000	3.000	3.000	3.000	1.500	1.500	1.500	1.500

SUPERVISORY BOARD 1963-2012

NAME	PERIODE			FUNCTION
S. Packshaw	1963	-	1964	
A.M. Schreuders	1962	-	1975	Chairman (1963)
Drs. J. de Winter	1969	-	1969	
Drs. C. van Rijn	1969	-	1978	
Ir. B. Volbeda	1970	-	1971	
Dr. Ir. F. Sonneveld	1970	-	1980	Chairman (1975)
Ir. W. Muller	1973	-	1977	
J. Muller	1976	-	1977	
Mr. C.J.A. van Lede	1978	-	1979	
Ir. P.M. van der Sluis	1978	-	1980	
Th.J. van Dijk	1978	-	1982	Chairman (1980)
Drs. C. van Rijn	1979	-	1982	
Ir. M. Zonneveld	1980	-	1982	
A. Stouthandel	1980	-	1982	
B. Schuil	1982	-	1985	Chairman (1982)
Drs. L.M.W. van Oosterom	1982	-	1987	
F.H. Schreve	1983	-	2011	Chairman (1985)
Ir. M.M.U. van Dis	1984	-	1987	
R. Smulders	1985	-	1986	
J.D.R.A. Bax	1986	-	1991	
R.J. Howe	1988	-	1989	
C. Pannevis	1988	-	1990	
R.M. Young	1989	-	1992	
B. McClelland	1990	-	1992	
B.E. Stallworth	1990	-	2002	
M. van der Vorm	1991	-	1992	
Drs. F.P. Luttmer	1991	-	1995	
G. Kaptein	1991	-	2000	
M.W. Dekker	1991	-	2005	
J.A.C. King	1997	-	2003	
P. Crawford	1997	-	2009	
P. Winsemius	2000	-	2006	
Th. Smith	2002	-	present	
J.A. Collingan	2003	-	present	
Dr. F.J.G.M. Cremers	2005	-	present	
Ir. G-J. Kramer	2006	-	present	
Mw Dr. M. Helmes	2009	-	present	
Ir. H.C. Scheffer	2010	-	2011	Chairman (2011)
F.H. Schreve	2011	-	present	Chairman (2011)

MANAGEMENT 1962 - 2012

NAME	PERIOD			FUNCTION
Ir. K. Joustra	1962	-	1983	President (1962)
Ir. J. de Ruiter	1969	-	1983	
A.J.A. van Overeem	1972	-	1978	
A.L.G. Goulmy	1972	-	1978	
Dr. Ir. A.C. Scheepmaker	1973	-	1978	
J.J. Schoustra	1978	-	1979	
W.J. Monahan	1979	-	1979	
Drs. J.M. Verweij	1982	-	1987	
Ir. G-J. Kramer	1983	-	2005	President and CEO (1983)
B. McClelland	1988	-	1990	
Ir. K.S. Wester	1996	-	2012	President and CEO (2005)
A. Jonkman	2004	-	present	
Ir. P. van Riel	2006	-	present	
Ir. A. Steenbakker	2006	-	present	Chairman Board of Management (2012)
J. Rüegg	2009	-	present	
W.S. Rainey	2011	-	present	

ORGANISATION MAP

Fugro provides a unique range of services and activities worldwide. These are organised in three divisions: Survey, Geotechnical and Geoscience.

SURVEY DIVISION

Supports the oil and gas industry, renewables and a broad range of commercial and civil industries, as well as governments and other organisations. It encompasses numerous offshore, subsea and geospatial activities, as well as positioning systems that support these and other Group activities.

GEOTECHNICAL DIVISION

Investigates the engineering properties and geological characteristics of near-surface soils and rocks, using in-house developed, proprietary technologies. It advises on foundation design and provides materials testing, pavement assessment and construction support services for onshore and nearshore regions, ultra deepwater environments and everything in between.

GEOSCIENCE DIVISION

Provides services and products associated with collecting, processing, interpreting, managing and storing geophysical and geological data. These data sets are used for evaluating the presence of natural resources, including oil, gas, water and minerals, and for optimising the exploration, appraisal, development and production of those resources.

The following map provides an overview of Fugro's three divisions, their business lines and the activities that the company delivers within each. When it comes to providing services to major projects and developments, Fugro delivers cross-divisional support based on the combined expertise and resources of its business lines and operating companies.

OFFSHORE SURVEY

1   Precise Positioning
- Differential positioning services
- Exploration seismic solutions
- Infrastructure positioning
- Rig move and VSP services
- Subsea acoustic positioning
- Fleet management
- Inertial Navigation System (INS)
- Remote positioning
- Dredging and coastal operations

2   Offshore Construction Support
- Dimensional control surveys
- Pipelay support services
- Spoolpiece and jumper metrology
- ROV support
- FPSO installation support
- IRM and decommissioning

3   Geophysical Surveys
- Inspection surveys
- Pre-installation surveys
- Deepwater field development surveys
- Geohazard surveys
- Shallow target exploration seismic surveys
- Pipeline route surveys
- Environmental surveys
- Renewables, port and coastal surveys
- Mineral surveys
- Charting and UNCLOS surveys
- State-of-the-art survey vessels

4   Marine Surveys
- Cable and pipeline studies
- Cable and pipeline route surveys
- UNCLOS and EEZ surveys

- Airborne hydrographic LiDAR
- Hydrographic surveys
- Environmental benthic habitat surveys
- Ordnance detection surveys

5   Meteorology & Oceanography (Metocean)
- Metocean measurement
- Metocean systems
- Metocean consultancy
- Weather forecasting
- Buoy monitoring systems
- Structural monitoring

SUBSEA SERVICES

6   Drill Support
- Site clearance surveys
- Jack-up spud can surveys

- Shallow gas monitoring
- BOP installation support
- Well completion support
- Wellhead monitoring and intervention
- Specialist tooling operations
- Debris clearance surveys and removal

7 Construction Support
- Pipeline/jacket installation
- Flowline and umbilical installation
- Pre- and post-lay surveys
- Subsea spoolpiece metrology and installation
- Suction pile installation
- Trenching, backfilling and rock-dumping support
- Subsea pressure testing

SURVEY DIVISION

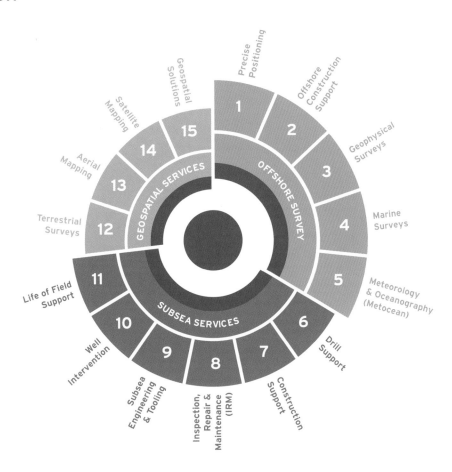

- · Flooding, gauging and stabilisation
- · Pipeline crossing preparation
  and construction

8 Inspection, Repair & Maintenance (IRM)
- · Platform and pipeline inspection
- · Flooded member detection surveys
- · FPSO hull and turret inspection
- · Anchor chain inspection
  and measurement
- · Mid-water arch inspection
  and measurement
- · Leak investigation and remediation
- · Bespoke repair tooling design,
  build and operation
- · Pipeline stabilisation and repair
- · Anode clamp design and retrofit
- · Structure repair clamp installation

9 Subsea Engineering & Tooling
- · Design and build of field
  intervention tooling
- · Innovative ROV-mounted
  tooling solutions
- · Design and build of
  Tool Deployment Units
- · Support, maintenance and
  tool management
- · Design, management and
  execution of subsea repairs
- · Subsea hardware
  component change-outs

10 Well Intervention
- · Subsea well intervention
- · Subsea tree/module installation
  and recovery
- · Well abandonment and
  decommissioning

11 Life of Field Support
- · Specialist field support vessels
- · Remotely Operated Vehicles
- · Air and saturation diving systems

GEOSPATIAL SERVICES

12 Terrestrial Surveys
- · Conventional land surveys
- · Precision 3D surveys
- · Mobile mapping

13 Aerial Mapping
- · Photogrammetric mapping
- · LiDAR mapping
- · RADAR mapping
- · Panoramic mapping
- · Thematic mapping
- · Rapid response mapping

14 Satellite Mapping
- · Satellite imagery
- · Image interpretation/elevation
  modelling
- · Ground/structure stability
  mapping
- · Oil seep detection

15 Geospatial Solutions
- · Online mapping
- · 3D modelling and visualisation
- · Consulting and advice

GEOTECHNICAL DIVISION

OFFSHORE GEOTECHNICAL

1   Geotechnical Services
- State-of-the-art geotechnical vessels
- Drilling, sampling and downhole in situ testing
- Seabed sampling and in situ testing
- Seabed and downhole rotary coring
- Downhole pressurised coring

2   Geophysical Services
- Integration of surface and borehole geophysical data
- Downhole geophysical logging
- Seabed refraction, resistivity and MASW
- Surface and downhole seismic cone testing

3   GeoConsulting and Engineering Services
- Desktop and feasibility studies
- Environmental impact assessments
- Data acquisition, integration and management
- Geophysical, geological and geotechnical modelling
- Geohazard risk assessment
- Geotechnical analysis and foundation design
- Soil-pipe modelling
- Sage 2D/3D software
- Numerical modelling

4   Laboratory Testing Services
- Soil and rock classification
- Static strength and deformation testing
- Dynamic properties and cyclic strength testing
- Foundation model testing
- Research and development
- Environmental, biological and chemical testing

5   Well Services
- Deep stratigraphic coring
- Top hole, exploration and appraisal wells
- Suction anchor installation and pipeline laying services

6   Pile Monitoring and Construction Services
- Pile driving monitoring
- Instrumentation of foundations
- Geotechnical assistance for foundation installation
- Installation and construction support

ONSHORE GEOTECHNICAL

7   Nearshore Construction Support
- Large diameter drilling
- Monopile installation
- Renewable and nuclear energy

8   (Ground) Water Services
- Geohydrological consultancy
- Risk assessment
- (Ground) water modelling
- Data management
- (Ground) water monitoring and data acquisition
- Hydropower and geothermal consultancy

9   Geo-Engineering Services
- Earthquake engineering
- Geohazard evaluations
- Geological mapping
- GIS services

10   Environmental Engineering Services
- Environmental consultancy
- Environmental investigations
- In Situ investigations
- Data management

11   Geotechnical Services
- Geotechnical consultancy
- Geotechnical investigations and drilling
- CPT services
- Geo- and structural monitoring services
- Borehole testing
- Pile testing
- Mineral exploration services

12   Geophysical Services
- High resolution shallow seismic
- Electrical methods
- Borehole geophysical logging
- Seismic cone testing
- Data processing and interpretation

13   Laboratory Services
- Material testing (geotechnical)
- Material testing (construction and infrastructure)
- Non-destructive testing (NDT)
- Organic testing
- Metallurgic testing and corrosion studies
- Certification services

14   Transportation Infrastructure
- Pavement testing and surveying
- Pavement management
- Structural testing
- Laser testing
- Non-destructive testing (NDT)

GEOSCIENCE DIVISION

INFORMATION SERVICES

1 Reservoir Services
- Feasibility studies
- Petrophysics and rock physics
- Seismic to simulation
- Reservoir characterisation
- Reservoir modelling and simulation Subsidence
- Field development optimisation and economics
- Software

2 Exploration Services
- General geologic services
- Geophysics and structural geology
- Satellite surface geology
- Geochemistry and seeps
- Screening and evaluation
- Training

3 Non-Exclusive Data & Products
- Interpretative services
- Wells
- Wells to seismic
- Seismic reprocessing
- TELLUS™ exploration database
- Geochemistry

4 Economics & Facilities Engineering
- Economics
- Fiscal and taxation
- Training
- Reporting
- Facilities engineering

5 Software Solutions
- Seismic reservoir characterisation
- Reservoir modelling
- Petrophysics
- Oil & gas data management

6 Oil & Gas Data Management
- Data remediation, transcription and copying
- Data storage
- Database development and management
- Bid round support

SEISMIC SERVICES

7 Marine Data Acquisition
- 2D/3D/4D seismic acquisition
- Modern fleet of seismic vessels
- Steerable streamer technology

8 Data Processing
- 2D/3D/4D time processing and depth imaging of land and marine seismic data
- Interpretative processing
- High resolution processing short offset 3D
- CRS processing
- Multi-vintage data matching

9 Non-Exclusive Data
- Seismic 2D data library
- Seismic 3D data library
- Seismic reprocessing

GENERAL GEOPHYSICAL

10 Airborne Data Acquisition
- Project planning and management
- Fixed wing and helicopter fleets
- Electromagnetics
- Aeromagnetics
- Gamma-ray spectrometry
- Airborne gravity gradiometry
- Airborne gravity

11 Land Geophysical Data Acquisition
- Gravity
- Electromagnetics
- Induced polarisation and resistivity
- Magnetics
- Borehole geophysics

12 Marine Geophysical Data Acquisition
- Gravity
- Magnetics
- Electromagnetics

13 Interpretation Services
- Potential fields (gravity and magnetics)
- Electromagnetics

14 Processing Services
- Airborne geophysical data
- Land geophysical data
- Marine gravity, magnetic and electromagnetic data

15 Non-Exclusive Data & Products
- Magnetic and gravity data sets (airborne/marine)
- Electromagnetic data sets (marine)

16 Software Solutions
- Potential fields (gravity and magnetics)
- Marine electromagnetics